Understanding M

Understanding Mental Health

Angelina Gibbs

Which?

BOOKS

Published by
Consumers' Association
and Hodder & Stoughton

Understanding Mental Health is published by
Consumers' Association, 14 Buckingham Street, London WC2N 6DS and
Hodder and Stoughton Limited, 47 Bedford Square, London WC1B 3DP

British Library Cataloguing in Publication Data

Gibbs, Angelina
    Understanding mental health.
    1. Mental health
    I. Title   II. Consumers' Association
    613   RA790

    ISBN 0-340-38161-2

Typographical design: Tim Higgins
Cover illustration: John Holder
Typesetting: Rowland Phototypesetting Limited, Bury St Edmunds, Suffolk
Printed and bound in Great Britain
by Collins, Glasgow

Contents

CONTENTS

Foreword

by Professor Anthony Clare

One of the most pressing needs in the area of mental health and illness is for a simple, informative, comprehensible and unbiased guide to help people decipher the language, understand what is and is not known about the causes and treatment of mental illness and become more familiar with the nature and extent of the services, statutory and voluntary, currently available. Psychiatrists, psychologists, social workers, even general practitioners are not exactly renowned for their ability to communicate such information. Despite unparalleled media interest in the subject, it seems doubtful that the average person knows very much more about emotional ill-health today than a decade ago. Professional journalists are often not much better informed while even some social workers, nurses and doctors exhibit prejudice and even ignorance when it comes to psychological aspects of health and disease.

In writing this book Angelina Gibbs has performed a notable and timely service to the public, to the voluntary and statutory organisations and to the various professions involved in the care and the treatment of the mentally ill. Her description of the current state of knowledge concerning major mental disorders such as schizophrenia and manic-depressive illness is enviable in its clarity and accuracy. Her handling of the commoner psychological symptoms of anxiety and depression, symptoms which are so often associated with physical disease as well as with such social stresses as economic hardship, unemployment and marital unhappiness, is most impressive. Contained in the book is much helpful, practical information concerning the various treatments and services available to sufferers and their families alike.

There are areas of controversy and dissent within the mental health field and Mrs Gibbs does not shun them. But, unlike so many who have written on this subject, she does not allow such issues to deflect her from her task of providing a factual, unemotive guide. And this is a positive, forward-looking book in that it emphasises the extent to which much mental disturbance is treatable and is no more chronic nor intractable than many physical diseases, a point which merits stressing over and over again. Yet she does not make exaggerated claims and at no time does she conceal the very real lack of fundamental knowledge that bedevils the field.

But such knowledge as we have is summarised and contained within the pages of this guide. It may not be enough to prevent any of us suffering from various emotional disturbances but it will go a long way to ensuring that such suffering need not be unrelieved. It will assist the relatives and friends of people undergoing serious mental disorders to understand a little more and to cope a little better. It is a valuable piece of ammunition in the long, weary war to remove the dreadful stigma that smears the whole area of mental disability and suffering and that constitutes an extra and often unbearable burden upon the mentally ill and those who care for them. Its blend of information and commonsense, of theory and practical advice, of treatments and services makes this guide an absolute necessity to anyone who wishes to have a better grasp of the nature and extent of mental ill-health, of the current status of our understanding and of the resources available to treat it. In short, it is an indispensable guide for every one of us.

Professor Clare is Head of the Department of Psychological Medicine at St Bartholomew's Hospital Medical College in London. He has written extensively, and is particularly well known for his B B C Radio 4 programme, 'In the Psychiatrist's Chair'.

I

Introduction

There are still mysteries in all aspects of medicine, so it is perhaps not surprising that the complexity of the human brain should pose so many dilemmas for those who wish to understand mental health. It is amazing enough that everything we say, think and feel is mediated by this organ. But it is even harder to accept that some people's minds lead them to believe that they are being spied on, or to feel so despairing that they commit suicide, or to find the sight of a cat unbearably frightening.

We can understand physical illness much more readily than mental illness, even without any medical training. We can identify more easily with people suffering from an infection or a broken limb. They are 'just like us', except that their illness or injury restricts their activity and they need medical treatment. When someone is mentally ill we find it harder to accept that he is 'just like us', and many sufferers therefore feel alienated and isolated by their illness.

What is mental illness?
This is the first of many questions on mental health which cannot be answered conclusively. Theories abound, and while there is a general consensus on many points, extreme views must also be considered. It is not the aim of this book to describe any particular conception of mental health as 'correct'. Often research lends convincing support to a theory, and it can therefore be put forward in this book with more confidence. Other theories are based on speculation by a small group of workers, unsupported by good research or the opinions of most doctors dealing with such patients. These theories are described here more cautiously.

The terms 'mental illness' and 'mental handicap' are frequently confused – see Chapter 7.

It is usually possible to say definitely whether someone is suffering from a particular physical problem – an x-ray shows the fractured bone; a laboratory analysis reveals the presence of bacteria. However, it is hardly ever possible to obtain physical proof of a mental disorder. Generally it can be deduced only from the way a person feels, behaves, thinks or perceives the world. The psychiatrist does not have access to the patient's mind in order to confirm a diagnosis. Mental illness is suspected when these aspects of a person's life are abnormal. But this raises another tricky question: What is normal? Just because someone feels depressed does not mean that he is mentally ill. Similarly, no one leads an anxiety-free life. Eccentric behaviour need not be construed as a sign of mental illness, any more than the vivid imagination of a great artist or poet, yet these are deviations from the norm.

The only mental health legislation in the UK to define mental illness is that being introduced in Northern Ireland, which describes it as 'a state of mind which affects the person's thinking, perceiving, emotion or judgement to the extent that he requires care or medical treatment in his own interests or the interests of other persons.' It is helpful to imagine mental health as a continuum from well-being to illness, although it is extremely difficult to define the point at which mental well-being becomes mental illness, and an individual's position on the continuum may frequently change. There is a grey area in the middle in which some cases of anxiety and depression fall. Generally, problems of feeling, thinking and behaviour are considered as mental illness only if they interfere with the individual's life, causing him, or those around him, distress. So it is not necessary to specify what is viewed as 'normal' to separate mental health and illness. The key point is what is normal *for that person*. Mental illness is signalled by a change from a previously balanced mental state in which the person has coped satisfactorily with life, to a situation where one mood or type of behaviour predominates. Whether the person's previous nature would generally be called 'normal' is not really relevant.

One type of problem falling in the grey area between mental health and illness may be called 'emotional problems'. These are understandable reactions to experiences, such as grief following a bereavement, or feelings of depression after an operation to remove part of the body. For some people, an extreme emotional problem will become a mental illness – the widow who eventually develops a depressive illness, for example.

Any of the following problems could be experienced to some degree without being signs of mental illness, but in combination they may indicate that the person is in need of help:

- a change in the person which lasts longer than seems appropriate after a disturbing experience
- changes in emotions, behaviour and relationships which are so severe or persistent that they cause the person to suffer
- difficulty interpreting one's inner experiences and telling others about them

- changes in the person causing distress or disturbance for those around him
- a change in the person which is unrelated to anything that has recently happened
- difficulty in making relationships.

Sometimes changes are so obvious, as in some cases of schizophrenia, that there is unlikely to be any question that the person is mentally ill. In the past there was, however, considerable disagreement about diagnosis, and a patient might be thought schizophrenic by one doctor and not by another. Though this situation is improving, there may still be disagreements of this kind.

A few people, particularly in America, take the view that the entire concept of mental illness is erroneous. They do not accept that the reactions shown by sufferers are signs of illness at all. Instead they consider them to be understandable in the light of these people's struggles to deal with the particular circumstances of their lives.

In view of the difficulties in defining mental illness and deciding whom to include in the definition, it is not surprising that estimates of the number of people affected should vary. However, it is generally estimated that one woman in every five or six, and one man in nine, will need professional help for a mental illness at some time in their lives. One woman in eight and one man in twelve will need at least one stay in a psychiatric hospital or unit. Only under the age of 17 are males more likely to need psychiatric help than females. Some studies have found that about ten per cent of the patients seen by general practitioners (GPs) each year have a 'mental illness', but it is estimated that the complaints of up to one-third of patients are based on emotional or mental problems.

It is thought that around one family in five is affected by mental illness. So the chances are that at some time in our lives we will either suffer a mental illness ourselves, or have a relative, friend or neighbour who does. Yet, despite its prevalence, there is still a stigma attached to mental illness, and fear, blame and rejection are still common reactions. Nevertheless, there have been radical improvements in the care of mentally ill people over the past two hundred years. At the beginning of the nineteenth century reformers started to campaign for asylums and hospitals to provide refuge for these sufferers. The isolation of mentally ill people in institutions continued until the 1950s when more reform was urged. It was discovered to be unnecessary and harmful to lock these patients away for years. Many were discharged back to the community – even if they were not fully recovered – and re-admitted to hospital if necessary. It was not just a change of attitudes in the 1950s which led to many mentally ill patients leaving hospital. New treatments, especially drugs, relieved many symptoms to the extent that sufferers could live much more independent, though perhaps limited, lives outside the hospital gates. Psychiatric services began to be geared towards patients living at home – day hospitals and out-patient care, for example.

Using this book

Some of the mental and emotional problems described in this book affect only, or predominantly, one sex. Those caring for a mentally ill relative at home are more likely to be female; consultant psychiatrists are normally men. However, to save space, 'he' has been used throughout the text, except for cases where the sufferer would usually or always be female. No offence or discrimination is intended – especially against the many women who voluntarily or professionally care for mentally ill people.

In describing the services available for mentally ill people and their families, the main text refers to the situation in England and Wales. Any major differences in Scotland and Northern Ireland are made clear. One key difference is the local authority arrangement for social services provision. In England and Wales this is through social services departments. In Scotland these are known as social work departments. Northern Ireland has a rather different system: health and personal social services of the kind described in this book are administered by the same authority – the Health and Social Services Board. This information is not repeated in the text every time social services are mentioned, but is indicated by the phrase 'or equivalent' after each reference to social services departments.

Within the text, words in SMALL CAPITALS indicate that the subject is dealt with more fully elsewhere. For specific mental illnesses this will be in Chapter 5, emotional problems in Chapter 6, broad categories of mental illness in Chapter 3 and types of treatment in Chapter 4.

There are several thousand addresses in the UK which might be useful for sufferers of mental illness and those who care for them. Many of the major national or widespread organisations are mentioned in this book – the names appear in **bold** type. The addresses and telephone numbers are given from page 226 onwards.

Most of the organisations listed in the book ask that a stamped addressed envelope or label be sent with enquiries – overheads are a major problem for the charities in particular.

2

What causes mental illness?

Perhaps the first question which occurs to sufferers and to their families is: Why? Why this illness, at this time, to this person? Usually only a partial answer can be given because not enough is yet known about the causes of mental illness to be more precise. For this reason it is also impossible to predict whether someone is going to become mentally ill.

Mental illness is generally thought to be caused by a combination of factors. Any of these on its own would probably not result in mental illness, but the factors may interact, or a particular incident may 'tip the balance'. Before looking at these various factors, it is important to note that there is disagreement among psychiatrists and researchers about the causes of mental illness. The most widely held view is that it is caused by the combination of several factors – that is, no illness has one, inevitable cause. A variety of causes can lead to the same disturbance of feeling or behaviour. Rejecting this 'multiple causes' view, a few workers feel that certain illnesses do have one specific cause – that is, every sufferer has inevitably been affected by this one factor.

The theories held by psychiatrists about the causes of mental illness are important for two reasons. First, they may affect the type of treatment which a psychiatrist recommends. However, most psychiatrists in this country do not espouse one theory to the exclusion of all other possibilities, and will consider available treatment of various types, depending on the patient's individual case.

The second important consequence of these theories is the possibility of preventing ill-health. If avoidable causes can be identified, there is scope for preventing mental illness. This will be discussed in more detail after a look at the various suggested causes. These are described separately but it will become clear that they are not really independent. For example, childhood experiences and personality are inextricably linked. This supports the view that mental illness is caused by a combination of factors.

Childhood experiences

It is thought that the first fifteen years have a greater influence than experiences during any other period of life. Adverse experiences during this time include an unstable family life where affection is never shown, or where it is taught that anger must never be displayed. A poor physical or emotional environment affects the development of some children, but for others there are compensating factors so that there are no lasting ill-effects on their social or emotional well-being. Research on this subject has not provided evidence that any aspect of early family life causes mental illness, though there has been much speculation. Some of this has caused parents to feel unnecessary guilt about mental illness in their offspring (see AUTISM and SCHIZOPHRENIA). Investigations into whether the death of a child's mother causes DEPRESSION in later life have been inconclusive.

The extent to which specific childhood experiences are responsible for later mental illness is debatable. There have been numerous theories, for example those of Freud, Jung, Adler, Meyer and Reich (beyond the scope of this book). It is reasonable to assume, however, that emotional development in general, and the way children learn to respond to life's challenges, do have an effect on later reactions to STRESS.

Personality

This is probably a mixture of the temperament someone is born with, and his childhood experiences. The resulting personality affects how the stresses of life are perceived and dealt with. Some people, for example, habitually view minor incidents as major crises, or fail to face up to challenges. Others are said to 'take everything in their stride' (see ANXIETY).

Those who later suffer from mental illness have often previously experienced personality problems but the nature of the link is unclear. PERSONALITY DISORDERS, such as schizoid or obsessional personalities are discussed more fully in Chapter 5 under SCHIZOPHRENIA and OBSESSIVE DISORDERS. It has been suggested that personality determines the form which mental illness takes, if it develops at all. However, those with an obsessional personality who become mentally ill do not necessarily suffer from an OBSESSIVE DISORDER. There is one personality type, though, which typically seems to precede severe DEPRESSION or MANIC-DEPRESSION. This does not mean that the personality causes the illness – both may be the result of some constitutional factor.

Heredity

Most people are aware that mental illness is not 'catching', but there is much more concern over whether children are likely to inherit it. This is a particularly interesting area of research, in which it has already been found that there is a genetic factor in some disorders. Precisely how this works is unknown except for HUNTINGTON'S CHOREA, which develops only in those who have inherited the gene. There is a 50/50 chance of a child inheriting the gene from a parent who is a carrier.

Other mental illnesses such as SCHIZOPHRENIA and MANIC-DEPRESSION have a genetic component which is not fully understood. A predisposition to the disorder seems to be inherited, but the illness probably develops only if other factors are also present. Close relatives such as offspring have a greater chance (though far from 100 per cent) of developing the illness than more distant relations such as cousins. This is not just because the children share the same environment as their mentally ill parent. Identical twins have the same genes, and even if they are brought up in different homes, one twin still has an increased risk of developing one of these illnesses if the twin brother or sister is a sufferer.

The possibility of a genetic factor in minor mental illnesses and PERSONALITY DISORDERS is less clear. Relatives of someone suffering from a NEUROSIS (see Chapter 3) have an increased chance of also developing a neurotic disorder, but this is because of the effects of living together, rather than sharing genes. It is, however, possible that certain personality traits may be inherited. As described earlier, these may play a role in determining how people cope with STRESS.

Changes in the brain and physical health

One of the most active areas of research into the causes of mental illness has involved chemicals released by nerve cells within the brain. The drugs prescribed for mental illness act on these chemicals, in ways not fully understood, and increased knowledge in this area will enable treatments to be improved. The brain chemicals being studied constantly transmit messages between the nerve cells. Some of these chemicals are believed to play a role in determining mood, and faults in the message transmission system seem in some way to produce mental illness. An excess or deficiency of a particular chemical, or more accurately an imbalance in the various messenger systems, affects the person's mental state. Research is complicated by many factors which regularly come to light – recent discoveries have been made of other chemicals which themselves seem to influence the 'message transmitters'. The roles which brain chemicals are believed to play in ANXIETY, DEPRESSION, PARKINSON'S DISEASE and SCHIZOPHRENIA are described in Chapter 5. See also DRUGS in Chapter 4.

DELIRIUM and DEMENTIA are examples of mental illnesses caused by physical disorders within the brain. This is often temporary in the case of delirium, but permanent in most forms of dementia because the brain cells die and cannot be replaced. Brain infections such as meningitis, and brain tumours, can impair the patient's mental health.

Various physical illnesses which do not originate in the brain can also produce symptoms of mental illness. For example, some of the symptoms of ANXIETY and DEPRESSION can be caused by disorders of the thyroid gland in the neck. Depression may follow prolonged debilitating illnesses such as influenza, glandular fever and hepatitis.

Stress

There are two aspects of the effect of stress on mental health. It has been suggested that relatively long-term stresses can make people more vulnerable or susceptible to mental illness. These stresses include living on a very low income, having no close friends or relatives to turn to (see next section), UNEMPLOYMENT and MARITAL PROBLEMS. Such strains can cause tension and irritability, and it is known that people in these situations do suffer higher rates of mental illness. But a cause-and-effect relationship is not yet proven. Perhaps being mentally ill results in the person living in these undesirable conditions – it is known, for example, that sufferers from SCHIZOPHRENIA tend to drift into a poorer lifestyle. Possibly the factors which cause the person to be mentally ill also result in the marital or occupational difficulties.

A slightly different aspect is the effect of a 'significant event' in someone's life triggering an episode of mental illness. This may be the 'last straw' for someone who, despite a predisposition to mental illness, had been coping with life while it presented no major challenges. Such events have been ranked for the degree of stress they entail, and the more that occur at once, the more likely the person is to suffer some ill-effects. This list is headed by the death of a husband or wife, followed by separating from a spouse, and the death of a close relation. Not all stressful events are unpleasant – marriage and marital reconciliation are near the top of the list. The consequences of 'life events' have been investigated particularly in relation to DEPRESSION, SCHIZOPHRENIA and to a lesser extent ANXIETY. A very broad generalisation is that depression is triggered in some people if they develop a feeling of hopelessness after a stressful event involving loss or disappointment. If the event involves danger or a threat, anxiety is thought to be a more likely – though certainly not inevitable – outcome. It seems that people vary in their susceptibility to the effects of stress – see later in this chapter.

Research has also looked at the effect of continued stress on physical well-being. This is discussed further in Chapter 3 under PSYCHOSOMATIC DISORDERS.

Lack of social support

It has been said that we now have fewer people to whom we can naturally turn with our problems. Living in crowded cities does not guarantee a correspondingly large circle of friends, and families tend to move apart geographically. Social support is more than just having someone to listen to your problems – though this is important. It is a feeling of being part of a group of people who care for and respect each other, and who will help each other.

A lack of friends – see LONELINESS – and of an intimate relationship with a partner who can be confided in, seems to be a relevant factor in mental illness. Apparently such people help to buffer the impact of strain and stressful events. For example, unmarried women seem to have a greater tendency to mental problems, especially DEPRESSION. Of course, the quality of these social relationships is important – a bad marriage can be a source of STRESS, rather than a help in coping with life.

Exactly how social support affects vulnerability to mental illness is not clear, though there does seem to be a protective effect. Once again the question of cause-and-effect must be raised. It may be that depressed people have lost their friends because of their mental illness, or report that they have no one to turn to because of their depressed view of life.

Diet

The idea of diet playing a role in physical health is familiar. Most people have at least heard the advice to eat less sugar or more fibre, even if they choose not to follow it. But there is now some evidence that diet may also play a role in mental health. This area of research is called clinical ecology, and investigates the adverse reactions of susceptible people to substances which may be found in food, drink, drugs and the atmosphere. The reaction is not the same as being allergic to strawberries or shellfish, which make some people feel and look ill almost immediately and are then carefully avoided. The theory is that it is usually frequently eaten foods, such as milk, eggs, sugar and wheat, which are likely to cause symptoms of mental ill-health in susceptible people. There may be no violent reaction to the food, so they have no suspicion that they should stop eating it. Some researchers believe that people with combinations of many physical and mental symptoms for which no explanation can be found may actually be suffering from a food intolerance. The mental symptoms could be caused directly by sensitivity to the foods, or arise as a result of the physical reactions.

The theory of adverse food reaction is perhaps best known in connection with HYPERACTIVITY in children. An abnormal reaction to certain foods has also been postulated as a possible factor in some EATING DISORDERS. Hypoglycaemia is the medical name for low blood sugar levels which continue to fall after sweet foods are digested, instead of stabilising. It has been suggested that this may cause DEPRESSION and irritability. Perhaps more surprising is research suggesting that DELIN-

19

QUENCY may be linked to diet. There is a suggestion that SCHIZOPHRE-NIA too may have a nutritional element in some sufferers.

Only a few doctors in this country have taken an active interest in clinical ecology, and there is a need for much more scientific research before firm conclusions can be drawn. However, if you are interested in the idea, four organisations can supply more information: the **National Society for Research into Allergy, Sanity**, the **Biosocial Therapy Association**, and **Action Against Allergy**. The Consumers' Association publication *Understanding Allergies* also covers this subject.

Can mental illness be prevented?

It is clear that there are several obstacles to preventing mental illness. The first is that much more remains to be discovered about the various possible causes before definitive statements can be made about their role. Secondly, how they interact is poorly understood and this would be vital knowledge for any prevention programme. Thirdly, only some of the factors could be changed anyway. Diet, some life stresses and some aspects of child-rearing could be altered, but changing personalities and decisions about whether certain mentally ill people should have children would be much more difficult problems. Except for HUNTINGTON'S CHOREA sufferers, the scope for genetic counselling is certainly very limited at the moment.

From what is already known about mental illness, the following general points can be made, but they do not constitute a guarantee against illness:

- it is wise not to have too many major changes which can cause STRESS occurring at the same time. Some stressful events can be predicted, such as marriage and changing jobs. Try to avoid combining these
- social support may play a role in protecting against mental illness, and in limiting how long it lasts. This suggests that when moving to a new area it is a good idea to become involved with people and build up a social network. This is very difficult to do if emotional problems are already developing
- those with a good social network of family and/or friends will always have someone to turn to with their problems. Talking over worries, difficulties and bad experiences is sometimes all that is needed to prevent them causing emotional problems. The 'good listener' need not be a relative or friend though – professional and voluntary COUNSELLING can also help
- everyone would like to bring up their children in a way that will prevent mental illness, but it is not yet known how to achieve this. It

is common sense that a warm and loving family environment is important, where emotions are openly expressed, and self-reliance is encouraged

- research has looked at how individuals vary in their methods of coping with STRESS, but so far the conclusions are only tentative. It seems to help if you have a variety of ways of dealing with problems, rather than a fixed response to every situation. It also appears to be important not to have a negative attitude to yourself – that is, not to feel that you are useless, unworthy and so on. It helps if you feel that you are in control of your life, rather than a powerless victim of other people's actions or 'Fate'. It may not always be possible to change stressful situations, but you can sometimes alter your attitude to yourself and to the circumstances

- some minor emotional and mental problems may resolve themselves within six months without any form of treatment. Other forms of mental illness tend to get worse if the person does not receive any help. For example, if the parents' unhappy marriage is causing their children emotional problems, getting help early on may prevent more serious difficulties later for the children. Getting help quickly in a crisis has been shown to help people cope with the situation more satisfactorily.

It is the final point which is the most relevant in attempts to reduce the suffering caused by mental illness. Whatever the problem – from emotional difficulties following a BEREAVEMENT, to the onset of SCHIZOPHRENIA – it is important to try to get help as soon as you are aware of it. For this reason Chapters 9 and 10 describe how to spot the warning signs of mental illness, and to obtain help for yourself or for someone else. Mental illness caught early is easier to treat and causes less disruption to the lives of sufferers and their families.

3

Types of
mental illness

Just as there is not yet agreement on what causes mental illnesses, there is also disagreement over how they should be classified. There is an International Classification of Diseases but this has not settled all the arguments.

This chapter looks at the various ways in which mental illnesses are grouped, so that terms such as psychotic and psychosomatic can be explained – the way they are used in everyday speech is often somewhat different. The chart opposite shows a generally accepted, but not definitive, classification of the problems covered in this book.

Taking mental illness first, the most basic distinction is between organic and functional disorders. In organic mental conditions there is an identifiable physical disorder either solely within the brain or elsewhere in the body which also affects the brain. An example of a temporary organic mental disorder is DELIRIUM – for instance, during a fever. More serious is DEMENTIA which is usually irreversible. Disturbances in the working of the thyroid gland in the neck can affect the brain.

The remaining mental illnesses are called functional disorders – that is, the working of the brain is affected but no physical disorder has yet been found. As described in the last chapter, research is currently looking at physical abnormalities in the brain associated with functional mental disorders, such as DEPRESSION and SCHIZOPHRENIA. Nevertheless, these chemical abnormalities have not been shown to be the sole cause of all cases of the illnesses, and they are still called functional disorders.

Neuroses and psychoses
One way of subdividing the functional problems is to separate the much more common minor mental illnesses from severe disorders. A mental illness is less severe if the sufferer has insight into his problem. He is aware of something being wrong with the way he currently feels – either in contrast to his past life or to the lives of others. These disorders are generally called neuroses (or psychoneuroses) – though there is no

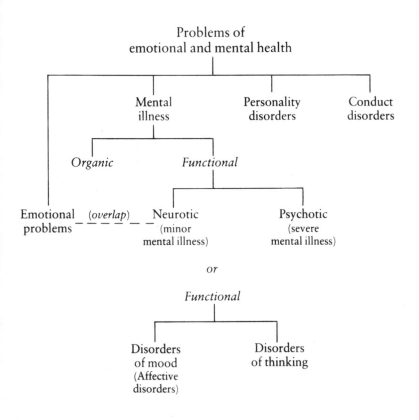

universively agreed definition of this term. Neuroses can be thought of as exaggerations of experiences with which everyone is familiar. For example, ANXIETY is a reaction common to most people in certain situations, but the neurotic anxiety state is out of all proportion to the circumstances. Similarly, neurotic DEPRESSION is an extreme version of the normal feelings of sadness and misery. PHOBIAS, OBSESSIVE DISORDERS, HYPOCHONDRIA and HYSTERIA are also classified as neuroses. Often sufferers experience symptoms of more than one type of neurotic problem – a combination of anxiety and depression is a common example.

The boundaries around neuroses are by no means clear. The chart above indicates the overlap between emotional problems and neuroses – for example, relationship problems could be considered in either category. There is a similar overlap with personality problems – for instance, excessive shyness. The justification for labelling neuroses as 'illnesses' is that they interfere with the sufferer's normal life. They prevent him forming relationships and being content with his life at home and at work. A neurotic person feels that he cannot cope alone, but also that he cannot tell others about his feelings. An argument against calling neuroses illnesses is made by those who view them as 'inefficient living'. These people argue that neurotics need to learn how to 'live properly' – facing life's challenges and accepting themselves as they are, rather than wishing to be someone different. A medical approach is therefore rejected on the grounds that treating the effects of the neurosis, such as disproportionate feelings of panic and anxiety, is irrelevant to the underlying suffering. The fundamental problem in the person's approach to life has to be resolved.

There is a middle ground between these two concepts of neurosis. Some people may have a 'neurotic approach to life' – they generally feel that they do not quite fit with those around them, that their lives are empty and unrewarding, and they avoid challenging situations. Such people might be described as mentally ill only when their ANXIETY, DEPRESSION or PHOBIA begins to interfere with their lives.

Traditionally neuroses have been thought of as reactions to STRESS. The latest International Classification of Diseases, however, describes two categories of emotional disturbance related to stress which are classified as neither neuroses nor psychoses. One is a relatively short-lasting reaction to severe stress; the other a prolonged reaction to less intense stress over a longer period. Examples of these conditions are considered in this book in Chapter 6 on emotional problems – reactions to BEREAVEMENT, MARITAL PROBLEMS and so on.

Neuroses are often chronic disorders – that is, the sufferer has had the condition for some time, perhaps for years. If a condition has come on suddenly and recently it is said to be acute.

While the arguments are likely to continue over whether all neuroses are really mental illnesses, there is far less controversy over the status of psychoses. The psychotic patient does not perceive the world as it really is (though the nature of 'reality' is, of course, subject to philosophical debate). What is meant here is that he is liable to experience hallucinations (for example, seeing and hearing things which are not there) or delusions (believing things for which there is no justification). Gradually the world in which the psychotic person lives becomes more one of fantasy than reality. His thoughts and emotions cease to be rational and it is not possible to discuss with him his ideas and feelings in a logical way. He probably does not realise how seriously ill he is, though he may well feel very disturbed and uneasy about what is happening to him. The psychotic patient cannot make an effort to resume a normal state since he no longer has any control over his thoughts and feelings. However, there are usually times when the psychotic symptoms subside and he can react rationally again to the real world. SCHIZOPHRENIA, PARANOID

DISORDERS and MANIC-DEPRESSION are examples of psychoses.

For those not suffering from a psychosis it is very difficult to imagine what it must be like – unlike neurosis it is not an exaggeration of anything normally experienced. In most cases a psychiatrist will have no problem in deciding whether a patient is psychotic. However, it may be more difficult when the psychiatrist and the patient are from different ethnic backgrounds. Occasionally what is normal in one culture may be assumed to be evidence of psychosis in another because it is incomprehensible.

Disorders of mood and of thinking

These descriptions of neuroses and psychoses have touched on another possible way of dividing mental illness. This is to separate disorders of mood from disorders of thinking. The first category includes DE-PRESSION, MANIA and MANIC-DEPRESSION which are also labelled affective disorders. ANXIETY states are also sometimes included. Disorders of thinking are generally SCHIZOPHRENIA and PARANOID DISORDERS, but these may also involve symptoms of mood disorder.

Personality disorders

These are not mental illnesses, and cannot be 'treated' in the usual sense. Nevertheless, people with personality disorders are referred to the mental health services and it is sometimes possible to teach them more satisfactory ways of interacting with and relating to others.

Once again, the problem is one of drawing a dividing line. When does an exaggerated characteristic, such as excessive shyness, or an eccentricity, become a personality disorder? Broadly speaking, the distinction is made on the basis of whether the problem has an adverse effect on the person or those around him. If the person is so withdrawn and unable to tolerate human company that he has no friends and cannot go out to work, a personality disorder may be the cause. Such habitual patterns of behaviour or ways of living are established by the time the person reaches adolescence, but often seem less obvious when he is middle-aged or older.

Many personality disorders have been described, the most serious being PSYCHOPATHY. Other examples are the schizoid personality (see SCHIZOPHRENIA) and the hysterical personality (see HYSTERIA). As pointed out in Chapter 2, those who have such personalities do not necessarily later develop the related mental illness – or indeed any mental illness at all. Sufferers from severe DEPRESSION and MANIC-DEPRESSION have typically had an affective personality, however, characterised by a predominant mood of marked depression or elation, or an alternation between the two in repeated mood swings.

Conduct disorders

Like personality disorders, these are not mental illnesses, though they are often brought to the mental health services for treatment. Generally, they involve abnormal behaviour which cannot be classified in any other way, either as a mental illness or as a personality disorder. When conduct disorders are seen within the mental health services, it is either in an attempt to abolish deviant behaviour or to improve inadequate behaviour. Psychiatric problems in children are often classified as conduct disorders. In later life, the problem is generally that the person does not behave in a way which is socially acceptable.

Psychosomatic disorders

As commonly used, 'psychosomatic' implies a physical illness caused entirely by emotional factors. However, this is probably quite rare and research studies have not fully established the extent to which it occurs. There are, for example, an above-average number of deaths among recently bereaved widowers. This does not necessarily mean that BEREAVEMENT causes their fatal illness. It is much more likely that the emotional STRESS, in combination with the man's existing poor physical health, produces a fatal disorder.

Psychological factors are much more commonly part of the cause of a physical illness, but not the sole one. It has even been claimed that emotional and social factors play at least a minor role in every case of illness. In this much wider definition, 'psychosomatic' therefore refers to the way psychological and social factors are related to the physical state of the body. The following are examples of how this can happen:

- a mental illness or emotional problem has physical symptoms – eg DEPRESSION affects the part of the brain involved in sleep patterns and appetite control, and these are therefore disturbed in sufferers
- emotional stress plays a part in the occurrence of some attacks of physical illnesses – eg migraine, asthma, high blood pressure, ulcer, skin diseases. This stress can be caused by the need to hold back strong emotions, such as frustration and anger (people vary in what they find stressful)
- a physical illness triggers a mental illness – eg DEPRESSION after glandular fever
- a physical disorder appears as a mental illness – eg meningitis or DEMENTIA (see ORGANIC DISORDERS earlier in this chapter)
- psychological factors determine the effect of a physical illness on the patient – eg he may deny that he is ill and refuse all treatment. About one-sixth of heart attack survivors develop long-lasting ANXIETY or DEPRESSION which interferes with their recovery.

See also HYPOCHONDRIA and HYSTERIA in Chapter 5.

4

Types of treatment

There are probably more misconceptions about the treatment of mental than of physical illness. It is sometimes believed to consist of either lying on a couch relating one's dreams or being strapped to a bed enduring electric shocks. This chapter explains what the treatments really involve and why they are used.

The treatments are described in alphabetical order for easy reference, but they do not in fact fall into discrete categories since many of the therapies overlap. There are two basic types which may run side by side as part of an overall programme for a patient: **physical treatments** (DRUGS and ECT – ELECTROCONVULSIVE THERAPY) and **talking treatments** (which can be considered under the general heading of PSYCHOTHERAPY). In any case, many doctors try to adopt a holistic approach which sets out to treat the whole person and not just the symptoms.

For more details of how these treatments are used for specific mental illnesses and emotional problems, see the section on 'What can be done' for the relevant disorder in Chapter 5 or 6. Details are given in Chapters 9 to 11 on the availability of these treatments within the NHS, private and voluntary services, and how to get them.

Abreaction

This treatment is used in special circumstances to enable a patient to discuss events or emotions which he could not otherwise even think about. It is used for some cases of severe ANXIETY or HYSTERIA in which the sufferer has 'buried' memories of a particularly distressing incident – such as a traumatic accident. To enable him to relax and talk about the problem, the therapist may use HYPNOTHERAPY or, more usually, inject a DRUG. Depending on the drug used, the patient may sleep for a while immediately after receiving it. Then, with encouragement from the therapist, he will start to recall his feelings. Despite the methods used to relax the patient, it is still very distressing to re-experience the incident. However, by doing so, and discussing his feelings with the therapist, the patient is more able to come to terms with them and accept what has happened.

There is an important distinction to be made between abreaction and the use of truth drugs. Abreaction is used to release information which the patient has 'repressed' – that is, he is not consciously aware of it. However, it seems that if someone has made a conscious decision not to disclose a fact, he will not do so under abreaction.

Abreaction can be used for patients who are not staying in hospital, provided they are accompanied home.

Behaviour therapy

This is a form of PSYCHOTHERAPY. It is based on the theory that behaviour is learned and can therefore be un-learned. There are several theories of how this learning takes place, but they all maintain that in some cases the 'wrong' behaviour occurs in a particular situation, thus causing distress – PHOBIAS are a good example. Behaviour therapy seeks to remove these unwanted behaviours and/or to help the patient to learn better behaviour patterns. What distinguishes behaviour therapy from some other forms of PSYCHOTHERAPY is that it concentrates on what the patient can be observed to do. There is no speculation as to why he behaves in this way. However, many therapists do combine a behavioural approach with other psychotherapeutic techniques, and may therefore spend some time discussing the patient's motivation and relevant history with him.

If behaviour therapy is to be used, the initial meeting(s) with the therapist will be used to decide together what specific goals are to be reached. A particular pattern of behaviour, such as a PHOBIA or COMPULSION, will be the target of the techniques to be used. It is likely that a time-limit will be set – for example, ten one-hour sessions at weekly intervals. At the end of this course, the therapist may decide to extend the therapy for a few more sessions if he thinks that this would help. Very often the therapist will set 'homework' to be carried out by the patient between therapy sessions. This might be practising alone a task which has been attempted during the last session with the therapist. Sometimes members of the patient's family are asked to become involved.

One important characteristic of behaviour therapy is that it requires the active co-operation of the patient – he has to want it to succeed and make a positive effort at all the assignments set. Behaviour therapy cannot be 'done' to a patient. It works for many types of NEUROSIS, but even with a dedicated patient it will not be effective in every case. Two problems are whether the patient can during therapy generalise the achievements to his everyday life, and whether the effects will last. It is not a lengthy process – a course will last no longer than a few months, and may achieve results much more quickly.

There are many behavioural techniques and whichever are selected for a particular patient will be fully explained to him first, so that he can agree to the proposed therapy. As a general guide to behaviour therapy, some of these techniques are briefly described below:

Desensitisation The patient is helped to relax in some way. Then whatever he fears is gradually introduced to him – perhaps by first showing him a picture, and then a model of it. By associating pleasant, relaxed feelings with the feared object or situation, it is hoped to change the patient's behaviour towards it.

Modelling The patient watches and usually copies the therapist doing the behaviour which is to be learned.

Operant conditioning The patient is rewarded for 'correct' behaviour – ie for achieving the goal of that part of the therapy. This might be a tangible reward if a 'token economy' method is being used with a group of long-stay hospital patients. The tokens they earn can be exchanged for small items such as sweets and magazines. Praise is always given as well, and this is often used alone as the reward for carrying out the behaviour which is being encouraged.

Flooding or implosion This involves bringing the patient face-to-face with the object or situation he fears (always with his prior agreement). He is encouraged to tolerate the resulting ANXIETY and even the panic, to learn that it does eventually subside and that there is no lasting catastrophic outcome. Sometimes hypnosis (see HYPNOTHERAPY) or tranquillising DRUGS are given on the first few occasions to help the patient to face the situation. This, and some other techniques, are sometimes carried out in the patient's imagination – he conjures up a picture of himself in the situation. This can be effective, and is the only possibility when the situation cannot practically be arranged for numerous practice sessions (eg for the PHOBIA of flying). However, it is difficult or impossible for some people to get their imaginations to work to order in this way.

Paradoxical intention This is used to remove specific symptoms. The patient is instructed to cause the symptom to appear, then to make it worse. Surprisingly, this can lead to the symptom disappearing – see for example HYPERACTIVITY and PHOBIAS.

Contracts These are used in FAMILY THERAPY and sometimes for MARITAL PROBLEMS. Each person involved specifies what he wants the other person to do in their home-life together, and what he is willing to do. They aim to keep this contract, and report on their progress at the next therapy session. If alterations in behaviour are achieved, it can produce changes in their attitudes towards each other, and so improve the relationship.

Aversion therapy This involves associating an unwanted behaviour with an unpleasant situation – such as a slight electric shock or feeling sick. It has been used with ALCOHOL DEPENDENCE and sometimes with certain SEXUAL PROBLEMS. The same rules about consent to treatment apply to this as to any other form of treatment – see the final section in Chapter 11.

Social skills training and **assertiveness training** These forms of therapy are for people who have generalised problems of poor self-confidence and difficulties in making relationships. They may be relevant for people with ANXIETY, social PHOBIAS and some PERSONALITY DISORDERS. The methods used may involve a therapist instructing a small group of patients and modelling (see above) a particular type of social behaviour for them to copy. Each patient then tries this out, perhaps swapping roles with the therapist or other patients in the group. A video recording might be used to help them to discuss each other's performances. Other forms of behaviour therapy, such as operant conditioning, may be incorporated into the training. For example, the therapist might praise the patient every time he smiles at the person with whom he is role-playing. There is some debate as to whether skills taught in therapy actually help patients to lead more socially fulfilling lives.

Cognitive therapy

This is a form of PSYCHOTHERAPY which incorporates elements of BEHAVIOUR THERAPY. It is based on the theory that changes in emotions and behaviour are determined by the person's thoughts about events that happen to him. Therapy is aimed at helping people challenge and change these patterns of thought. It is used mainly for ANXIETY and DEPRESSION. The patient's way of thinking is to believe that life is frightening or gloomy – everything tends to be interpreted in this light. For example, he might always blame himself if relationships go wrong or he might think that he is a complete failure because he made a small error. The therapist helps him to monitor this style of thinking and to consider alternatives. Thus errors become just errors, rather than evidence of complete failure. The person must test out his beliefs using graded tasks or experiments. Sometimes these aspects of the therapy are called behavioural because the person is asked to change or engage in certain forms of behaviour. An example would be a RELAXATION technique, with therapy to help the patient change his habitual way of thinking by imagining himself facing specific situations calmly.

Counselling and befriending

This is sometimes viewed as one type of PSYCHOTHERAPY, but most counsellors would probably describe it as an informal alternative for certain problems. Counselling falls between what a friend does when listening to someone's problem and the specialised techniques used in BEHAVIOUR and COGNITIVE THERAPY and PSYCHOANALYSIS.

Befriending This is a service offered by some voluntary organisations for specific problems, such as BEREAVEMENT or LONELINESS among elderly people. It aims to do what a good friend might – offering an attentive and sympathetic ear and a shoulder to cry on if needed. The befriender does not claim to have any special skills or expert advice but will offer support.

Counselling This goes a step further but still without providing answers to problems experienced by the client (counsellors do not call the people they see patients). The counsellor aims to help the person to help himself. Using his experience, and perhaps training, he will discuss the client's current problems, encourage him to look at relevant areas of his life and possible alternative ways of looking at them. There is far less emphasis than in some forms of PSYCHOTHERAPY on the client's earlier life and relationships. The counsellor helps him to examine his feelings, thoughts and actions, but will not tell him how to change any of them – the client must come to these realisations himself. A counsellor may, however, make suggestions or comment on how certain behaviour by the person or those close to him might be interpreted in various ways. More than a befriender, a counsellor is concerned with how the client is reacting to the comments put to him, and how his self-awareness is developing. The counsellor wants the person to discover better ways of coping with life's problems. If solutions cannot be found, counselling can help the client come to terms with an unalterable situation. A good relationship with the counsellor is important, so that the person feels confident to talk about possibly painful emotions. It may then be possible for the client to try out new approaches – perhaps displaying his feelings more openly – without fearing what the counsellor's reaction will be. The counsellor will encourage and support the person, but will not respond emotionally as a friend might. There are no instant cures for emotional problems, and while a few counselling sessions may be all that is needed to find a more satisfactory course, it is wise not to expect too much too soon.

The best reason for distinguishing counselling from PSYCHO-THERAPY is that counsellors help clients with emotional problems, but are not able to be the sole source of help for those who are mentally ill. Not all those who offer counselling have the word Counsellor in their job-titles. It can be provided by social workers, psychologists, nurses and doctors, among others. More information can be obtained from the **British Association for Counselling**.

Drugs

Since the 1950s more and better drugs have been available to help mentally ill people to cope with their symptoms. Sometimes the illness disappears naturally during the treatment and the drugs have merely made it easier to tolerate the illness. In other cases the drug must be taken continuously or intermittently for many years to keep the symptoms at bay. Drugs reduce the mental suffering of millions of people whose lives might otherwise be intolerable because of mental illness, enabling them to live outside hospital instead of becoming and remaining long-stay in-patients, and by paving the way for other forms of treatment. It is arguable, however, whether drugs ever cure an episode of mental illness and whether they should be prescribed at all for emotional problems, or some cases of minor mental illnesses. Relieving a depressed or anxious mood can make it easier for the sufferer to face up to, and deal with, his problems. His mood may also be making life very difficult for his family or work colleagues, so that it is better for others for his symptoms to be treated. The argument against drug treatment for emotional problems and neurotic illnesses is that the sufferer may feel that this is all that is necessary, and not consider ways in which he can help himself.

Individual drugs are not discussed in detail in this book. There are many paperbacks for non-medical readers on the composition and effects of the widely prescribed drugs. In this section, the main groups of drugs for mental disorder are described, with information on how and why they are believed to work. General advice on being prescribed drugs is given in Chapter 9. Practical information for those taking the various types of drugs (for example, on side-effects) is given in Chapter 5 in the 'What can be done' sections under the relevant mental illness.

To understand something of how the drugs work it is necessary to go back to the 'Causes of mental illness' described in Chapter 2. One of the theories described there refers to chemical messengers in the brain – substances which transmit information between the nerve cells. Much of this theory is based on the observation that many drugs which relieve mental symptoms also affect these chemical messengers. It seems that by correcting imbalances in the various message-transmission systems the drugs restore a more normal mental state. Predictably, the situation is far more complicated than this simple explanation – for example, two drugs may differ in the way they affect the chemistry of the brain yet have the same effect on mental symptoms. There may well be other chemical messenger systems as yet undiscovered, so the effect on them cannot be monitored. As more is learnt, drugs are likely to be developed which have more specific and predictable effects.

Below are the main groups of drugs prescribed for mental illness:

Antipsychotic drugs As their name suggests, these are for the severe mental illnesses or PSYCHOSES. They are also known as neuroleptics or major tranquillisers, though the latter name is rather misleading. Their main effect is to remove the severe symptoms of psychoses such as hallucinations and delusions, and severe agitation (see SCHIZOPHRENIA, PARANOID DISORDERS and MANIA). The side-effects of this type of drug are discussed under SCHIZOPHRENIA, but the reason for one effect can conveniently be described here. If the imbalance of chemical messengers present in schizophrenia is over-corrected, the balance will be tipped too far in the opposite direction. The resulting imbalance is that found in the brains of sufferers from PARKINSON'S DISEASE, and thus similar symptoms can be produced in those taking neuroleptics for schizophrenia. This is called Parkinsonism, and to alleviate the muscle tremor, the drugs used for Parkinson's disease are prescribed. There are ways of reducing the risk of Parkinsonism, as discussed under SCHIZOPHRENIA, and it is often argued that it is in any case less debilitating than schizophrenia.

Antianxiety drugs Again the name describes the effect – reducing the symptoms of ANXIETY and tension. They are also used for EPILEPSY and insomnia. Another name for this type of drug is minor tranquillisers, but they are in no sense a mini version of the major tranquillisers used for psychoses. Because of their effects, they may be known as sedatives and sleeping pills, though there is little difference between the drugs.

Until the 1960s barbiturates were commonly prescribed as sedatives and sleeping pills, but they have now been largely replaced by the benzodiazepines. The latter affect the brain's chemical messengers and also relax muscles throughout the body. Though safer in many respects than barbiturates, benzodiazepines are not without their problems, one of which is the risk of tranquilliser addiction. Not everyone who takes the drugs is at risk of becoming dependent on them but some people find it extremely difficult to stop taking tranquillisers. This is discussed again in Chapter 5 under ANXIETY, and advice for those who feel they might be dependent on benzodiazepines is given under DRUG DEPENDENCE.

Antidepressants These can be divided into three groups, depending on how they appear to affect the brain's chemical messengers – tricyclics, MAOIs and a third miscellaneous group of newer formulations. As well as DEPRESSION, the first two groups have also been used for some PHOBIAS, and tricyclics are thought by some doctors to help with OBSESSIVE DISORDERS. Because of the effect of MAOI antidepressants on chemicals in the brain, it is very important to avoid eating foods containing certain chemicals (see DEPRESSION).

Lithium salts These stand somewhat alone since lithium is the only drug found to be effective in preventing recurrent episodes of MANIC-DEPRESSION. It has also been used with less spectacular success as a treatment for MANIA.

Drug trials

There are two ways of testing a newly developed drug. One is to compare it with a known, effective drug. The other is to test whether it works better than a placebo – a pill without any active chemical ingredient. Placebos are sometimes called 'sugar pills', but they do, surprisingly, sometimes have a therapeutic effect. This is because the patient, not knowing that they do not contain any active ingredient, believes that they will help. Exactly how this placebo mechanism works is still the subject of research.

When drugs have been passed as safe, they are tested on patients to determine their effectiveness. A doctor must ask those patients he wishes to participate in a drug trial for their permission – which they can refuse to give. These days, trials usually compare new drugs with established ones. Though the doctor will not necessarily tell the patient which he is prescribing, he must explain that it might be the new drug. Similarly, if a placebo forms part of the trial, the doctor must tell the patient that he might receive the placebo. He cannot tell him definitely if he is prescribing the 'sugar pill', because this would ruin the placebo effect.

Medical research is discussed in more detail in the Consumers' Association/Patients Association publication *A Patient's Guide to the National Health Service*.

Electroconvulsive therapy (ECT)

This treatment, known also as electroplexy, consists of passing a small electric current through the brain. It is now used almost exclusively for severe DEPRESSION, though it is occasionally given for SCHIZOPHRENIA and MANIA. Doctors do not fully understand why it works (and some dispute that it does), but it seems to affect various parts of the brain and its chemical messenger systems.

As a general anaesthetic is given, it is essential not to eat or drink anything for several hours before the treatment. A muscle-relaxing drug is injected, and then the anaesthetic. (Strictly speaking this is modified ECT – unmodified ECT without these preparations is used only in exceptional circumstances.) An electrode is placed over each temple (bilateral ECT) or just over the right temple in right-handed patients and the left one in left-handed people (unilateral ECT). The small current delivered from the electrode(s) causes a convulsive fit but the drug and anaesthetic reduce the visible effect of this to a slight trembling at most and the patient is quite unaware of it. Within a few minutes the patient begins to come round from the anaesthetic and may well feel confused for up to an hour. During this time he will rest in bed. Some people suffer certain after-effects such as headache, stiff muscles and feeling sick. These should be mentioned to a nurse or doctor who may give the patient some medicine on this occasion or at the next session. Out-patients can be given ECT, but there needs to be someone to accompany them home afterwards.

It takes several days for ECT to have any effect, and it is always given as a course of sessions. The frequency and number of sessions varies, from once to three times a week for up to 20 sessions, or even more. Generally four to 12 sessions are needed. Being elderly or pregnant does not pose any special risks – in fact, results seem to be especially good with elderly patients. Having ECT is probably no more dangerous than receiving a general anaesthetic for any other reason. The after-effect which causes most inconvenience is memory disturbance. While the patient is having a course of ECT he may (especially if he is elderly), begin to have problems remembering people's names, or find it very difficult to learn new information. Within a few weeks of completing the course, these problems should have disappeared. Research suggests that unilateral ECT has less effect on the memory.

See CONSENT TO TREATMENT in Chapter 11.

Family therapy

This is not a type of PSYCHOTHERAPY but a way of using various psychotherapeutic methods. It involves an approach to mental illness which sees the sufferer as a member of a network of people – most importantly as part of his family. Therapists using this approach are concerned with how members of this family communicate and with the relationships between them. They believe that to consider a patient in isolation from his family would often be to miss much of the problem and ways of resolving it. Getting to know the patient's family better may reveal that there are rigid alliances dividing the members into two camps. Or it may be that no one in the family has a strong sense of identity – the members function as a single unit, but do not develop as individuals. If a therapist suggests family therapy for a patient, it does not mean that he believes the family to be responsible for the patient's mental illness. Therapists are concerned with resolving distress and conflict, not with apportioning blame.

Any of the methods of PSYCHOTHERAPY can be used, depending on the therapist's training. He may use a psychodynamic approach (see PSYCHOANALYSIS), or a BEHAVIOURAL method such as contracts between members of the family. Some therapists aim to teach better methods of communication, or to help parents develop better rela-tionships with their children – not just with the person who was the original patient. Family therapy can be used with almost any mental illness or emotional problem, though it is not relevant for every case. It is particularly appropriate for many problems suffered by children and adolescents, and for MARITAL PROBLEMS.

The therapist decides which members of the patient's family he would like to be involved and invites them to attend at least some of the sessions. This always includes those living in the same household as the patient, and probably any brothers or sisters who have left home. It is thought that even young children can attend these therapy sessions without harm. Grandparents and other relatives may be thought by the therapist to have a significant role – and even some friends and neighbours may be invited. This group will not necessarily always be invited to the same sessions. On occasions the therapist may wish to see the parents, or members of the immediate household, alone. The therapist may wish to hear about the lives of members of the family going back several generations. He will be interested in patterns of illnesses, personality and specific types of behaviour which sometimes appear in successive generations. Co-operation from all those invited to the sessions is clearly an advantage, and successful therapy requires a positive commitment from at least the patient and most of his family.

Often the therapist will decide at the beginning of the therapy how many sessions are to be held. These may be at the patient's home, or at a clinic or surgery. Sessions may be held only once every three or four weeks, but therapists using a psychoanalytic approach will make more frequent appointments. Assignments may be set as homework between sessions, particularly if behavioural methods are being used.

Sometimes two therapists work together, perhaps one taking the lead and the other commenting to him from time to time. Family therapists in at least one area use a system whereby one therapist watches the session from behind a one-way screen, communicating with the other therapist by telephone. Sometimes the family's permission is asked to record the session. The recording may later be discussed with the therapist's colleagues or for teaching purposes.

The mental health professions listed in Chapter 8 do not include a job of 'family therapist'. Those using this approach are usually employed in other capacities – such as psychologists, social workers and psychotherapists.

Group therapy

Like FAMILY THERAPY this is a way of providing PSYCHOTHERAPY and may use any of the available methods. It is more widely available than individual therapy within the NHS. Families are clearly a sort of group, but the groups to be discussed here are of people who did not previously know each other and are invited to join in order to help with their individual problems. Some groups are made up of similar people suffering from the same problem. Most, however, are mixed groups of males and females of various ages with different but probably related problems. No one is made to feel unique, so there would never be just one woman or just one sufferer from AGORAPHOBIA. Most groups have between six and twelve members who are usually asked not to meet socially between the therapy sessions. These last one or two hours and are held once or twice a week for up to two years. In closed groups new members cannot join after the first session. Open groups accept new members at any stage. The other conditions of entering group therapy are that members arrive on time for the sessions, keep confidential what they hear during discussions and try to be honest about their feelings.

Discussing personal problems in front of a group of strangers may not seem a helpful form of therapy but it does have several advantages over individual PSYCHOTHERAPY. Members realise that they are not alone in their problems – others experience ANXIETY, DEPRESSION, PHOBIAS and so on in very similar ways. They can encourage each other and in some types of group are able to discuss practical ways of coping with the problems caused by their illness. Group therapy is especially valuable for sufferers who have difficulty in making or maintaining relationships, or in expressing emotions. They are helped to contribute to the group by the other members who will not let one member remain silent every week, and by the group leader who is the therapist (there may be two). Those who are shy or unsure about their relationships with others can try out new ways of behaving in the 'protected' environment of the group. This may give them the confidence to act differently in their everyday lives.

Depending on the therapeutic methods being used, and on his own style, the therapist may participate as a member, talking about himself and his own feelings. Other group leaders intervene only if they feel it necessary – for example, to encourage the group to comment on what someone has said, or to support one member who is being shut out by the rest. Being in a group where the therapist does not really act as a leader, but sits back to observe and listen, can be disconcerting at first.

Group behaviour therapy This uses the BEHAVIOURAL methods described above, usually with a group of people who are suffering from the same problem.

Group analysis This adapts the principles of PSYCHOANALYSIS to take into account the ways in which groups differ from one-to-one relationships.

Encounter groups These are not designed for people who are mentally ill or suffering from emotional problems and they could be dangerous for vulnerable people. The leaders are not usually professionals and may have no training in group therapy.

Group counselling This uses the principles of COUNSELLING described above. More than in other forms of group therapy, group counselling encourages the members to exchange information on their difficulties, without such definite aims of resolving them. Such groups are unlikely to operate within the NHS, and many of the groups held by national voluntary organisations fall into this category.

Homoeopathy

This is one of the complementary or alternative therapies which some people prefer to the orthodox medicine usually practised in this country. Homoeopaths aim to treat the cause of the problem and free the patient's own mental and emotional resources, so that he can look at his problems with a fresh eye and handle them himself. Unlike conventional DRUGS, homoeopathic remedies do not suppress symptoms.

Homoeopathic prescribing involves giving a minute amount of a substance to relieve symptoms which in its original state it would actually cause in a healthy person. For example, a remedy for emotional disturbance is made from a substance which would induce the same symptoms had it not been homoeopathically prepared.

Further information can be obtained from the **British Homoeopathic Association** and the **Institute for Complementary Medicine**.

Hypnotherapy

Hypnotherapy is PSYCHOTHERAPY in which hypnosis is used. It can be helpful for emotional problems and neuroses. Many definitions of hypnosis have been proposed, but a common way of describing it is as being in a state of 'altered awareness'. Someone under hypnosis is neither asleep, nor unconscious, but he is not fully awake either in the usual sense. One way of trying to understand what it is like to be under hypnosis is to think what happens at a very emotional moment – you are not consciously aware of anything irrelevant to the immediate situation. Suddenly your state of awareness has been altered. Being totally absorbed in a day-dream, for example, also resembles the state of being under hypnosis.

There are two main approaches to hypnotherapy. One uses the relaxed state of hypnosis to enable the patient to recall and talk about experiences and emotions which he would not otherwise have brought to mind. This allows the therapist to be of more help to the patient in trying to understand the nature of his problems. Hypnosis is thus used as an aid to gaining insight during the psychotherapy session. The therapist may take a psychodynamic approach (see PSYCHOANALYSIS) and this type of therapy is called hypnoanalysis. The aim is to help the person uncover the causes of his present problems. The **British Hypnotherapy Association** uses this approach. For a small charge they will provide more detailed information on hypnotherapy.

A different form of hypnotherapy involves suggestion. The person under hypnosis is more susceptible to suggestions made to him, which might be of increased confidence or of decreased fear and tension. Minor ANXIETY and some PSYCHOSOMATIC DISORDERS can be treated in this way, perhaps incorporating aspects of BEHAVIOUR THERAPY. The **School of Hypnosis and Advanced Psychotherapy** trains people in a form of hypnotherapy which includes the use of suggestion.

Members of the **British Society of Experimental and Clinical Hypnosis**, the **British Society of Medical and Dental Hypnosis** and the **Association for Applied Hypnosis** may use either approach, depending on the circumstances.

Some people fear that under hypnosis they may do something outrageous that they would ordinarily never consider doing. While their conscious inhibitions might be reduced to a very small degree, this would never extend to doing something contrary to their normal moral standards. Hypnosis cannot make a person do something he does not want to, and successful hypnotherapy therefore relies partly on the patient's willingness to co-operate positively with the therapist.

Industrial therapy

This helps to prepare people for returning to the working environment after a medium or long stay in hospital, and perhaps to doing jobs very different from their previous occupations. Hospitals have Re-Employment Training and Industrial Units where factory-type work is provided. Mental illness can often impair self-motivation and social skills, so industrial therapy acts as a re-introduction to the discipline of arriving for work on time, and to working alongside other people. Industrial therapy organisations outside hospitals are much less common than industrial units within them, but provide valuable training and employment experience. REHABILITATION (helping people to resume as near normal lives as possible after illness) and EMPLOYMENT are discussed at greater length in Chapter 13.

Occupational and related therapies

Occupational therapy is the use of any activity related to ordinary living – such as self care, domestic chores, social and leisure activities – chosen to promote independence in all aspects of the patient's life. Except where the patient is likely to have to remain in hospital, the aim is to prepare him for leaving, especially after a long stay. The activities may take place in the patient's ward or in the hospital occupational therapy department.

Occupational therapists also work with people with acute mental illness and use a variety of techniques to assess and treat specific problems such as ANXIETY states and PHOBIAS. Some occupational therapists also work in the community. Therapists promote new skills and help patients to practise old ones, so that they can look after themselves as much as possible in their own homes. The activities should increase the patient's self-confidence and self-sufficiency. Domestic skills are practised and developed with a view to the person gaining greater independence. Crafts are used for the purpose of stimulation and creative achievement. Music, drama, art and movement may also be used by the occupational therapist.

Discussion groups on various subjects provide information (perhaps on everyday matters such as bank or post office services), and broaden social skills. Occupational therapy also tries to improve the patient's ability to make decisions and use initiative.

Of the related therapies sometimes used in occupational therapy departments, **art therapy** is especially useful for those who find it difficult to express their confusion and distress in words. Putting their feelings into a picture may reduce tension and distress, and can also help those trying to treat them to understand their problems more quickly. **Play therapy** can be used in a similar way with children.

Dance therapy, which is offered at a few hospitals as part of the rehabilitation programme, is one way of helping patients to increase their self-confidence and co-ordination. Dance therapy and **movement therapy** are also methods of releasing emotion, as is **drama therapy**. This has some links with the role-play in social skills training described under BEHAVIOUR THERAPY. For example, a patient might adopt the role of someone else in his family, with the rest of the group playing other family members. Drama therapy can also be used less intensively as a source of enjoyment for hospital patients, and is useful for developing social skills. **Music therapy** is another example of using an art form both for entertainment (which is probably therapeutic) and in specialised ways as a therapy.

Physiotherapy and remedial gymnastics
These therapies aim to improve physical well-being and thereby mental health. A physiotherapist may teach exercises, lead sports activities and provide RELAXATION classes.

Psychoanalysis
This is one specific form of PSYCHOTHERAPY. Strictly speaking, only those who have trained at certain Institutes are psychoanalysts, but the term is often used loosely to cover forms of psychotherapy derived from a number of theoretical schools. These are psychodynamic theories,

which hold that the reasons for a person's current behaviour and mental state are to be found in his earlier experiences – especially those which happened during his childhood (see Chapter 2).

Freud's analysis of his patients, based on this theory, was called psychoanalysis. This involves the patient lying on a couch, with the analyst sitting out of his line of vision. The patient then 'free associates' – that is, he says everything that comes into his mind. The analyst does not encourage him to talk about any particular subject, nor does he offer support and sympathy. His only role is to interpret what the patient says in terms of its significance to the unconscious reasons for his current problems. This usually continues for years, often with the same material being repeated by the patient and interpreted by the analyst again and again. One aspect of psychoanalysis is 'transference', during which the patient transfers to the therapist his feelings about someone who has played a key role in his life. The therapist might thus 'become' his father for a time, while these emotions are discussed and interpreted.

Other psychodynamic theories developed from Freud's work, leading to related forms of interpretive (or insight) psychotherapy. Therapists offering these are sometimes called analytical and individual psychologists. The techniques and theories vary, some stressing the importance of interpreting dreams, day-dreams or aspirations, for example. The central aim of all these psychodynamic therapies, however, is for the patient to achieve insight into what is presumed to be contained in his 'unconscious mind'.

One of the major drawbacks of interpretive psychotherapy is the time it takes. Sessions last 50 to 60 minutes and are held four or five times a week, usually for years. To overcome this problem, **brief insight therapy** was developed. The therapist plays a more active role than in psychoanalysis, encouraging the patient to talk about specific aspects of his life. The problems to be tackled are defined at the outset as goals for the therapy. Sessions of 30 to 45 minutes are held weekly, usually for up to 15 weeks.

Transactional analysis The basic premise is that the 'transactions' or experiences a child has with his parents influence how he lives later. If he grows up with the assumption that 'I am not OK', but that the rest of the world is OK, he will live in such a way as to prove that he is a failure.

Of those people for whom psychotherapy is relevant, only a small proportion are suitable for psychoanalysis. By definition, much of the material which is brought up during a session can be very painful to re-live. Anyone who is not willing to examine these areas and find out information about himself which he may not like would not be suitable for interpretive psychotherapy.

Psychosurgery

This is also known as leucotomy, functional neurosurgery and (in the USA) lobotomy. These names all refer to surgery on part of the brain to relieve intolerable mental illness which has not improved despite years of treatment by all other known means. Those considered for surgery have almost invariably been in hospital for some time. Psychosurgery is now extremely rare in this country and, as with any treatment, there is no guarantee of the operation being successful. However, some patients have been greatly helped, and even for those who do not improve, the risks these days are slight. The operation does not seem to reduce the patient's intelligence, nor affect his personality. He may be less creative or able to learn new skills. However, psychosurgery is not even considered unless the patient already has an extremely poor quality of life. Such people may be suffering from severe DEPRESSION, ANXIETY or OBSESSIVE DISORDERS. The benefit of psychosurgery in SCHIZOPHRENIA is less clear.

There is considerable debate about how psychosurgery works and whether it should be performed at all. It probably affects the brain's chemical messenger systems, in common with the other physical treatments of DRUGS and ECT. After the operation the patient may experience changing moods for a while. Then a steady, improved mood should develop, at anything up to a year after surgery. Despite improved techniques there is still a very small chance of the change in mood being too extreme – for example, causing a previously severely agitated person to become 'lifeless'.

There are special provisions concerning consent to psychosurgery – see Chapter 11.

Psychotherapy

Any treatment for a mental or emotional problem which does not use physical methods could be called psychotherapy. The main therapeutic tool is talking, and it is the ways in which words are used, and the additional activities by the therapist and patient, which differentiate the forms of psychotherapy. Some people feel that a few of these methods do not truly constitute psychotherapy – those most commonly excluded are COUNSELLING and HYPNOTHERAPY. Such arguments on classification abound in psychiatry.

Supportive psychotherapy provides reassurance, encouragement, and a degree of sympathy – certainly more than PSYCHOANALYSIS, though rather less than would be expected from a close friend. The therapist interprets the nature of the problem and explains how the patient's difficulties have produced the symptoms of which he is aware. Therapy thus relieves much of the patient's confusion and worry about what he is experiencing. 'Am I going mad?' is a question often put by clients to their therapists. (Psychotherapists often refer to the people they see as 'clients', rather than patients, as do counsellors.) Unlike those using interpretive psychotherapy, as described under PSYCHOANALYSIS, these therapists are not particularly concerned with the patient's early life unless this appears to have a specific relevance to the present problems. The help given by the therapist may take the form of suggesting other attitudes which the patient might adopt towards himself, others and life in general. The therapist may help the person to change his emotional reactions to circumstances which cannot be changed or avoided. Therapists never tell their patients what to do – they can only help them to reach more satisfactory conclusions themselves. If psychotherapy is successful the patient will feel more confident, contented and able to face life's challenges. Sessions with the therapist may be 30 to 60 minutes long and are held one to three times a week.

As has been said several times in this chapter, the patient's commitment and co-operation are essential. Another vital ingredient of psychotherapy is a good relationship with the therapist. This does not mean warm friendliness but the patient should feel a degree of trust and confidence in the therapist's ability and commitment to the problem.

Neurolinguistic programming is a form of psychotherapy being used by some therapists. It offers a model of how people communicate and aims to provide the client with different ways of responding to situations of stress, other than the way which is currently causing him to feel ANXIETY, DEPRESSION and so on.

Psychotherapy may not appeal to every patient, but if other methods of treatment are to be used it is probably necessary to have at least some form of COUNSELLING or supportive psychotherapy in addition. With the more intensive forms of psychotherapy, the patient needs to be able to express himself and to be interested in the workings of his own mind. All forms of psychotherapy stem from psychology – the study of how the mind works, as opposed to the physical functioning of the brain.

It is possible for patients to feel worse after psychotherapy. This is generally claimed to be because the patient did not really want to change his attitudes or behaviour, so resisted the therapist's efforts. Patients who do not improve with psychotherapy may also feel worse because this failure further reduces their self-confidence. A different approach, with a different therapist, might produce better results – provided the patient is honestly intent on improvement.

Reality orientation

This method is used only for sufferers from DEMENTIA and other confused elderly people living in hospital or special accommodation for elderly mentally ill people, or attending day facilities for such patients. It has been used in the UK since the 1970s and its effectiveness is still being studied. With patients who are so confused that they cannot give their name or the day of the week, all attempts to help are worth investigating. The overall aim is to improve their orientation – most fundamentally the patient's awareness of who and where he is, the time and date.

In informal or 24-hour reality orientation, those caring for the elderly person continually provide this information when they speak to him. They will remind him of the date, describe what they are doing, ask him what he is wearing and so on. If the patient replies correctly he is encouraged. But the staff will ignore or discourage incoherent rambling. To help the patients, signs are put on doors, large clear-faced clocks are prominently placed and so on.

Some homes and hospitals also use formal reality orientation. This is a more intensive session of encouraging patients to be aware of who and where they are. Small groups work with one or two therapists, gradually tackling more advanced information, such as accurately recalling their past lives.

It does seem that patients receiving this therapy do become increasingly able to answer orientation questions but other aspects of their behaviour (see DEMENTIA) do not improve.

Relaxation and self-help techniques

This forms part of several types of therapy, such as HYPNOTHERAPY and some BEHAVIOUR THERAPY. Used alone it is also one self-help method of coping with STRESS and tension. There are various books and cassette tapes giving instructions for relaxation exercises (see pages 157–158). It does not matter which method is used, so long as it leads to complete relaxation.

Relaxation does not just mean reducing muscle tension. It is equally if not more important to achieve a peaceful state of mind. This is often done by concentrating on a single image, phrase or word (the 'mantra'). Attaining this state is called **meditation**. Again, manuals are available for learning how to relax in these ways. Meditation is sometimes used with PSYCHOTHERAPY. The experience of meditating can alter the person's view of himself, helping him to approach life differently.

Yoga is another useful technique for physical and mental relaxation. Though teach-yourself books are available, it is perhaps best to start with personal tuition from a qualified instructor.

Biofeedback training is much less widely available and special equipment is needed. The aim is to learn to change aspects of the body's functioning which have in the past been considered to be purely automatic rather than under conscious control. Examples are muscle tension, heart rate and brain wave activity. For instance, an increased level of one type of brain wave produces a feeling of relaxation. Special equipment connected to the body gives a continuous measure of the particular function being used – eg the tension of a muscle in the forehead. The machines provide information by a needle on a dial, or by emitting a tone, for example. The person concentrates on this feedback and the therapist encourages him to control his body's activity in the desired way. The ultimate aim is for the person to be able to achieve this control without receiving continuous feedback. He will probably be asked to practise this at home between sessions with the therapist.

Auto-suggestion is a technique by which the patient imagines himself to be in the physical or mental state he desires. For example, if he feels himself becoming anxious, he repeatedly tells himself 'I feel calm and relaxed' until the feelings of anxiety disappear. Auto-suggestion, which is basically a 'positive thinking' technique, can be used in combination with yoga or biofeedback.

All relaxation methods are relevant to ANXIETY sufferers and to many people with emotional problems. Any condition in which stress plays a major role (see also PSYCHOSOMATIC DISORDERS) may benefit from using a relaxation or self-help technique of the type described here. Professional guidance is always recommended.

Speech therapy
Communication with other people is of great importance to maintaining social function and to helping people lead a life that is as worthwhile as possible. The relatively small number of speech therapists work directly with individual patients and help others working with patients to improve their communication skills. Speech therapy is being more widely used now in mental illness hospitals.

Which treatment?

There is no Best Buy treatment for most illnesses or problems, and the choice depends on many factors specific to the individual case. These include the symptoms and possible causes of the illness, various characteristics of the patient such as his homelife and attitudes towards his disorder, and the local availability of different types of treatment. Ideally, there would always be a choice for patients but this is often not the case for NHS patients. The availability of NHS and private services (and also local authority and voluntary provisions) is covered in Chapters 9 to 11. If you do have preferences about your treatment, Chapter 11 gives some advice under OUT-PATIENTS APPOINTMENTS.

There are two problems in comparing the effectiveness of various treatments. One is the placebo effect discussed under DRUGS. The other is spontaneous remission, which is when a disorder suddenly clears up by itself – at least temporarily. If treatment has been given, the improvement is then wrongly attributed to the therapy, when in fact the patient would have got better anyway. This has been known to happen even in serious cases of mental illness, but spontaneous remission is more likely in certain circumstances:

- this is the first time the patient has been mentally ill
- the illness developed suddenly and recently
- the illness followed a very stressful incident or period
- the sufferer has no personality disorders or social difficulties
- there are relatives and friends to offer support.

5

Mental illnesses

Despite the title of this chapter, not all the conditions described are invariably classified as mental illnesses: there is no precise definition of what constitutes a mental illness. Some of the conditions listed here would be almost universally recognised as such – MANIC-DEPRESSION and SCHIZOPHRENIA, for example. Others, such as ALCOHOL DE-PENDENCE and PSYCHOPATHIC DISORDER, may not properly be called mental illnesses. These, and disorders such as AUTISM and EPILEPSY, which are neither mental illnesses nor emotional problems, are included in this chapter because those concerned about mental health may well require more information on them.

If you are seeking information on a condition which you do not find in the alphabetical lists of this or the next chapter, look it up in the index – it may be included under another name.

Agoraphobia

This is the commonest form of PHOBIA. It is also the most serious because, in its severest form, the sufferer is housebound despite being healthy in every other way. Agoraphobia is often wrongly defined as a 'fear of open spaces'. The central feature is actually a fear of leaving home (especially alone) and of going into a particular situation, or more usually, into a number of related situations (especially where there are crowds). These situations include travelling by public transport, shopping and walking in the street. In a mild case, it will be only one of these situations which provokes fear and panic, and this can be avoided, although at some inconvenience. A severe case of agoraphobia, however, involves not only a fear of going out, but also of being left alone at home. In such instances the lives of the phobic person and of the family are totally disrupted.

Fear is experienced not only when the situation has to be faced, but also if it is anticipated. Thus an agoraphobic person may feel anxious for the entire day before an evening trip to visit friends. The actual visit may cause less anxiety.

The agoraphobic person often also suffers from ANXIETY or DE-PRESSION which makes the symptoms worse. These symptoms are described under PHOBIAS. Two types of fear seem to characterise agoraphobic people. One is of fainting, dying or in some way losing control in the situation they fear – for example, 'going berserk' on a bus or in a shop. The other fear is of being looked at by all the other people in the situation – other shoppers, pedestrians, and so on. Suffering from agoraphobia does not rule out having other PHOBIAS too.

There does not seem to be any adverse effect on the children of agoraphobic parents – they are no more likely to develop phobias themselves than other children are.

Many agoraphobic people find that they can cope with a feared situation in certain circumstances – for instance, if they have a friend or relative with them. Others can manage if they go out only at night, or even if they wear dark glasses or carry an umbrella. For those whose fear is strongest about being confined in a crowded place from which there is no easy way out, it often helps to choose a restaurant or theatre seat, for example, near the exit.

Agoraphobia is more commonly found in women than men, and usually begins between the ages of 15 and 35 – often beween 25 and 30. As with other phobias there is speculation as to what causes agoraphobia. Childhood events may occasionally be the trigger, but personality traits, and stresses or traumatic events experienced in later life, seem more often to be the cause. A common way for agoraphobia to start is for the person to suffer a panic attack (see ANXIETY), without warning and for no apparent reason, while away from home. Though it may not be evident to the sufferer, this attack is probably the result of recent stress, perhaps combined with his own predisposition to anxiety. It is a frightening experience and those who subsequently develop agoraphobia associate the panic with the place where it happened. They then fear that going into a supermarket, for instance, will bring on another attack. If they are sufficiently anxious this may well happen. But it may also happen anywhere else and the person gradually begins to fear being away from the familiar surroundings of his home.

Agoraphobia may develop suddenly, or gradually over a number of years. It is usually long-lasting, unless treated. It does disappear in occasional cases, perhaps reappearing in the future, but this is unlikely if the agoraphobia has lasted over a year.

What can be done

BEHAVIOUR THERAPY is an effective form of treatment, using the same methods as described for other PHOBIAS. Research studies have found that most agoraphobic people improve with this type of therapy. Group treatment is very often used, though practice of the therapeutic exercises will also have to be carried out alone. The group may approach their goals gradually under the guidance of the therapist – for example, travelling just one stop by bus as a group at first, then building up to a half-hour journey alone. Some therapists encourage immediate confrontation of the situation – entering a supermarket on the first excursion, for instance. The type of treatment is always agreed first with the patient. If an agoraphobic person cannot leave home under any circumstances, the behaviour therapist is often willing to visit at the beginning of the therapy programme.

Other treatments are described in the section on PHOBIAS.

Self-help programmes encourage the sufferer to face the feared situations, thereby breaking the 'habit' of avoiding them. The programmes vary in their suggestions for how this is done, but the constructive support of a sympathetic relative, friend or volunteer is always helpful – even essential. If you are concerned about someone who suffers from agoraphobia the most helpful thing you can do is to encourage the person to tackle the problem – either by asking a GP for a referral to a therapist, or by using a self-help programme. Merely assisting the sufferer to avoid the feared situations may seem kind, but it is not helpful in the long run.

One problem with which the long-term sufferer will need help is the difficulty of changing, after many years, to a new way of life. If treatment is to be successful the sufferer must not be afraid of the changes it will entail. Sometimes marital therapy (see MARITAL PROBLEMS), or social skills and assertiveness training (see BEHAVIOUR THERAPY) may also be recommended, along with treatment for the agoraphobia.

The best-known organisation for agoraphobia sufferers is The **Open Door Association**. Others include the **Northern Ireland Agoraphobic Society**. There are also local self-help groups, and community action groups providing volunteer support. All organisations to help people with PHOBIAS have a large proportion of agoraphobic members.

Alcohol dependence

Some agencies working with people who drink heavily are no longer using the terms 'alcoholism' and 'alcoholic'. Their reasoning is that there are many more drinkers whose lives are adversely affected by alcohol than those previously classified in this way. Some also find the terms offensive and feel that people may seek help as 'problem drinkers' but would refuse to approach a service for 'alcoholics'. This is not to say that agencies still using these terms are any less effective, and drinkers will receive as much sympathetic understanding there as at any of the services adopting a different approach.

One way in which heavy drinking has been classified is to separate those whose drinking has no serious effects from 'problem drinkers'. These are people who suffer mental, social, economic, legal or physical problems related to their drinking. For example, they may become irritable and depressed, quarrelsome and unpredictable, have difficulty concentrating and sleeping. Some develop a PARANOID DISORDER. They may have hallucinations, hearing voices insulting or threatening them. Frequently a paranoid delusion takes the form of jealousy – believing despite all reassurances that their partner has been unfaithful. There may be MARITAL and SEXUAL PROBLEMS (which are not necessarily relieved by giving up alcohol), and a worsening relationship with their children who lose respect for them. Their friends may be reduced to only a group of fellow-drinkers and their social lives revolve around alcohol. The expense of alcohol, and perhaps losing a job for consistently poor performance, may lead to financial difficulties. Criminal offences, from being drunk and disorderly to stealing in order to buy alcohol, may bring the drinker to court. Many problem drinkers experience amnesia, but only a minority will suffer serious physical harm including DEMENTIA because of brain damage. This can sometimes be permanent – even if the person gives up alcohol.

Women are able to tolerate less alcohol than men before physical harm is caused. Some research suggests that they are more susceptible to its ill-effects before a period. Severe PRE-MENSTRUAL TENSION and the MENOPAUSE sometimes make women drink more. The proportion of problem drinkers who are female is steadily increasing.

People with any alcohol-related difficulties are thus defined as 'problem drinkers'. They may believe that they drink because of their problems – because they have a poor marriage or are in debt – but these are more likely to be the result of their drinking. A proportion, around one quarter, of problem drinkers are also alcohol-dependent. They show the characteristic signs of drug addiction (alcohol is a drug – see DRUG DEPENDENCE). If they stop drinking for up to 12 hours they experience withdrawal symptoms: headache, trembling, sweating and nausea. Some even have visual hallucinations – see DELIRIUM tremens. In order to avoid feeling this way, or to relieve the symptoms, the dependent drinker will consume more alcohol. He becomes tolerant to alcohol and can therefore drink increasingly large amounts. Someone experiencing alcohol dependence shows little variety in his drinking – every day he has the same drinks at the same time. Alcohol comes to play the major role in his life. Dependence has two aspects – psychological (which usually comes first) and physical. At first the drinker has an emotional dependence on and preoccupation with alcohol but this develops into a physical craving by his body for alcohol.

Why some people become problem drinkers, and some go on to develop alcohol dependence, is the subject of research and debate. To some extent theories about the causes of alcohol dependence determine the treatment provided. If it is seen as an illness (as is the view of **Alcoholics Anonymous**, for example), the person is held always to be a sufferer and must therefore avoid alcohol for the rest of his life. Others do not view alcohol dependence as a disease, and the mental health legislation throughout the UK excludes it as a mental disorder, though it may co-exist with a mental illness.

Research is examining the effect of alcohol on brain cells, and it may be that the reaction is different in some people, explaining why they become alcohol-dependent. There is a view that the only relevant factor is how much a person drinks and for how long – at a certain point he will become dependent on alcohol. Others feel that there is a combination of causes – psychological, biological and environmental. Some people start drinking after an event which has caused them to suffer DEPRESSION. The event, the person's mental reaction to it (which itself may involve biological factors), and perhaps an abnormal physical reaction in the brain to alcohol, may all combine to produce alcohol dependence. A genetic component has also been proposed based on the fact that between a quarter and half of the male relatives of those with severe alcohol dependence are themselves addicted to alcohol. There may thus be an inherited tendency to develop the most serious form of problem drinking. Less severe problem drinking can also be passed on in families by children copying their parents.

There is no one personality type which leads to problem drinking although there is some connection with PSYCHOPATHIC DISORDER. Depression and MANIC-DEPRESSION may also lead to problem drinking. Some people with SCHIZOPHRENIA may drink to mask their symptoms and unhappiness. Indeed, anyone may drink to try to escape those problems that seem insurmountable.

What can be done
Nothing can be done until the person acknowledges that he is a problem drinker, and if he is dependent on alcohol, that he has an addiction. Having taken this step, the person should see his GP or go to one of the many agencies for problem drinkers. The sooner he seeks help, the easier it will be to cure his problem drinking.

As described above, some authorities believe that total abstinence is the only possibility for someone who has been alcohol-dependent. Others believe that while this is the ideal goal, for some drinkers it is an impossible one, and therefore it is better to aim for more controlled drinking. A third type of agency does not set total abstinence as a goal at all, but aims to help problem drinkers to reduce their consumption to a safer level. There is undoubtedly a group of alcohol-dependent people for whom total abstinence is the only answer. With continuing support and determination they can avoid drinking, and this is the best solution for them. But not every problem drinker either can or needs to give up alcohol altogether. A minority, but probably not those who are alcohol-dependent, may be able to return to having just a few drinks socially. If they cannot maintain this level, then total abstinence may be necessary.

Services are provided through the NHS for alcohol dependence but for less serious problem drinking voluntary organisations are the usual source of help. Their emphasis may be on providing help at an early stage, to try to prevent more serious problems developing. No referral by a GP is necessary.

An alcohol-dependent person who has been drinking very heavily for a long time will probably experience severe withdrawal symptoms at the start of treatment. DRUGS (tranquillisers) may be needed to cope with these. Detoxification or 'drying-out' is an essential first step to rid the body of all alcohol and to get it used to not receiving a regular intake of alcohol. Most patients are able to do this at home, receiving care from a GP or community nurse. Some attend out-patient units specialising in alcohol dependence. Others have to stay in hospital if they are to manage this critical stage of treatment. They are admitted to Alcohol Treatment Units which may be attached to mental illness hospitals. Some patients are admitted to general hospitals for this drying-out period which may last several weeks. Until recently the in-patient care at Alcohol Treatment Units often involved three months of PSYCHOTHERAPY aimed at total abstinence. Some are now advocating shorter stays followed by out-patient care. BEHAVIOUR THERAPY is being used as one of a variety of approaches at such Units, and a goal of controlled drinking as opposed to abstinence is chosen for some patients.

One form of behaviour therapy is aversion therapy using a tablet called Antabuse or Abstem. This is taken every day, or a preparation can be implanted in the body. It has no effect unless the person drinks alcohol, in which case he suffers nausea, sweating and fever. This unpleasant experience, associated with alcohol, should deter him from drinking again. If the person is living at home, another member of the household may be asked to ensure that the tablet is taken each morning.

There are private clinics offering treatment, and private medical insurance schemes may cover the costs. One is **Clouds House** run by the **Life-Anew Trust**, where the Alcoholics Anonymous programme is used. GROUP THERAPY, COUNSELLING and RELAXATION are provided during stays of five to eight weeks on average. Aftercare continues for up to two years and former patients are encouraged to join their local AA group.

Alcoholics Anonymous has over 2,000 groups in the UK. Anyone who wants to stop drinking can join, and they are encouraged to give up alcohol 'one day at a time'. Mutual support is given at the once- or twice-weekly meetings. 'Twelve Steps to Recovery' are suggestions for ways of living a happier life. It is not a religious organisation but there is a spiritual theme to the Twelve Steps. AA provides all the support which some problem drinkers need in order to stay sober; for others it is an important part of a treatment programme. Some people find it does not suit them but it is worth attending at least a few meetings to find out. AA produces a wide range of literature on drinking problems.

Al-Anon Family Groups UK **and Eire** is a separate organisation which grew out of AA. It is for the relatives and friends of problem drinkers, even if they are not receiving any treatment. The groups provide mutual support and discuss how they have coped with various problems. Like AA, they suggest Twelve Steps leading to a less anxious and more comfortable life.

Alateen is the teenage counterpart of Al-Anon Family Groups and its meetings are attended by the children of problem drinkers. Both organisations produce literature.

Local councils on alcohol exist throughout the UK providing services and information on other help available locally, and advising problem drinkers and their families. One such council is the **Greater London Alcohol Advisory Service**. Those who live in the City of London or Hackney may receive COUNSELLING through the service.

Alcohol Concern can tell you where to find your nearest local council on alcohol and other services in your area. They offer information, publications and a large library, but no treatment or counselling services.

Samaritans branches (see SUICIDE) may also be able to tell you how to obtain help for problem drinking.

The **Alcohol Counselling Service** is for problem drinkers, and for their relatives and friends, and operates in Lambeth, Lewisham and Southwark. COUNSELLING is usually individual, but there are also regular group meetings, including a women's group.

Aquarius offers free COUNSELLING at one of its day centres or residential houses in the Midlands. Relatives are also welcome to attend or telephone the centre for counselling.

Turning Point operates a number of residential centres and counselling services for problem drinkers.

ACCEPT provides free services at eight centres in and around London. COUNSELLING, PSYCHOTHERAPY, GROUP THERAPY of several types and numerous activities such as RELAXATION training are used to create an individual programme for each client. Total abstinence is advocated for alcohol-dependent drinkers. Similar services are available to relatives and friends, even if the problem drinker concerned is not using ACCEPT services. Advice is available on legal, financial, MARITAL and SEXUAL PROBLEMS related to problem drinking. Literature is also produced.

The **National Drinkwatchers Network** is another aspect of ACCEPT's services. This is a chain of self-help groups and clubs for mild problem drinkers in England and Wales who want to be able to control their drinking habits.

Residential projects are run around the country for alcohol-dependent people who have stopped drinking, but who are not yet ready to return to their homes, or who are homeless.

Alzheimer's disease

This is the commonest form of DEMENTIA, and does not differ in many ways from the other forms. The description of its symptoms is therefore given under DEMENTIA. It is the cause of the brain cell degeneration which distinguishes Alzheimer's disease from the other dementias. For some reason as yet unknown, the brain cells undergo several types of change, including an accumulation of abnormal fibres. Another abnormal feature is collections of degenerating nerve endings called plaques. These features can be seen only under a microscope and their effect is eventually on the whole brain's functioning. It is known that small quantities of plaques exist in the brains of middle-aged and elderly people who do not have dementia, and this has been proposed as an explanation for their slight difficulties of recall (see CONFUSION). Another difference in the brains of people with Alzheimer's disease is a deficiency of certain chemical messengers (see CHANGES IN THE BRAIN in Chapter 2).

Despite its close similarities to the other forms of dementia, sufferers from Alzheimer's disease as a group show some differences. Those with the disease are more likely to be female but this may only be because they are on average older (women have a longer average lifespan). Sufferers from Alzheimer's disease are more likely to make abnormal movements, such as pouting and grasping, but only in the later stages of the illness.

The possibility of a genetic factor in Alzheimer's disease has not been fully established. The consensus seems to be that there *may* be an inherited predisposition to develop the disease – more likely among the younger pre-senile sufferers. This should not, however, lead the children of sufferers to believe that they run a high risk of developing the condition. If there seems to be an inherited predisposition in your family, you can ask your GP to refer you to a genetic counsellor.

What can be done
There is no cure for Alzheimer's disease. The treatment available is the same as for other sufferers from DEMENTIA.

The **Alzheimer's Disease Society** helps the families of those suffering from the disease, and from related conditions for which there is currently no specialist voluntary organisation. The Society provides literature and information on the help available. Self-help groups exist in many areas, and funds are available for people in financial need who are caring for a sufferer. COUNSELLING is offered on legal, social and family matters from the Society's headquarters. Several day centres have now been set up. More information about them, and about regional and local offices, is available from the Society's head office.

Anorexia nervosa

Sometimes called the 'slimmer's disease', this condition may develop after more normal dieting to lose weight. It is, however, different from dieting in several respects, and is certainly not a 'nervous loss of appetite' as is sometimes imagined. Anorexia nervosa is much more common in females – only five to ten per cent of patients are male. Sufferers are rarely younger than nine years old nor older than 25 when they develop anorexia. Most teenage girls are conscious of their weight and figure, and dieting is common. In many this will be a passing phase but the girl who is going to develop anorexia becomes increasingly engrossed by the thought of losing weight. Her diet becomes stricter as her determination to be thin increases. Anorexia nervosa can therefore be thought of as an obsession with thinness – an overriding ambition to lose weight, far below a 'healthy' level. The sufferer in fact has a fear of gaining weight akin to a PHOBIA. Her dread of becoming fat is so intense that she will starve herself to avoid it.

This fear does not, however, lead to a total avoidance of food. Nutrition and cooking fascinate the sufferer – she knows the number of calories in every food and may spend hours cooking, only to watch everyone else eat what she has prepared. Many sufferers will not eat if anyone is watching. Even alone, their 'meals' may consist of nothing more than a spoonful of cottage cheese.

Controlling and reducing their weight is seen as virtuous by many sufferers. They typically set themselves high standards in other areas, too – such as academically. Setting a low target weight for themselves is a standard to be reached, and to do so gives them a rewarding feeling. Then the target is set still lower. As well as dieting, they may exercise for hours every day to burn up calories.

It has been said that anorexia sufferers do not consider themselves or others to fall between two extremes. They describe others as 'good' or 'bad'; themselves as 'fat' while the ideal is 'thin' – there can be no compromise. This fat self-image is typical of most sufferers – some doctors say that it is true of them all. A girl with anorexia will stubbornly insist, and probably truly believe, that she is fat, or that her thighs are too big, when she is actually pathetically thin. However their bodies look to themselves or others, they hate their shape.

It is not surprising that the life of someone with anorexia can be unhappy, and DEPRESSION is quite common. The sufferer feels that if only she weighed one stone less life would be wonderful again. Her preoccupation with losing weight leaves no time for friends or a social life, and she becomes increasingly withdrawn. Her family find her hard to live with – stubbornly refusing to eat, flying into a rage if she is nagged, and using inventive cunning to conceal the extent of her dieting. Despite all these difficulties, a sufferer is very unlikely to seek help for her condition – she does not realise that she needs it. She may, however, consult a doctor because her periods have stopped – an early symptom of the disease. This is caused by a disruption to the hormonal system and is one characteristic feature of the disorder.

The signs of anorexia are well documented; the causes are less clear. There are many theories ranging from the purely psychological to the purely biological. It is almost certain, however, that a combination of factors are involved. A teasing remark to the girl about her plumpness sometimes sparks off concentrated dieting, but this is very unlikely to be the cause of anorexia. Several other factors would already be present and this remark is just the trigger. Before then, aspects of the girl's thinking, and perhaps personality, would have predisposed her to this disorder. She may well have low self-esteem and feel unable to cope with herself in some way. Some theories say that sufferers have difficulty in accepting the role of a young adult with its attendant independence and sexual maturity. Teenagers with anorexia do not show a normal interest in the opposite sex. The hormonal changes and severe weight loss also prevent their bodies maturing. Achieving an ever-decreasing weight may represent for the girl perfect control over her life and body in a way that she feels she used to lack. In fact she is trapped in a vicious cycle of starvation and weight loss because some of the symptoms of anorexia help to perpetuate this abnormal behaviour.

As an additional safeguard against weight-gain, some people with anorexia resort to vomiting or the use of laxatives to rid their bodies of any small amount of food they have eaten. Some sufferers develop a related condition – BULIMIA NERVOSA.

What can be done

It is imperative that treatment is sought as soon as possible – the longer the condition continues, the harder it is to treat. Also, the older the girl when she develops anorexia, the more difficult it is to reverse. Cures are possible, though they are not always complete. Some sufferers who regain a near-normal weight continue to be over-concerned with food and their weight and may suffer another episode in the future.

A young girl who is showing signs of becoming increasingly obsessed with dieting can be reasoned with. She will accept a rational explanation of the dangers of anorexia – one of the books written by women who have recovered from anorexia might convince her of this. Someone with anorexia will not listen to such reasoning and will not modify her eating at all – except perhaps to diet with more determination.

If you suspect that someone has anorexia, try to persuade her to see her GP. If she flatly refuses, you could obtain some information from one of the organisations listed below and give it to her. She might be willing to attend one of their meetings, or they may suggest other sources of help in your area. If all else fails, go to the GP yourself. Prepare a list of the reasons which make you suspect anorexia. At the very least a GP should be monitoring the weight of someone thought to have anorexia. In a serious case he will refer her to a specialist. There are few clinics specialising in EATING DISORDERS, and there may be a long wait for an appointment. Treatment can be on an out-patient basis, but at least a brief stay in hospital is often recommended in more serious cases. The girl's poor physical state may necessitate this, as a small proportion of sufferers will literally starve themselves to death. Admission to hospital may also force the patient to admit to herself that she is ill, and this is an essential step if she is to be cured. Supervision of her eating is much easier in hospital, though this should be handled sensitively. The use of rewards and punishment, BEHAVIOUR THERAPY of an operant conditioning kind, does not seem to be helpful.

It is, however, vital that the patient gains weight as part of her treatment. This is not only necessary for her physical health, but also so that she can learn to come to terms with weight gain. COUNSELLING and PSYCHOTHERAPY should be an integral part of the treatment programme and continue after her discharge. As many different forms of psychotherapy as exist have been tried for anorexia. PSYCHOANALYSIS explores the mother–daughter relationship; COGNITIVE THERAPY concentrates on the sufferer's thoughts and attitudes. Whatever form is used, the patient's view of life and of herself must be changed in order to correct the abnormal attitudes described above. Social skills training (see BEHAVIOUR THERAPY) may be included in the treatment.

Some patients are discharged to a hostel enabling them to make further progress before returning home.

FAMILY THERAPY may be offered if family problems arose while the patient was ill. A patient's low self-esteem and reluctance to be independent can sometimes be improved by changes in the way a family works together. Even if family therapy is not used, the doctor will almost certainly want at least the parents to be involved in the treatment programme.

DRUGS of various kinds, including tranquillisers and antidepressants, have been tried, but none of these cures the condition.

One recently tried remedy is zinc, for sufferers who are found to be deficient in this element. The deficiency seems to perpetuate the condition, although it is not suggested as a cause of anorexia.

Anorexic Family Aid offers support and advice to sufferers and their families. It has two aspects, the first being fortnightly group meetings in Norwich led by a trained therapist. Individual COUNSELLING is available. Membership is also available to those who live too far away to attend the meetings. The second part of Anorexic Family Aid is a National Information Service. Literature on anorexia and BULIMIA is produced and a telephone helpline service is available. There are many books on anorexia which families and sufferers may find helpful – Anorexic Family Aid produces a list of recommended reading, as does Anorexic Aid.

Anorexic Aid is a network of self-help groups run by people who have recovered from anorexia or BULIMIA. Their aim is to provide support and information for sufferers and their families. Some groups have meetings while others maintain communication between members by letter or telephone. Groups endeavour to offer guidance to improve eating, and counselling to resolve the underlying problems.

Other self-help groups run by recovered patients are being set up around the country. Some are more helpful than others, but it is always worth going to at least one meeting to see if the type of support they offer is useful for you.

Anorexia Anonymous is not a support group, as its name suggests, but a private psychotherapist who uses a form of PSYCHOTHERAPY called trance therapy to help the patient overcome her problem.

The **Women's Therapy Centre** runs a one-day workshop from time to time on anorexia. The main purpose is to discuss the problems faced by sufferers, though it may also be possible to help them find individual or GROUP THERAPY.

Anxiety

There is nothing abnormal about the feeling of anxiety and it is felt by everyone, with good reason. The actor's belief that 'nerves' are essential for a good performance is quite true – being 'keyed up' helps us to perform better. Anxiety is felt as we prepare for 'fight or flight' – either to achieve the most in whatever we stay to do, or to escape as quickly as possible. The symptoms of anxiety (see below) have a biological function in preparing us for 'fight or flight'. Thus, if anxiety is felt before giving a speech, running a race or sitting an exam, it is both understandable and useful. However, as the activity is begun, or at least when it is completed, the anxiety subsides and it is important for the body – and the mind – to achieve a more relaxed level.

Anxiety becomes a mental problem when:

- it occurs for no reason
- it is excessive in view of the demands of the situation provoking it
- it is unremitting
- the sufferer cannot 'escape' it by thinking of or doing something else
- the sufferer is distressed by it.

In these cases anxiety is no longer a useful mechanism, but evidence of a personality disorder or mental illness. Trait anxiety is characteristic of a personality which causes the individual to feel continually tense, frightened or apprehensive. This is the person who 'makes a mountain out of a molehill' – reacting to a minor upset as a major catastrophe. He cannot forget past incidents and worries about whether he said or did the right thing, what the implications might be, how events might turn out badly in the future. As a result he is always suffering a degree of stress and is prone to develop the mental illness of anxiety.

An anxiety state is a mental condition, often suffered by someone with trait anxiety. It may be experienced as an isolated mental disorder, or as part of another illness. DEPRESSION and anxiety are commonly combined, and sometimes referred to as 'atypical depression'.

Anxiety has two components – physical and mental. They always occur together, but some people are very much more aware of one type of symptom. In the course of an anxiety state (which may continue for years), many sufferers experience panic attacks. The background anxiety is sometimes called generalised or free-floating anxiety, because it is not connected to any event, situation or object, as is a PHOBIA. However, people who have phobias often experience generalised anxiety as well. Occasionally, people have only recurrent panic attacks without the generalised anxiety in between. HYPOCHONDRIA is a common feature of anxiety.

The psychological features of anxiety are worry and apprehension, irritability and restlessness, and poor concentration which sometimes seems to affect the person's memory. Elderly sufferers frequently experience a loss of self-confidence, fear and a feeling of isolation or insecurity. Anxiety sufferers ruminate on the negative aspects of life – the possibility of accidents, failures and dangers. They see the darkest side of the situations they face. These feelings come and go, and are not the same as the continuous despondency of someone suffering from severe depression.

The physical features of anxiety are tension, which may produce aches and pains, difficulty getting to sleep and then disturbed sleep until the person wakes in the morning, often feeling tense. (Depression affects sleep in a different way.) SEXUAL PROBLEMS are common with anxiety and may in turn cause the sufferer to feel more anxious.

During a panic attack the anxious feelings are intensified and the physical symptoms may in themselves be frightening – a racing pulse and thumping heart, a dry mouth, parts of the body sweating, nausea, diarrhoea and a frequent need to urinate. Some people hyperventilate or over-breathe and this causes them to feel dizzy or faint, and can make the fingers tingle. Psychological features of a panic attack may include a feeling of unreality. This may take several forms, such as that part of oneself is watching the rest, or that one's surroundings are distant or dream-like. A panic attack begins suddenly, usually for no obvious reason, although it is often preceded by some form of increased stress. It will then stop as suddenly as it began.

Anxiety rarely reaches the proportions of a PSYCHOSIS (see Chapter 3), but if it does the sufferer may experience hallucinations (hearing voices, for example), or delusions that he is being plotted against (see PARANOID DISORDERS).

An anxiety state is generally produced when the sufferer is experiencing STRESS with which he cannot cope. If his personality has been characterised by trait anxiety, it will take a lower level of stress for him to develop an anxiety state. People with obsessive personalities (see OBSESSIVE DISORDERS) may also develop an anxiety state. Some people seem to develop an anxiety state without any trigger in the form of stress. The symptoms of anxiety can be produced by physical illnesses, such as disorders of the thyroid gland, or EPILEPSY affecting a certain part of the brain. Hypoglycaemia (unstable sugar levels in the blood – see DIET in Chapter 2) can also cause the symptoms.

Some research is investigating a chemical in the brain which apparently causes anxiety. There are a number of theories on how changes in the brain's chemical messenger systems might produce an anxiety state, but none has been widely accepted.

The psychoanalytic theory (see PSYCHOANALYSIS) of anxiety is that it results when instincts are repressed by what are called 'neurotic defences'. The person is not consciously aware of this, but the effort of repressing the knowledge produces the symptoms of anxiety.

What can be done
The steps to be taken depend on the severity of the anxiety state. If the condition is clearly due to a currently stressful experience, the solution is to deal with this situation if at all possible. Someone who is not predisposed to anxiety, for example by a personality problem, will almost certainly recover once the anxiety-provoking situation no longer exists. COUNSELLING or supportive PSYCHOTHERAPY is useful for explaining the condition of anxiety state to the sufferer, so that he does not fear its symptoms. A counsellor may also be able to help him reach conclusions about how to tackle a problem.

Some sufferers may need more intensive psychotherapy if an anxiety state is their habitual reaction to the minor stresses of everyday life. They may need to adopt different attitudes if they are to cope satisfactorily with life in future. One approach is COGNITIVE THERAPY. The aim is to help the person to recognise his negative view of himself, of his own ability to cope, and of life in general. Instead of brooding on the difficulties and dangers of life, he learns to look for alternative attitudes and to stop thinking of things as 'black and white'. He tells himself to concentrate on how he is going to tackle a situation and praises himself for each achievement.

RELAXATION can help many sufferers, even if it is only a part of their treatment. There are many self-help methods for learning relaxation – see 'self-help' in Chapter 9. Yoga and meditation, for example, have been found helpful in reducing anxiety. Biofeedback training in relaxation is available in some places. Relaxation classes are run by some local associations for mental health and other organisations. These classes teach people how to cope with panic attacks as well. Those whose personality predisposes them to anxiety state may find that relaxation skills can prevent them developing the mental illness of anxiety. This requires dedication and determination, however – attending a relaxation class once a week is not enough if there is no attempt to change in between. Some hospital departments of clinical psychology may be able to sell or recommend tapes for practising relaxation exercises at home.

HYPNOTHERAPY has been used in several ways. Hypnoanalysis may be used to uncover the roots of anxiety if a psychoanalytic interpretation is made of the anxiety state. Hypnosis also induces a state of deep relaxation which is beneficial to sufferers. While the person is in the hypnotic trance during a therapy session, the therapist may use suggestion to encourage him to adopt new approaches and attitudes.

A combination of several techniques is used in anxiety control (or management) training, which is available in some areas. The first stage consists of relaxation techniques until the person is able to bring about this deeply relaxed state easily. The therapist (usually a clinical psychologist) then asks him to imagine scenes in which he would feel anxious. Sometimes the therapist describes such scenes. When a scene can be imagined without anxiety, a slightly more anxiety-inducing scene is chosen – and so on until the person is able to imagine all his feared situations without getting anxious. Sometimes, an anxiety sufferer also learns how to deal with the feelings aroused, with elements of cognitive therapy to alter his attitudes. An example would be learning that an increased heart rate does not mean that he is going to suffer a heart attack. The training is thus a cognitive-behavioural technique. The course usually involves about ten sessions and those who have attended it may then wish to form a self-help group to encourage each other to continue with the progress they have made so far. The course therapist may be willing to keep in contact with the group.

Clearly, there are many ways of tackling anxiety apart from the prescription of DRUGS. However, tranquillisers and other antianxiety drugs do have their place in the treatment of some cases. They should be used only for an anxiety state – not for people who have trait anxiety as a personality problem. Precisely how tranquillisers work is not known. They have two types of effect – one is to alter the brain's chemical messenger systems and the other is to relax the muscles of the body. Most cause a certain degree of drowsiness and it is dangerous to drive or operate machinery while affected by tranquillisers. Elderly people may also experience difficulty in co-ordinating their movements, or CON-FUSION (see also DELIRIUM). Alcohol should be completely avoided by people taking tranquillisers. Some patients suffer side-effects which include nausea, headache, dizziness and irritability. A very few people become extremely excitable or even aggressive. The dangers of becoming addicted to tranquillisers after taking them for long periods are discussed under DRUG DEPENDENCE. There are drawbacks to taking tranquillisers and their use should therefore be limited to the cases in which they are really needed. There is no doubt that tranquillisers help those whose anxiety state is interfering seriously with their lives. Once the symptoms are more manageable (usually within a week), counselling, psychotherapy and/or relaxation techniques can help the person to tackle the problems he faces. In severe cases ABREACTION may be used if the person cannot even begin to discuss the causes of his anxiety.

The benzodiazepines prescribed as tranquillisers will have a therapeutic effect on anxiety for only about four months and it is therefore unnecessary (and indeed undesirable) to take them for much longer.

Other antianxiety drugs are not benzodiazepine tranquillisers. Sometimes an antidepressant is prescribed which also has an effect on anxiety. Or another type of drug may be used to control very troublesome physical symptoms of anxiety, such as a racing heart or tremor. Such symptoms should always be discussed with a GP so that he can determine whether they have a physical cause.

Some people find that a HOMOEOPATHIC approach to treating anxiety works for them.

Autism

This rare condition is usually detected by the age of three years. It is therefore often called childhood autism but this does not mean that it is suffered only during childhood. Some improvement does come with age but it may be only slight.

Its cause continues to puzzle psychiatrists and researchers, though early ideas such as attributing it to the parents' handling of the child have now been discredited. Autism is also no longer classified as childhood SCHIZOPHRENIA. Impaired brain function is being found as one cause, and this probably arises in several ways – for example, injury at birth and infections during babyhood. The condition is more common in boys than in girls.

Parents' anxieties may first be raised by their child's lack of response to cuddling. An autistic baby does not stretch out his arms to be picked up, or look up into his parents' eyes. The children fail to develop normal relationships and normal speech. They do not react 'sociably' to other people. Autistic children are often described as being in a world of their own. This does not mean that they are day-dreaming in a make-believe world, but that they are aware only of themselves and not others. They may scream for hours, or lie or sit perfectly still. At times autistic children seem to be deaf because they do not react to what people say. But at other times their acute sense of hearing is obvious from their sudden reaction to quite soft noises.

About half remain mute, others use language in a strange way – for example, repeating the same phrase endlessly or speaking in a mono-tone. This repetition is apparent in their behaviour, too, with the same action, such as rocking, being performed again and again like a ritual. Routine and order must be preserved – their toys arranged in a certain way, for instance. Any disruption of this order may provoke a prolonged tantrum. This form of OBSESSIVE DISORDER may also be apparent in their fascination for a particular object – perhaps a ball of silver paper.

Only a minority of autistic children are of normal intelligence, with over half having IQs below 50. A very small group are extremely gifted in mathematics, art, music or memory skills.

Though classic autism is rare, a larger number of children have social and language difficulties to a lesser degree.

What can be done
The outlook for a child diagnosed as autistic is sadly not very bright. Most will eventually have to live in some form of residential facility, although a few are able to live independently. Their future depends on how well they learn to speak, to communicate and to form social relationships, and to perform necessary skills.

DRUGS may help to control severe behaviour problems, such as excessive noisiness, restlessness and attempts to injure themselves.

BEHAVIOUR THERAPY is sometimes successful in improving specific aspects of the child's behaviour. It may be used to reduce the obsession with a particular item. At regular intervals an almost imperceptible change is introduced – for example, slightly modifying a routine or reducing the size of an object to which the child is attached to the exclusion of all else. The aim is to transfer the child's attention to other matters.

Another method of behaviour therapy is operant conditioning which rewards the child (perhaps with sweets) for the behaviour being encouraged, and punishes him with a gentle slap – for example, if he bites himself. As the child progresses, the therapist can praise or speak sharply to him, but at the outset this has no effect as reward or punishment. The technique has been criticised, and more research is needed to compare its efficacy with that of other methods.

SPEECH THERAPY may also employ conditioning to teach autistic children to speak. This seems to help while it is being used but the therapy must be used continuously for progress to be maintained. Sign language is used with some children who are mute, sometimes as a first step towards teaching them to speak, although this may never be achieved. Even those who do learn to speak will probably never talk normally because they cannot be taught abstract language. However, a child who is able to communicate in even some limited fashion can lead a more rewarding life.

There are specialist schools for both day and boarding pupils, a few of which arrange for the autistic children to mix with children who are not handicapped in any way. State schools accepting autistic children are run by some local authorities, but other specialist schools are voluntary or private. Those who do not attend school, either because no suitable place can be found, or because they are classified as unsuitable for education, live in mental handicap hospitals or at home, from where they attend training centres or special care units.

PSYCHOTHERAPY with a psychodynamic approach is occasionally used but is not generally very successful.

The **National Autistic Society** helps parents by supplying information and arranging meetings between them. The Society also provides day and residential centres for the care and education of autistic children.

Bulimia nervosa

Bulimia is an EATING DISORDER which is a form of compulsive eating often connected with ANOREXIA NERVOSA. The majority of sufferers are female and in their late teens or early twenties. It is sometimes referred to as the 'binge and vomit syndrome' as this is the sufferer's typical behaviour. She indulges in sporadic 'binges', during which she gorges food uncontrollably. The urge to start this binge is irresistible and, once she has begun, she does not stop until she runs out of food, is discovered by someone, or feels too exhausted or uncomfortable to continue. Then, partly from a sense of guilt, and partly to avoid gaining weight from the food, she makes herself sick. Some people use laxatives to get rid of the food.

This cycle of gorging and purging may be repeated every day or only once every few weeks, much to the distress of the sufferer. This is one respect in which she differs from someone with anorexia who has no idea of the seriousness of her condition.

Sufferers from bulimia do, however, share certain characteristics with those who have anorexia, such as an intense fear of becoming fat. They may have had anorexia themselves. Sufferers are desperate to control their weight but unlike those with anorexia are unable to starve themselves. Realising this lack of self-control, they live in constant fear of a craving to binge which they will not be able to resist. After the first few mouthfuls, which they may savour, the food – usually sweet and high in carbohydrate – will give them no pleasure. In between binges their attitude to food will still not be normal, and they may try desperately to diet. Those with bulimia, in common with sufferers from anorexia, seem to link their self-esteem with the way their bodies look. They also tend to set themselves very high standards.

The term bulimia is sometimes used for people who alternate between gorging and fasting. Compulsive eating of this and other kinds is described under EATING DISORDERS.

People with bulimia do differ in some ways from those with anorexia. They tend to form more relationships, especially sexual ones, though never with any satisfaction. They tend to be heavier, though some are underweight, and females are less likely to lose their periods. They suffer more severe DEPRESSION and are more likely to commit SUICIDE.

Although binges are always in private, frequently at night when the family is asleep, the sufferer will eat in front of other people – unlike the person with anorexia. However, if at all possible someone with bulimia will get rid of the food she has eaten immediately after the meal.

What can be done
In so far as bulimia resembles ANOREXIA NERVOSA, the treatment may be similar in its attempts to control the abnormal behaviour and alter the person's attitudes to herself and life in general. As a hospital in-patient she does not have access to the foods on which she would ordinarily binge, and vomiting is strongly discouraged. However, this alone is a short-term measure. A brief hospital stay may be recommended for similar reasons as in anorexia, but it may also be required because of the physical damage which gorging and excessive vomiting cause to the body. Some of the damage may be irreversible in severe cases. While she is in hospital PSYCHOTHERAPY is begun and this is more likely to involve GROUP THERAPY than when anorexia patients are first treated. COGNITIVE THERAPY is being used in some places in the form of

cognitive-behaviour therapy. The desired behavioural change is better self-control by the patient over her eating patterns. At the same time she is encouraged to change her attitudes and learn other ways of coping with the emotional pressures which may have triggered off her binges.

Anorexic Family Aid and **Anorexic Aid** help sufferers from bulimia as well as ANOREXIA.

The **Maisner Centre** offers private help to bulimia sufferers and compulsive eaters. Applicants first complete a questionnaire and then receive an eating plan and a cassette tape. They then fill in daily food charts and return them weekly to the Centre for assessment. Advice is given by telephone to help sufferers understand why they should change their diet, and lifestyle if necessary. Personal consultations are available at the Centre.

Compulsions

Four compulsive behaviours are described in other sections – ALCOHOL DEPENDENCE, DRUG DEPENDENCE, EATING DISORDERS and GAMBLING. Certain SEXUAL PROBLEMS may have a compulsive element – for example, some cases of exhibitionism. Other compulsions are sometimes said to be part of an obsessive-compulsive disorder. The obsession is a thought, idea or impulse which cannot be dispelled or resisted, while the compulsion is an irresistible urge to carry out an activity. In practice, these two components are very often linked and the preferred name for this problem is now OBSESSIVE DISORDER.

Confusion

This is a symptom, not a specific disorder. Confusion is an inability to think as clearly as one normally would. It can be found as a part of two mental conditions – DELIRIUM and DEMENTIA. Elderly people may also appear to be confused because their sight and/or hearing are very poor. The correct glasses, hearing aid and ear-care can make an appreciable difference in their ability to understand what is happening around them.

The term 'confused', when applied to elderly people in hospitals and residential homes, can have a number of meanings. It may be used to describe those whose behaviour is unacceptable. However, there is always a reason for this – dementia, delirium, personality disorder, or even just an unwillingness to conform to the community life. Confusion may also be caused by a sudden change in the elderly person's life – such as moving to a new environment or BEREAVEMENT.

Although these definitions and examples all involve elderly people, confusion is neither confined to the elderly nor an inevitable result of getting old. It is no longer believed that people's intelligence declines noticeably as they age, thus increasing the likelihood of confusion. The only faculties which do generally show a slight deterioration are the ability to think quickly and to recall facts easily. It may therefore take an elderly person slightly longer to perform mental arithmetic or to remember someone's name, but as the section on DEMENTIA emphasises, this does not herald senility.

What can be done

The treatment for confusion is to deal with the underlying cause, if possible – see DELIRIUM and DEMENTIA. It is therefore important for a GP to see an elderly person who is confused. The person is unlikely to recognise the need for this himself, so you will either have to persuade him to make an appointment, or contact the GP yourself.

Delinquency

Delinquency is not a mental illness though it is a problem which may sometimes come to the attention of the mental health services. Some dictionaries define it as an offence committed by a juvenile. However, mental health experts often extend the definition to cover other antisocial behaviour which does not constitute an offence. Antisocial behaviour may include persistent truancy (see also school PHOBIA), lying, vandalism and under-age drinking, as well as cruelty, aggressiveness and stealing.

A single minor offence such as shoplifting is not likely to come to the attention of the mental health services. However, adolescents who persistently offend in this way, or more commonly through a variety of antisocial forms of behaviour, may face the measures described below.

The causes of delinquent behaviour are numerous and probably every case involves a combination of them. The child may be under stress at home or at school. There may be poor family relationships. One recent survey found that delinquents were not as close to their fathers as non-delinquent youngsters. Delinquent girls did not feel close to their mothers either. Some psychiatrists consider them to be unhappy, angry adolescents who express this in antisocial behaviour, rather than in DEPRESSION. The reasons for their feelings taking this form might be their inborn temperament, or immaturity. Some have a greed, impulsiveness, lack of judgement and desire for immediate gratification, typical of children much younger than themselves. In these ways they resemble the adult who has a PSYCHOPATHIC DISORDER. Low self-esteem is a common characteristic of delinquent youngsters, and one of the barriers to improving their behaviour is their rejection of attempts to befriend and help them.

Some experts feel that delinquents lack social skills. They argue that the youngsters do not know how to deal with criticism or teasing, so they act aggressively or destructively. The influence of those around them may be a key factor for easily led adolescents. Relatives or friends who consistently flout the law may encourage these juveniles to do the same.

A recently proposed theory, as yet not widely accepted, is that diet may play a role in susceptible children. (See DIET in Chapter 2 and HYPERACTIVITY later in this chapter.) It is proposed that some children are sensitive to certain chemicals in their diet – commonly in the food they consume in large quantities, such as milk. The theory is that this affects the chemical messenger systems in their brains, and thus their behaviour. Some may also have deficiencies in vitamins and minerals. In conjunction with the social and other factors mentioned above, this could lead to delinquency in certain youngsters.

What can be done

In many cases delinquents are brought to court for their offences. They may be placed under a Probation or Supervision Order, depending on their age. It is then the job of the probation officer or local authority (effectively a social worker) to ensure that the youngster does not offend again. Probation officers are social workers attached to the courts; you may ask their advice about delinquent behaviour, even if your child is not in trouble with the law. Intermediate treatment under the supervision of the local authority, or less commonly a probation officer, may be used as an alternative to detention centres, youth custody or taking the youngster into care. (See also SERVICES FOR CHILDREN in Chapter 11.) A combination of activities is chosen for the juvenile – including social skills training (see BEHAVIOUR THERAPY), drama therapy (see OCCUPATIONAL THERAPY) and COUNSELLING. Parents are involved in the programmes, but the youngster can be removed from home for up to 90 days in order to participate in these activities. Courts are also able to direct young offenders not to engage in certain activities and may impose curfews.

Children placed in the care of the local authority may be accommodated in community homes, and social skills training is being used in some of these. Residents who are disruptive may be sent to secure units or youth treatment centres where various forms of behaviour therapy are used.

Delinquent behaviour which does not lead a youngster to court may still sometimes be brought to the attention of the mental health services.

Behaviour therapy may be used, as may FAMILY THERAPY. This might involve changing the way the parents react to their child's behaviour. Generally, consistency, firmness and moderation are advocated – therapists would try to correct a couple who alternated between punishment and indifference to their child's misdeeds.

Experiments in the USA have shown that the antisocial behaviour of male juvenile offenders has improved by altering their diet. The **Biosocial Therapy Association** is now promoting the idea in Britain that diet is one of several factors affecting behaviour.

Delirium

This has a number of synonyms, such as acute confusional state, acute organic psychosis and acute brain syndrome. If only for brevity, 'delirium' is used here. There are three types of symptom:

- disorientation – the person does not know what time it is, and later may be unsure where he is, especially if he has recently moved to a new environment. In rare cases a patient may even be confused about his own identity
- impaired consciousness – the patient sometimes appears awake and alert, but at other times he is drowsy and may need a gentle shake to attract his attention. (However, this may frighten him in view of the third set of symptoms.) When the person is in this state, he soon becomes incoherent, or rambles about several unrelated subjects. He may speak only a few words, or only to himself
- impaired perceptions – this happens most commonly with the things he sees – or believes he sees. He might mistake an inanimate tall object for a person, or a small one for an animal. This is called an illusion. If he suffers from hallucinations he will 'see' things which are not there at all – people climbing through his window, for instance. These illusions and hallucinations are often frightening, and someone touching him while he is in a drowsy state and experiencing them may frighten him.

A delirious patient suffering from these three types of symptom may develop PARANOID ideas. His strange experiences, all attributable to the delirium, may cause him to believe that he is being attacked or persecuted. He may well show terror at some stages, or even aggression, but will then lapse into an apathetic state. Some patients are irritable and restless; a few are exceptionally elated. The delirium is often worse at night.

A delirious state may last only a few hours or continue for weeks, although a doctor should be called long before this. It can start suddenly or develop gradually, depending on the cause.

DELIRIUM

In elderly people the most common cause is the adverse effect of prescribed DRUGS. This may be a side-effect from a newly prescribed medicine, but it is much more likely to be because the dose is too high or too many drugs are being taken in combination. Elderly people sometimes forget whether they have taken a dose of each of several medicines they have been prescribed, and so take them all again.

Delirium can also be caused by suddenly ceasing to take a drug – including alcohol. People who suffer from ALCOHOL DEPENDENCE have withdrawal symptoms if they stop drinking. In some cases these symptoms are severe – delirium tremens (DTs). It may not start for up to three days after the person's last drink, but begins with a trembling and visual hallucinations. Sometimes this is followed by convulsions, over-activity, CONFUSION and illusions. Most cases last one to three days, but they can continue for over a week.

Other causes of delirium are more common than alcohol-withdrawal – for example, infections and fevers. Children who have a high temperature with an infectious disease, such as measles, may be delirious for a few hours. Various other physical conditions may also cause delirium – anaemia, certain forms of EPILEPSY, DEPRESSION, thyroid disorders, abnormal sugar levels in the blood (see DIET in Chapter 2), vitamin deficiencies and head injury. Elderly people who are already taking prescribed drugs are especially susceptible to delirium when they develop a physical illness. (A couple of studies have described it as occurring after childbirth, but this is a controversial diagnosis, and not accepted by many doctors.)

What can be done
Children who are delirious with an infectious disease do not need medical attention specifically for the delirium, but this may be necessary for other aspects of the illness. An elderly person with delirium should be seen by a doctor so that he can determine and treat the cause. This might involve changing the person's medication.

DRUGS are sometimes given, either to treat the illness causing the delirium, or to relieve severe ANXIETY caused by paranoid ideas.

If you are nursing a delirious person keep his room well lit, or totally dark if he is asleep – half-light can create illusions. Keep it quiet, too, so that noises cannot be misinterpreted. Speak clearly and reassuringly, repeating yourself if necessary.

Unlike DEMENTIA, delirium can be reversible and may therefore usually be treated.

Dementia

This is not a single disorder, but a group of conditions which produce a deterioration in the sufferer's intellectual ability, memory and personality. This deterioration is progressive and the majority of the conditions causing it are irreversible. Unlike DELIRIUM, the consciousness is not affected so the person does not appear drowsy. However, some of the other symptoms are common to both conditions, and a patient may suffer from both. 'True' dementia is caused by degeneration of the brain in the ways described below. The same symptoms may occasionally be due to other causes and treatment for these may prevent the patient's condition deteriorating. They include ALCOHOL DEPENDENCE, DRUG DEPENDENCE, chronic lung or kidney disease, thyroid disorders, DEPRESSION, brain tumour and vitamin deficiencies.

The most common types of dementia are ALZHEIMER'S DISEASE, followed by multi-infarct dementia. Some sufferers have both forms together. The phrases 'senile' and 'pre-senile dementia' do not refer to different types, but merely to the age at which the sufferer develops the condition. If he is younger than 60 or 65 he is said to have pre-senile dementia. The only difference between senile and pre-senile dementia is that the deterioration seems to be more rapid for sufferers under 60.

The less common forms of dementia include HUNTINGTON'S CHOREA.

At most, ten per cent of those aged over 65 have dementia, and it is severe in only half these cases. The proportion rises with age – about 20 per cent of those aged over 80 are sufferers. Nevertheless, it is clear that dementia is not the inevitable fate of those who live a long life.

Those who develop multi-infarct dementia are likely to be 60 to 80 years old. The typical age for developing Alzheimer's disease is a much wider range, from about 50 to about 80 years old. Other forms of dementia may, however, affect young children. Sometimes this is a degenerative condition first noticed in the child's third year. The child loses the skills he has learnt and is then severely handicapped. After the initial stage when he may realise something is wrong, the child does not know what is happening to him. As with adults, some causes of this type of deterioration are treatable.

The characteristics of ALZHEIMER'S DISEASE are described elsewhere. The rest of this section looks at multi-infarct dementia and at information common to all forms of dementia.

Multi-infarct dementia has been given a number of other names such as arteriosclerotic and cerebrovascular dementia. It is related to other problems of the blood circulation, such as high blood pressure and heart disease. This type of dementia is caused by damage to small areas of the brain because of strokes. The blood supply to those areas is suddenly reduced and the cells die. This stroke may be so small that the person is unaware of it, or it may have a temporary effect such as speech problems or paralysis. Serious strokes, or a series of small ones, cause a gradual deterioration in the sufferer's mental functioning and this is dementia. It is possible to differentiate this type of dementia from Alzheimer's disease by the speed of its onset (faster) and of its progress (more uneven). The symptoms are very similar, but sufferers of multi-infarct dementia are more prone to DEPRESSION and to unprovoked fits of crying. Their personality, however, may be less damaged.

No form of dementia is caused by 'under-utilising' the brain, or by working too hard, or by traumatic events – though stress may make it worse once it has begun. An elderly relative is sometimes found to be suffering from dementia after BEREAVEMENT. This is not because of the death of the spouse, but because the partner used to be able to 'cover up' the effects of the dementia in its early stages. The partner may have taken over the shopping, remembered the chores to be done and so on, so that no one living outside their house was aware of the person's failing capacity.

Because dementia affects all the mental functions, an enormous variety of symptoms are possible, but however severe his condition, no sufferer will have them all. The first signs may be a slightly reduced short-term memory – the person finds it difficult to recall what he has just done, but has no trouble remembering a distant event. Because slight loss of memory is such a common feature of increasing age, this symptom may be ignored. But it is important not to worry unnecessarily about memory-lapses. It must be stressed that only a doctor can advise on an individual case. As an example, however, it is quite normal to forget an item you were going to buy at the shops, but to forget that you have just been to the shops and set off again is more serious.

Another early sign of dementia is a slight change in personality. The person might lose interest in his job or hobbies, or be uncharacteristically lazy. His work may become shoddy and his appearance scruffy. At later stages personality traits may be exaggerated. For example, a tidy person may become obsessive about neatness, and perhaps frustrated at his decreasing ability to be tidy. Other sufferers show complete changes in their personality – the mild-mannered becoming aggressive, the quiet becoming noisily domineering.

In the early stages of the illness the sufferer may be aware of his failing abilities, and understandably suffer DEPRESSION. Other problems at this time may be ANXIETY, HYPOCHONDRIA and PARANOID DISORDERS. As the deterioration progresses, at a rate which varies greatly between sufferers, this insight is lost and the person is unaware of his condition.

As intellectual skills are lost the ability to cope with problems and use judgement declines, and new information is difficult to take in. The memory impairment increases and the person becomes disoriented (see DELIRIUM). Some people with dementia behave as if night were day – wandering about and wanting to eat in the middle of the night. In the final stages of the illness the sufferer may become incontinent.

What can be done

If the dementia is due to a curable condition, that disorder must be treated. Dementia resulting from the two commonest causes – multi-infarct and Alzheimer's disease – cannot be cured. Treatment can relieve some of the behavioural symptoms, possibly slow down the rate of intellectual deterioration, and keep the sufferer physically mobile for as long as possible. Research may in the future find a cure for at least some types of dementia.

DRUGS are used to control the more unmanageable behaviour problems, such as agitation and aggression. Sedatives help the person to sleep through the night and avoid the risks of wandering alone in a confused state. Antidepressants may be prescribed. Initial enthusiasm for a number of drugs aimed at improving the functioning of the brain has been replaced by disappointment and they are little used now. It was also hoped to follow the rationale used in treating PARKINSON'S DISEASE by replacing the missing chemical messengers, but this has so far been unsuccessful.

PHYSIOTHERAPY exercises help the person to remain mobile for a time.

REALITY ORIENTATION is used exclusively for patients with dementia. Relatives can help with the person's disorientation and failing memory by providing lists of things to do according to his ability, putting up calendars and clocks, signs on the doors to rooms and so on.

SPEECH THERAPY can help the person to make the most of his ability to speak. Properly fitting dentures also make speech clearer. Speech therapists may also be very helpful in demonstrating alternative methods of communication in individual cases.

A district nurse can advise you on nursing care of the sufferer when this becomes necessary – ask your GP to arrange for one to visit you. As the person becomes more disabled, aids from the social services department (or equivalent) will help – ask the occupational therapist to visit.

Specialised advice can be obtained from the voluntary organisations set up to help sufferers from dementia and their carers. Examples are the **Alzheimer's Disease Society** and the **Association to Combat Huntington's Chorea**.

Further information on caring for someone with dementia is given in Chapter 14 under ELDERLY RELATIVES.

Depression

As with ANXIETY, feelings of depression are sometimes perfectly under-standable reactions to problems. Few would call grief and despondency after BEREAVEMENT, DIVORCE or serious SURGERY, a mental illness. Generally, people begin to feel a little better after a while, and although they may continue to grieve about the event, it does not colour their whole view of life for very long.

The mental illness of depression is rather different. It prevents the person living the sort of life he enjoyed before. He may feel isolated and LONELY even though he has the same number of people around him. Despite this he appears to reject those who try to comfort him, and is unable to feel affection for them. He frequently cries, but as the illness progresses tears bring little relief and he may even reach a point of being unable to cry any more. His energy and interests disappear, and gradu-ally the effort of talking and concentrating becomes too demanding. Those around him may start to give up trying to help. He finds it difficult to remember day-to-day things, but may dwell excessively on the past. Generally, depressed people show very little activity, except perhaps for wringing their hands, but some elderly sufferers in particular become very agitated and restless, and this may be misconstrued as DEMENTIA. At times the sufferer's mood seems 'flat', with no emotion obvious; at others a deep gloom is apparent. He is pessimistic and hopeless, and sometimes also anxious. HYPOCHONDRIA is quite common. People suffering from severe depression frequently find it difficult to get to sleep and then wake early in the morning, unable to get back to sleep. Their mood is often lowest at this time, though a minority find the evening the worst time. Almost all sufferers lose their appetite and some weight, although a few gain weight. Constipation is common, as is a loss of libido or sex drive (see SEXUAL PROBLEMS). Another key feature of more severe depression is a feeling of unworthiness or guilt. Seriously depressed people often feel that it is their own fault that they are ill, that it is a punishment for the way they have acted in the past. They criticise themselves for being unable to cope with their present lives, and this makes them feel even more depressed. When these feelings become marked, especially with an attitude that others would be better off without them, SUICIDE is a risk. The risk is greatest when the person wakes early in the morning, perhaps around 5 am, feeling that there is no point in continuing. Some people drink heavily to relieve their depressed feelings, but alcohol only makes their mood worse.

It is also possible for sufferers to experience psychotic delusions – including PARANOID states – and hallucinations. The most extreme cases of depression can result in stupor: the person sits or lies unmoving and unresponsive. He does not eat, drink or talk, and urgent medical attention is needed. Such cases are, however, rare.

Several main causes of depression have been proposed and it is likely that each case involves a combination of factors. One theory concerns changes in the brain's chemical messenger systems, and antidepressant drugs do apparently restore a balance as the depression lifts. However, it has not yet been proven whether an imbalance in these biochemicals causes the depression in the first place.

The cognitive theory holds that sufferers have developed a distorted view of themselves and of the world, so that they see everything in a gloomy way. Every experience is then interpreted in such a way as to produce the mood and behaviour typical of depression. Another theory states that people who develop depression have been unable to cope in the past with problems, and to control how their life evolves. They begin to feel helpless, and then depressed. Both these theories have yet to be proven.

A new theory currently being researched is whether the length of the day, and thus exposure to light, has any connection with depression. Some sufferers become ill at the same time every year – in the autumn when the days are becoming shorter. The **Biosocial Therapy Association** is interested in this particular aspect of depression.

One of the obvious causes of depression is as a reaction to 'life events' – incidents which might cause sadness in anyone, but which trigger a mental illness in some people. The relevant life events seem to have a meaning of loss or failure for the person. BEREAVEMENT, LONELINESS, UNEMPLOYMENT, MARITAL PROBLEMS and DIVORCE, and some forms of SURGERY are examples. Relationship difficulties and a lack of support seem to produce a background of STRESS against which a 'life event' can be the trigger for depression. Some research suggests that being at home with several young children and having no intimate, confiding relationship to provide support, makes depression more likely. However, the causal link between these problems and mental illness is not firmly established. Similarly, there are inconclusive results from studies of the impact on later mental health of losing one's mother at an early age.

Depression is diagnosed more frequently in women than in men, and this has led to research into the possible hormonal causes of the illness. The connection between depression and PRE-MENSTRUAL TENSION and the MENOPAUSE seems to confirm this possibility. The fact that women sometimes develop depression while taking the contraceptive pill also seemed to support the theory, but many researchers now think that there is no chemical or hormonal basis for this.

Other drugs, do, however, seem to cause depression in some people. Among them are neuroleptics for SCHIZOPHRENIA, drugs for high blood pressure, and perhaps some for PARKINSON'S DISEASE.

A personality type which appears to predispose some people to depression is the affective personality. Such people have a depressed mood, or less commonly an elated mood, or an alternation between the two, without the other symptoms of depression or MANIA (see MANIC-DEPRESSION).

Several illnesses can cause symptoms of depression, including hypo-glycaemia (unstable sugar levels in the blood – see DIET in Chapter 2). As described under PSYCHOSOMATIC DISORDERS in Chapter 3, depression sometimes follows a physical illness such as glandular fever or flu.

Depression is the most common mental illness among elderly people. Some experts believe that children do not have depression; others hold that they do, but that it appears as DELINQUENCY, HYPERACTIVITY, school PHOBIA and so on.

The various causes of depression have been used as a basis for classifying cases, but this has led to little agreement about what the categories should be. The term 'reactive' was originally used for cases which arose as a reaction to stress, and 'endogenous' for cases which had no external cause but resulted from changes within the sufferer's brain. However, this is often an impossible distinction to make. Many experts feel that every case has an external trigger – an event which causes the symptoms to appear – but this may not be the sole cause of the depression as the term 'reactive' implies. In some instances the sufferer may have an in-built predisposition to depression (as 'endogenous' suggests), and thus a less serious event will trigger a bout of depression.

An additional problem has been the parallel use of the labels 'neurotic' and 'psychotic'. They have been used to divide minor and severe cases, and have sometimes been employed as synonyms for 'reactive' and 'endogenous'. But a patient for whom no external cause of the depression is apparent is not necessarily psychotic, nor even more seriously ill than someone whose grief in bereavement has developed into depression.

Another method of categorising cases of depression is to separate those which result from another illness or from taking a drug or abusing alcohol (secondary depression), from those in which depression occurs alone. However, it is this latter category of primary depression which researchers and psychiatrists are still trying to subdivide. A distinction which has received some agreement is that between unipolar and bipolar affective illnesses. These are mood disorders (see Chapter 3). Unipolar disorder involves only depression, but bipolar disorder includes depression (probably of a different type) and MANIA. This disorder is described in more detail under MANIC-DEPRESSION.

Perhaps the most satisfactory summary which can be given at this stage is to talk of Type A and Type B depression, either of which may be minor or severe. These may be two extremes of the same condition, or two separate disorders. In this classification, Type B depression can be described as a reaction to a STRESS in the person's life which represents a loss to him. His reaction is an exaggerated form of the feelings one would have expected him to have. He does not show a severe loss of appetite nor of libido. Anxiety is more commonly associated with this type of depression than with Type A. He finds it hard to go to sleep but does not wake in the early morning feeling suicidal.

Type A depression, on the other hand, generally develops more slowly, and typically when the sufferer is older. There are changes in the brain's chemical messenger systems, although whether these are the cause or the effect of the depression has not been established. This condition has a more marked effect on the sufferer's ability to continue his normal life, and feelings of guilt and self-blame come to dominate. He loses more weight and typically wakes early. Agitated depressives are restless and anxious; retarded depressives show little movement. Once the depression has lifted, it is liable to reappear. There seems to be a genetic factor in this type of depression.

Post-natal depression – even this is not a clear-cut category. There is disagreement about the causes and nature of the condition. The majority of women experience the 'blues' shortly after giving birth. It lasts one or two days during which they feel tearful, depressed or anxious. It is sometimes called 'mother's', 'maternity', '3rd (or 4th) day' blues, and is not the first sign of post-natal depression. Even the ten per cent of mothers who develop post-natal depression usually recover from the blues first. A change in hormone levels is probably the cause of the blues, but is not proven as a cause of post-natal depression. This may take up to three months or more after the birth to develop, and can be mild or severe just like any other bout of depression. The symptoms are the same, with the additional problems of tiredness and a helpless baby to look after. Theories specific to post-natal depression include the stress of birth and of being a mother as the trigger for depression. Some sufferers have had previous episodes of depression. A lack of support from the baby's father sometimes appears to be a contributory factor in combination with a series of recent 'life events', including the birth.

What can be done

If a personality disorder with a predominantly depressed mood, or a minor case of depressive illness is the problem, COUNSELLING or supportive PSYCHOTHERAPY, with self-help methods, is the answer.

Self-help groups for people with depression often provide support for sufferers currently receiving help from the health and social services. Especially if former patients attend these meetings, those who are still depressed are able to see that recovery is possible, and this gives encouragement.

A self-help group meets regularly at the **Northern Ireland Association for Mental Health**.

Depressives Anonymous has several local groups, a quarterly newsletter and a penfriend scheme. It is a mutual help organisation and sees itself as a source of support complementary to professional help.

Depressives Associated, by contrast, believes that most doctors do not understand depression. There are local groups and information leaflets, and again the importance of mutual help is stressed.

The most widely-used treatment for depression is DRUG therapy using the three groups of antidepressants listed in Chapter 4. The tricyclic antidepressants do not have a noticeable effect for two to four weeks and it is therefore important to continue taking them as prescribed, even though they seem not to be working. Some people find the side-effects quite unpleasant in the first few days, but these usually fade. They include drowsiness, having a dry mouth, constipation and sometimes difficulty in seeing or thinking clearly. Some drugs cause less drowsiness than others, so a doctor may be able to prescribe an alternative, or reduce the dose, if this side-effect is really troublesome. Once the drugs have improved the symptoms of depression, they must be continued for a time to prevent the depression reappearing.

MAOI antidepressants are used less frequently, but may be chosen if the patient has anxiety as well as depression. A noticeable improvement may take even longer than with a tricyclic drug. The possible side-effects include insomnia and an increased appetite, but these are usually temporary. These drugs are not prescribed for longer than a year because there is a slight risk of DRUG DEPENDENCE. One of the major drawbacks with MAOI drugs is that certain foods must be avoided. These include cheese, yeast and meat extracts, herring, red wine, cough and cold remedies. There is a new MAOI which does not, however, react with these products.

If you are prescribed antidepressants, ask whether you should avoid any foods, and take the drugs as your doctor advises – never stop them suddenly without his advice.

Lithium salts are sometimes used for recurrent severe depression, and in some cases may help to prevent a further attack if the sufferer has already had three bouts of severe depression. However, they are more commonly used to treat MANIA and MANIC-DEPRESSION.

If depression occurs as part of a psychotic illness, for example with delusions, neuroleptics as prescribed for SCHIZOPHRENIA may be used, at least initially.

As with anxiety, drugs are often not the sole answer to depression, but in severe cases they are a necessary first step if the patient is to be able to benefit from PSYCHOTHERAPY. Mild cases may require only COUNSELLING or supportive psychotherapy. When a combined treatment programme is used the drugs improve symptoms such as insomnia, loss of appetite and other physical problems. The psychotherapy (perhaps as GROUP THERAPY) improves the way the patient functions within his family and with other people. It also seems to alleviate ideas of guilt and suicide. COGNITIVE THERAPY has been used to show the patient how his habitual way of thinking about himself and his life is causing him to be depressed. He is taught how to interpret events differently so that they do not make him feel low, and to encourage and praise himself to improve his self-esteem.

BEHAVIOUR THERAPY and cognitive-behavioural approaches aim to decrease the negative or unpleasant aspects of the person's life, and to increase the pleasant aspects. This may take several forms, and will involve the patient in homework assignments. For example, the therapist may encourage him to remember happy events from the past, to participate in activities which he finds enjoyable and to use newly acquired skills (such as being more assertive). The therapist emphasises the patient's achievements and the person gradually changes his gloomy view of life. Social skills training and communication training may be used to help him achieve more satisfying relationships.

FAMILY THERAPY is sometimes offered, but if not, the patient's partner may at least be invited to attend some of the counselling or psychotherapy sessions.

RELAXATION may be useful, especially when the person is suffering from anxiety as well as depression.

All these treatments take time to work and this cannot always be afforded. A very severely depressed, suicidal patient often requires more urgent treatment, and ECT is used in these cases. Sometimes, antidepressant drugs and psychotherapy fail to help a depressed patient and ECT may be tried in such cases, too. Research continues into the effectiveness of ECT. The present conclusion seems to be that it is best for severely ill patients, including those suffering from psychotic delusions and those with a strong suicidal intent.

PSYCHOSURGERY is very occasionally used for intractable depression which has resisted years of treatment by all other methods.

Post-natal depression – the self-help methods include getting enough rest, if necessary by asking friends or relatives to help you, but not to take over the job of looking after the baby unless the mother is severely ill. Talk to your midwife, health visitor or GP who will be able to offer advice. Discuss your feelings with your partner – and perhaps invite him to attend any discussions you have with a professional health worker. If you feel isolated the section on LONELINESS in the next chapter may be useful. The **Meet-A-Mum-Association** described there aims to help prevent cases of post-natal depression by providing support and friendship. **National Childbirth Trust** post-natal groups are also a source of friendship and support. They also offer help on a one-to-one basis and publish a booklet on post-natal depression.

A more serious case of post-natal depression may require treatment with antidepressant drugs. Research is looking at the use of drugs to restore the normal hormonal balance. Rarely will hospital admission be necessary but in this case every effort is made to admit the baby, too. Some hospitals have mother and baby units, but otherwise general hospital psychiatric departments normally accept a few patients with babies. Help with MARITAL PROBLEMS is sometimes necessary.

The **Association for Post-Natal Illness** can put you in touch with a local mother who has had post-natal depression.

Drug dependence

A drug is any substance which changes the functioning of the body or the mind. DRUGS as therapeutic substances are discussed in Chapter 4. It is possible to become addicted to some of these – 'tranquilliser dependence' – as described below. ALCOHOL DEPENDENCE is another form of drug addiction. Drug dependence, however, usually refers to the misuse of substances obtained illegally.

A classification of drug misusers has been proposed which is similar to that for heavy drinkers – see ALCOHOL DEPENDENCE. Many young people experiment with drugs but only a minority use them regularly and become problem drug-takers. The definition is the same as for problem drinkers – the habit may cause social, psychological, physical, legal and financial difficulties. Many of the problems are the same as those suffered by problem drinkers. Habitual drug-takers also tend to have low self-esteem, and may drop their previous interests and friends, except those who share their drug-taking. Some users, especially young people, compound their problems by heavy drinking.

Some problem drug-takers become drug-dependent. As with dependent drinkers they may suffer withdrawal symptoms if they do not use the drug regularly – this is especially so with drugs such as opiates (eg heroin), cocaine and barbiturates. Tolerance may also develop so that they need increasingly large doses to achieve the same effect. However, not all drugs produce physical dependence in this way. The dependence may be primarily psychological – there is an emotional urge to keep taking the drug because of its effects on the user's mind. Using the drug regularly gives him confidence. For this reason, there may be psychological withdrawal symptoms of anxiety or depression.

Taking very large amounts of amphetamines can produce feelings of paranoia, but these almost invariably subside if the person stops. Use of hallucinogenic drugs such as LSD can also produce a psychotic reaction closely resembling SCHIZOPHRENIA.

Probably most parents of teenagers worry about the possibility of them taking drugs. All the agencies listed at the end of this section will advise parents who suspect this. It is important to remember that one experiment with drugs does not make an addict, and that many of the signs suggesting drug use are in fact merely 'symptoms' of adolescence. Nevertheless spotting the problem quickly means that help can be sought before the youngster is tempted to try hard drugs. You might, for example, be alerted by:

- loss of appetite
- loss of interest in hobbies, sport or friends
- marked change in mood or sleeping habits
- money or belongings disappearing.

Tranquilliser dependence – as described under DRUGS in Chapter 4, the benzodiazepine drugs were introduced as safer antianxiety drugs than barbiturates. It is now known that it is also possible to become dependent on minor tranquillisers such as diazepam (sold as Valium). These drugs seem to lose their antianxiety effect after about four months, and to lose their sedative effect as sleeping pills in under two weeks. There is therefore no point in taking them for long periods. Some people have been taking benzodiazepines for many years and are now dependent on them. If they stop taking the medicine they experience withdrawal symptoms which in some people can be quite severe. Dozens have been listed, including feelings of panic and agitation, nausea and poor appetite, trembling and dizziness. In some ways the result of giving up the tranquilliser is like the ANXIETY for which it was originally prescribed. Rare but frightening symptoms are hallucinations, feelings of persecution and AGORAPHOBIA.

There is no agreement on the likely duration of the withdrawal symptoms, but it probably depends on how long the person had been taking the tranquilliser and the size of the dose.

What can be done
Withdrawal can be a very difficult process and some drug misusers are never able to manage it. It may be achieved by gradually decreasing the dose, perhaps while the person is an in-patient or an out-patient at an NHS Drug Dependence Clinic or Centre. Nearly all the places at these clinics are taken by drug misusers who have been using heroin or similar drugs. There are waiting lists for most hospital drug dependence services, and places are particularly scarce in Scotland where addicts may be referred to facilities in England. Many of the clinics will accept only patients who are referred by their GPs, but some can be approached directly.

As an aid to withdrawal from heroin, methadone is prescribed at some clinics. The theory is that in time the addicts can be weaned off drugs, but critics of the method say that it is simply substituting one addiction for another.

Treatment at a specialist clinic may involve PSYCHOTHERAPY, social skills training and contract therapy (see BEHAVIOUR THERAPY), COGNITIVE-behaviour THERAPY, marital and FAMILY THERAPY, and rehabilitation (see Chapter 13). Meditation (see RELAXATION) has been found useful in the treatment of drug dependence.

In addition to the NHS facilities there are voluntary and private treatment centres. However, if a private place is found by the parent of a drug user who is not determined to break the addiction, the money spent is very unlikely to buy a cure. Like those dependent on alcohol, drug addicts must be motivated to give up. **Clouds House**, a private clinic treating ALCOHOL DEPENDENCE, also accepts drug addicts.

Some voluntary facilities are residential rehabilitation centres for people who have stopped taking drugs (this is usually a condition of living at the house), but who are not yet ready to return to their homes. Some may stay for up to two years while they learn a new approach to life and better ways of coping with stresses. Some are run as Christian or therapeutic communities (see ACCOMMODATION in Chapter 13). COUNSELLING may be offered, sometimes on alcohol dependence. Other residential facilities are halfway accommodation, providing an understanding environment for those who are ready to return to work, but not to a completely independent life.

SCODA will provide advice on drug dependence and lists of facilities in your area.

Families Anonymous has some similarities to Al-Anon Family Groups (see ALCOHOL DEPENDENCE). It is a self-help organisation providing weekly meetings for relatives and friends of problem drug-takers. The 'Twelve Steps' formulated by Alcoholics Anonymous have been adopted, and literature on drug-taking is produced.

ACCEPT, in addition to its services for problem drinkers, can also help those addicted to prescribed medicines such as tranquillisers (see below), and to illegal drugs.

Drugline offers advice and support to parents in the form of a telephone helpline. A monthly meeting is held in London. They will advise you if you want to set up a similar organisation in your area. A booklet on drugs is produced.

The **South Wales Association for the Prevention of Addiction** has a 24-hour telephone helpline, and provides COUNSELLING and information on local facilities for drug and solvent abusers and their relatives anywhere in Britain.

Turning Point has a number of rehabilitation and counselling services for drug users.

The **Samaritans** (see SUICIDE) can tell you how to get help locally for drug dependence.

Some addicts worry that by seeking help for dependence on illegal drugs, they will face prosecution. Doctors will not inform the police if such a drug user contacts them. They must notify the Home Office of people dependent on certain drugs including heroin and cocaine. (In Northern Ireland notification is made to the Department of Health and Social Services.) A list of drug users is kept by the Home Office for statistical purposes and as a record for a patient's future doctors to consult. The police do not have access to it, and no one should avoid seeking medical help through fear of legal action.

Tranquilliser dependence – if you have been taking tranquillisers for many months or years, and would like to stop, discuss it first with your GP. Never stop taking any drug suddenly. Discuss with your GP how to go about reducing the amount you take. Some experts advocate a very slow decrease, others think it better to do it in a few weeks.

Tranx is the National Tranquilliser Advisory Council. They offer support by telephone or at a group meeting and will give you practical advice on a withdrawal programme. They continue to help after people have stopped taking tranquillisers, while they readjust to life without drugs. Tranx has twenty affiliated groups (three of them abroad) and personal COUNSELLING can be arranged for people who do not want to join a group.

The **Northern Ireland Association for Mental Health** has a tranquilliser group meeting weekly at its head office.

Other self-help groups are being formed throughout the UK – ask your GP or local mental health association if there is one in your area.

Eating disorders

Two of the most common disorders are described earlier in this chapter – ANOREXIA and BULIMIA NERVOSA. A third group are compulsive eaters who do not 'binge and vomit' like those with bulimia. A compulsive eater may be someone on a diet who frequently 'slips' and has a bar of chocolate, and feels guilty and angry with herself. Then, because she has spoilt the day's diet anyway, she eats whatever she feels like – and it will probably be all the foods forbidden by her diet. She does not necessarily binge as in bulimia, where food is crammed into the mouth at disgusting speed – and often in distasteful combinations. The compulsive eater simply cannot control her appetite. If compulsive eaters do not diet strictly after their 'lapses', or purge as in bulimia, they inevitably put on weight, and many are obese.

From practical necessity, compulsive eaters, including those with bulimia, sometimes shoplift to obtain the food they crave. The cost of frequent binges can be enormous, and sufferers may resort to stealing other items because all the housekeeping money has been spent on food. Despite their very frugal eating habits, those with anorexia also sometimes shoplift, though not necessarily food.

The causes of all eating disorders are unclear, although many theories have been put forward, as described under ANOREXIA and BULIMIA. The more general disorder of compulsive eating may arise through the person trying to comfort herself for other aspects of her life which she finds disappointing. She might feel lonely or depressed, and find solace from eating foods which she regards as 'treats' – sweets and cakes, for example. It might be a food which has happy memories for her – such as of being a child.

One theory for compulsive eating falls into the area of clinical ecology described under DIET in Chapter 2. It has been proposed, though not proven, that an abnormal reaction to certain foods causes the compulsive eater to binge. The theory is that she has an 'addiction' to one or more foods and therefore craves them, but her body is hypersensitive to them and she reacts abnormally. A sufferer may thus wake in the middle of the night with a panicky feeling (likened to the withdrawal symptoms of any addict), and gorge on a variety of foods trying to satisfy the craving. Other sufferers may find that eating a particular food (to which their body reacts abnormally) triggers off a binge. According to the theory, if this food can be identified, compulsive eating can be controlled. This theory is not accepted by all doctors, but it is being used at the **Maisner Centre**.

Those who eat compulsively have a higher risk of SUICIDE than others of their age and sex. Feeling at the mercy of their irresistible craving for food, and constantly fearing another attack, in very severe cases they may take their own lives.

Some women with eating disorders find that their problem is worse just before or during their periods – see PRE-MENSTRUAL TENSION.

What can be done

The sections on ANOREXIA and BULIMIA describe treatment for these conditions. The help available for compulsive eaters is the same as for those suffering from bulimia. The **Maisner Centre**, for example, accepts clients who are compulsive eaters.

The **Women's Therapy Centre** runs groups for compulsive eaters. After the initial sessions working with a leader on individual problems, the groups continue on a self-help basis in the participants' homes, followed by a later session with the leader.

Epilepsy

This is not a mental illness but a disorder of the way the brain functions. Nerve cells which make up the brain are continuously releasing electrical energy, but fits, seizures or 'attacks' result if there is a sudden, excessive and abnormal discharge of energy. This happens on the odd occasion to many people, but epilepsy is a tendency for fits to recur. It is often not known why someone has a single or repeated fits. There may be an inherited predisposition to develop epilepsy. Such people often have other problems concerning brain functioning. Epilepsy may be caused by injury to the brain cells – for example, during birth or a stroke. In this case the damage may cause other problems, physical, intellectual or psychiatric. Thus epilepsy does not cause mental illness or handicap, but sometimes occurs with them. Fits can be caused by a very high temperature – young children occasionally have these febrile fits and this does not necessarily herald epilepsy. Most epileptic fits do not have a clear cause, but some sufferers learn to avoid their 'trigger' situations – such as lack of sleep, too much alcohol, or sitting close to a flickering television screen.

Those who suffer from epilepsy have usually started having fits as a child or adolescent, but it can begin at any age. As there is a genetic element, many sufferers worry about the risk of passing it on to their children. This risk is often very small, but varies according to the type of epilepsy suffered by one or both parents. At most there is a one in four chance of their child developing epilepsy.

There are many types of epilepsy, only one of which causes convulsions or 'major' fits. One form of this is known as 'tonic-clonic' or 'grand mal' and causes the sufferer to fall down, perhaps with a cry, and to begin jerking his limbs. The fit may last several minutes; then the person regains consciousness. Minor fits, without convulsions, occur in 'petit mal' or 'absence'. The person stops what he is doing and may stare blankly, blink frequently or appear to day-dream. Consciousness is lost for a few seconds, but he does not fall down and he may even be unaware of what has happened. It is more common in children than adults and often disappears by early adulthood.

These major and minor fits are caused when a large part of the brain is involved in the abnormal discharge of electrical energy. Sometimes the disturbance is in only part of the brain, though it may spread. This causes 'partial' fits of various types. The person may involuntarily twitch one leg, or feel 'pins and needles' in one hand, for instance. Some sufferers sense a strange smell, or feel as if they have already experienced something that is currently happening ('déjà vu'). In other forms the person may pluck at his clothing, appear confused or be unable to speak. Some types involve a changed state of consciousness but the person will not necessarily fall down. Sometimes a major fit follows.

Suffering from epilepsy can affect your eligibility for a driving licence – see DRIVING in Chapter 13.

What can be done

Someone living with a person who starts to have fits can be very helpful to the doctor considering a diagnosis of epilepsy. Because the sufferer does not usually remember what has happened, an 'eye-witness' account is essential for a proper diagnosis.

DRUGS can successfully control most forms of epilepsy, though a minority of people suffer side-effects, particularly if they are taking more than one type of prescribed drug. Those taking drugs should inform their doctor if they develop slurred speech, unsteadiness, drowsiness or nausea. Antiepileptic drugs or anticonvulsants must be taken continuously and although some fits may still occur, the drugs reduce their frequency. It is often necessary to take the drugs for a few years after the fits have stopped.

HYPNOTHERAPY and HOMOEOPATHY are other forms of treatment which have been tried, although there is less scientific evidence of their value. However, some people who object to taking drugs may wish to try them. BEHAVIOUR THERAPY and biofeedback (see RELAXATION) are being used experimentally to see if people can learn to control the electrical activity of their brain. PSYCHOSURGERY is very rarely used and then only for epilepsy caused in certain ways.

Some women with epilepsy have fits more frequently before or during their periods (see PRE-MENSTRUAL TENSION). Hormones and diuretics to prevent 'water-retention' are sometimes prescribed, but not all doctors advocate this type of treatment.

There are special centres for epilepsy, which are NHS facilities where sufferers from severe epilepsy can usually stay for up to three months. Some people then return to their homes; others need long-term or 'halfway' ACCOMMODATION (see Chapter 13). One of the special centres is at the Chalfont Centre for Epilepsy (see opposite).

Most children can attend ordinary schools unless their epilepsy is disabling, in which case limited special facilities are available. The organisations listed below can provide information on these, and general advice on explaining epilepsy to a child who has fits, or who lives with a sufferer.

Some people find it hard to accept a diagnosis of epilepsy. There is an increased rate of SUICIDE and attempted suicide among sufferers. Put all your questions to the doctor making the diagnosis and contact one of the specialist organisations for additional advice. These include:

British Epilepsy Association – about 80 local self-help groups. Literature is produced and other books recommended. Advice is available on all aspects of epilepsy, and visits to provide COUNSELLING can be arranged. The Association can provide small grants to help in a crisis and give information about holiday facilities for adults and children with epilepsy.

National Society for Epilepsy at the Chalfont Centre for Epilepsy – long-term and halfway accommodation, with medical, occupational and leisure facilities. The Society runs a sheltered workshop and a sheltered industrial group (see EMPLOYMENT in Chapter 13). Leaflets are produced and other books recommended, and queries on epilepsy are answered.

Epilepsy Association of Scotland – produces literature, provides an information service and supports about 15 local branches and groups. Three centres in Glasgow offer further education and social skills training, occupational training and workshops. Social workers based in Edinburgh and Glasgow provide COUNSELLING for anyone with epilepsy. All the branches organise social events and summer holidays.

A few areas have social clubs organised specifically for people with epilepsy.

Gambling

Gambling can be thought of as a COMPULSION, and the term 'compulsive gambler' is often used for those who have an irresistible urge to bet and a passion for the excitement of the 'gambling life'. Some people feel that this is too narrow a view of the form excessive gambling takes. For example, it may be a symptom of an OBSESSIVE DISORDER. The sufferer realises that his behaviour is irrational, he gets no pleasure from it and therefore tries hard not to gamble, but he invariably does. This condition is seen as quite distinct from the 'impulsive gambler' who gambles uncontrollably, but has mixed feelings about it – an urge to bet, but a fear of the intensity of this longing.

Sub-divisions of the problem of excessive gambling are of little importance to the family of someone who will beg, borrow, steal, cheat or lie to obtain the money to support his 'addiction'. Severe financial difficulties, MARITAL PROBLEMS, trouble at work, and a loss of friends outside the gambling circle may all add up to a situation in which the only answer seems to the gambler to be SUICIDE.

Denial is a central feature of excessive gambling. Like the ALCOHOL-DEPENDENT drinker, he refuses to accept that he has a problem. He is convinced that the next bet will bring a huge win, and he is 'working on a system' to beat the odds. As long as this denial persists there is no hope of the habit being broken.

What can be done

While a few gamblers may be able to overcome their problem alone, most require some form of PSYCHOTHERAPY, COUNSELLING, or at least support. Aversion therapy (see BEHAVIOUR THERAPY) has been tried. The person is asked to think about gambling, to imagine himself playing roulette, for example, and then he is given a slight electric shock. Desensitisation has also been used: the person is relaxed and then instructed to think about gambling. The idea is to make gambling seem less attractive to him, because in a state of deep relaxation thoughts of it should not be so exciting.

Gamblers Anonymous has over 100 local groups in the UK which meet at least once a week. As in Alcoholics Anonymous the only requirement for membership is a desire to break the addiction. GROUP THERAPY, a recovery programme, practical advice and discussing their experiences help some compulsive gamblers to recover.

Gam Anon provides support and encouragement for relatives and friends of compulsive gamblers. As in Al-Anon Family Groups (see ALCOHOL DEPENDENCE), the sufferer himself does not have to be seeking help.

Huntington's chorea

This is a form of DEMENTIA which usually affects the body's movements, so that they become totally uncoordinated. The first signs appear slowly and increase gradually, perhaps for years, before becoming serious. The person's handwriting may become untidy. Then the hands may start to make jerky movements or fidget, while unsteady feet cause the person to trip or appear clumsy. Uncontrollable twitching of the fingers and toes, then a shaking and swaying of the arms, follow. At first sufferers may be aware of these changes, although some gradually lose insight into the seriousness of their condition as the illness slowly becomes more severe. Walking becomes difficult, speech is often slurred and the ability to swallow is affected.

In some sufferers changes in mood are the first indications of the disorder. They become uncharacteristically depressed, moody or angry. Some later have spells of CONFUSION, and may be unreasonable, even violent.

As in other forms of progressive dementia, the degeneration of brain cells is the cause of the condition, together with an imbalance of chemical messengers in the brain. The condition usually starts when the sufferer is between 30 and 50, though it can develop in young children and elderly people. It is the only dementia for which the genetic factor is precisely known. The child of an affected parent has a 50 per cent chance of inheriting the gene which causes Huntington's chorea. Everyone who inherits the gene develops the disease, if they live long enough. The age at which the disease is first apparent is very variable, and some people die before developing the condition. It is this fact which makes it hard for young people to make informed decisions about whether to have children. For example, a young woman may know that her grandfather had the disorder. Her father, at only 45, could still develop it, but has not yet done so. If he never does, the girl could not have inherited the gene (unless her mother's family was also affected, which is extremely unlikely). The older someone at risk becomes, without having the disorder, the less likely he is to have inherited the gene. But there is always a slight risk until he reaches about 75. By that time the young woman in this example will either have taken the risk and had children, or will have decided not to have a family – perhaps unnecessarily. Although there is not yet a test which shows whether someone has the relevant gene but has not developed the disease, current research indicates that there will be a predictive test available for some people in the fairly near future. This will probably be mainly used pre-natally and will depend on blood samples being taken from a number of family members.

Sufferers and their relatives face many psychological problems – such as feelings of guilt at having passed on a fatal disease to their children and fears of developing it themselves. There is also the need to explain the illness and its consequences to children and adolescents at risk.

What can be done

There is no cure for Huntington's chorea, although research to find one is in progress. DRUGS can be given to control the jerky movements, but otherwise the treatment is the same as for other forms of DEMENTIA.

Knowledge of how the disorder is inherited presents those at risk with extremely difficult decisions about having children. Each Regional Health Authority has a genetic counselling clinic which can help. A GP's referral is necessary.

An invaluable source of help for sufferers and their relatives is the **Association to Combat Huntington's Chorea** – often called Combat. They have publications on various aspects of the disorder and its consequences. There are nearly 30 branches, plus representatives and local contacts in other areas. Advice is available through the Family COUNSELLING Service by telephone, letter or individual and group meetings. There are three family support schemes in England in which volunteers offer practical help and befriending. Combat also runs a short-term Care Home in Essex. Here sufferers are cared for by staff experienced in this condition, while their relatives have a break.

Hyperactivity

This condition, which first appears in childhood, has been defined in several ways. One of the major sources of confusion is that 'hyperactivity' refers to a type of behaviour, and to a disorder in which this is a key symptom. The disorder has also been labelled 'hyperkinesis', 'hyperactivity syndrome' and 'attention deficit disorder with hyperkinesis'. The rest of this section considers hyperactivity as a disorder which may have a number of symptoms.

The main symptom is not simply overactivity, but excess, inappropriate activity in view of the situation and the child's age. No amount of remonstration by adults or the child's friends will control the behaviour. Most hyperactive children are boys. Such children sometimes describe themselves as feeling out of control. To others they may appear fidgety, unable to sit still and excitable. Parents understandably find this behaviour extremely wearing, and avoid taking the child to public places. They also often feel guilty, especially if others criticise their ability to control the child.

A hyperactive child is sometimes very much better in one situation than another. Some, for example, may be calm and quiet at home but hyperactive at school. Being in a group of people may trigger their hyperactivity. Doctors usually diagnose hyperactivity syndrome only if it occurs in several situations.

Diagnosis also usually depends on a second key feature – an inability to concentrate on one subject for more than a few minutes. These children are unable to pay attention and are easily distracted. Hyperactive children often have quickly changing moods. An outburst of tears (a frequent problem) may seem to have no cause, and will change just as suddenly to gleeful play. Some are very impulsive, apparently never thinking before they act about the consequences of their behaviour. This often leads to accidents and clumsiness. Again, it is important to compare this with what would be expected of a child their own age – young children are always more impulsive than older ones.

Hyperactive children may have one or more other problems which are thought to be effects of their behaviour, rather than central symptoms of the disorder. These include low self-esteem, poor performance at school, difficulty making friends and playing with other children, and sleep problems. Sometimes these problems remain after the main symptoms of hyperactivity are gone.

A link between hyperactivity and later antisocial behaviour or psychiatric problems has never been clearly demonstrated. In some children the disorder simply disappears as they get older; in others it is relieved by various forms of treatment. For some, adolescence and adulthood bring different problems. Some research suggests that if a child has hyperactivity syndrome and is aggressively antisocial, his outlook is less hopeful than if he is not aggressive.

Parents may be disturbed by unusual behaviour in their baby and this is sometimes a sign that hyperactivity will follow, although other such babies develop normally. Parents often report that as babies their hyperactive children were extremely restless, had sleeping problems and would cry continually. It is important to seek help for this kind of behaviour, because irritability and frustration felt by parents with such a baby could affect their later relationship with him.

Why children become hyperactive has yet to be fully established. Researchers are tending to look for a combination of factors which can result in the disorder. Hyperactivity sometimes has a physical cause (such as an infection), so a GP should be consulted to see if this is the root of the problem. Among the explanations for hyperactivity that have been proposed are imbalances in the brain's chemical messenger systems, high levels of lead or aluminium in the blood and problems at school (although the latter are more likely to be a result of the disorder). Food intolerances – such as hypersensitivity to milk, sugar and wheat – and food allergies have also been investigated (see DIET in Chapter 2 and DELINQUENCY). The **Hyperactive Children's Support Group** (see below) promotes one of the best-known theories linking diet and mental health. This was developed in the USA and states that in certain predisposed children, food additives (particularly colourings and flavours) can cause hyperactivity. By eliminating these from the child's diet, the hyperactivity will be cured. Some are also said to be sensitive to substances occurring naturally in certain fruits and vegetables, such as oranges and tomatoes.

What can be done

Relying on punishment for 'bad' behaviour will not cure hyperactivity, but it might damage your relationship with the child and possibly make the problem worse. Ways of handling a hyperactive child have been suggested which may help to reduce the symptoms, but specialist advice should always be sought. Advice which has been given to parents includes establishing routines in the home, not allowing the child to get exhausted, and keeping to consistent rules about behaviour.

DRUGS have been more widely used in the USA than here. Stimulant drugs, such as amphetamines, increase the child's ability to pay attention, and reduce his impulsive behaviour. However, there does not seem to be a long-term benefit, and it is undesirable to prescribe such drugs to children for any length of time. Sleeping pills are sometimes prescribed but these may not help much.

BEHAVIOUR THERAPY, perhaps the most widely-used technique, employs several methods (described in Chapter 4). Modelling may be used to illustrate the desired behaviour to the child – he may be shown a film of children playing quietly and be asked to copy them. Operant conditioning for younger children involves giving a reward for quiet, attentive behaviour. At first this is often a material item, but gradually praise alone is introduced as the reward. The child may receive reward tokens at school for his good behaviour, as well as during the therapy sessions. Parents, too, may be involved in such a treatment programme.

Older children may receive social skills training, and use contracts as a form of therapy. A hyperactive adolescent and his parents would agree a contract stating that the youngster would behave in specified, calm ways, and the parents would do something he wanted in return. COGNITIVE THERAPY can also be used for older sufferers. The youngster learns phrases which he says to himself to influence his own behaviour. For example, every time he begins a task he might say to himself 'Stop: think first' to reduce his impulsive behaviour. Paradoxical intention is another form of behaviour therapy which sometimes works for these children. The therapist asks the child to throw a tantrum, for instance, tells him to make it worse, continue crying loudly and so on. One possible explanation for the effectiveness of this method is that the child learns to have control over his behaviour, which he previously felt controlled him.

Behaviour and cognitive therapy may be used individually or as GROUP THERAPY. FAMILY THERAPY may also be necessary if relationships are being strained.

There is less evidence for the value of HOMOEOPATHY and for RELAXATION using biofeedback, although these methods may help some children.

The **Hyperactive Children's Support Group** has about 150 groups in the UK for parents of sufferers. They meet to offer support to each other, and some visit parents who cannot attend the meetings. The organisation provides information on the nutritional causes of hyperactivity, a book list, and lists of foods which do not contain the additives and natural substances to which these children may be sensitive. They recommend a 'safe' diet based on fresh foods, and will advise parents on providing this. If parents find it difficult to get specialist advice, the Group can put them in touch with medical consultants interested in the dietary approach to hyperactivity.

Whether this diet works has been the subject of heated debate. Some research which seems to disprove the theory has itself been criticised. Perhaps the only conclusion which can be drawn at present is that some parents find that it works, and it can do no harm in any case if properly followed. Recent research lends tentative support to the theory of food allergies being responsible for hyperactivity in some children.

A combination of treatments seems to be indicated for hyperactivity, if the idea that it has a combination of causes is correct. Sufferers left with poor self-confidence and an inability to make friends may need PSYCHOTHERAPY to help overcome these problems.

Hypochondria

This term may be used in a number of slightly different ways, but the general definition is 'a conviction of being ill, when there is no disease present, and despite all reassurances from a doctor'. Such a person believes himself to show symptoms of a disease, sees his GP and is either immediately, or after examinations and tests, told that he is in perfectly good health. He may remain as convinced as ever that he is ill, but he is often reassured for a short time before the fear returns. Often the illness imagined is quite serious – cancer, a heart condition or venereal disease, for example. This is clearly connected to illness PHOBIAS and to some cases of OBSESSIVE DISORDER, although these generally involve excessive fears of contracting a particular illness, rather than a conviction of already having it. There have been cases of hypochondriacal conviction of serious illness resulting in the person committing SUICIDE in preference to 'dying from the disease'.

Those described as having hypochondria are not always convinced of major health problems – some have a range of worries, including concern about possible bad breath, excessive perspiration, hearing loss and so on. Elderly people sometimes have an excessive concern about whether their bowels or bladder are functioning correctly.

Used in a slightly different sense, hypochondria may refer to a preoccupation with the state of one's health. Such a person might devote all his time and thought – even a great deal of money – to caring for his body. While people who take this to extremes are creating a very narrow range of interests, and would probably benefit from spending less time thinking about their health, they could at most be described as eccentric.

Hypochondria is common in cases of ANXIETY. This may be because anxiety magnifies the experience of a slight bodily symptom. A vague pain is felt to be very unpleasant, whereas it would have been almost ignored had the person not been suffering from a mental illness. Anxiety itself causes a number of physical symptoms. These may be misinterpreted by the sufferer – for instance, assuming a panic attack to be caused by heart disease.

HYSTERIA is linked with hypochondria, and there is no clear dividing line between the two disorders. However, in hypochondria the sufferer shows excessive concern about the possibility of having a particular illness, and feelings of anxiety are a major feature. The hysterical development of a symptom is not necessarily against a background of a preoccupation with physical illness. Thus the person who suddenly becomes 'blind' when there is no visual defect, has hysteria. The person who consults a doctor or optician every month, despite reassurances that his eyes are healthy, has hypochondria.

A mental condition which is probably very rare is hospital addiction syndrome or Munchausen's syndrome. Such people are repeatedly admitted to hospital with symptoms of serious illness, have numerous investigations and may even have frequent operations, but no physical cause can be found for their symptoms. They appear to be addicted to undergoing physical medical procedures, but refuse to cooperate with any psychiatric examination.

DEPRESSION sometimes causes hypochondria – usually when it is combined with anxiety, or in elderly people with an agitated type of depression.

In more serious cases a hypochondriacal conviction can become a psychotic delusion, as in SCHIZOPHRENIA. It then has a bizarre quality – for example, the person believes his intestines are rotting. Such beliefs may also be held by people with DEMENTIA.

All these instances involve people who are not physically ill, but believe they are. However, it has been suggested that some of these cases do have a physical cause – food intolerances (see DIET in Chapter 2). It is well known that some people have allergies resulting in various physical symptoms – rashes or migraine, for instance. Some doctors believe that people who suffer from a variety of symptoms, for which no physical causes can be found, may actually be sensitive to certain components of their diet.

What can be done

No one should diagnose his own physical symptoms as mere hypochondria. If you have symptoms which worry you, see your GP.

When hypochondria is a feature of a mental illness, treatment consists of treating that illness – anxiety, depression, schizophrenia and so on.

Hysteria

'Hysteria' has a rather different meaning in psychiatry to its everyday use. While all psychiatrists would say that it does not mean uncontrollable screaming and crying, they do not agree on what hysteria does mean. Many have argued against using the term at all because of the lack of an acceptable definition. There are broadly two theories, one based in psychodynamic thinking (see PSYCHOANALYSIS), the other concentrating on how behaviour is learnt.

However it is explained, hysteria basically involves a physical symptom for which there is no physical cause, but which can be said to have a relevance in the context of the person's life. (See also HYPOCHONDRIA, and PSYCHOSOMATIC DISORDERS in Chapter 3.) Hysteria can be manifested in a number of ways, but it is probably quite a rare condition, especially after early adulthood. Freud described some of his patients as having paralysed limbs; patients seen today are more likely to have aches, pains or tremors for which no physical cause can be found. More dramatic are the cases of blindness or loss of speech. These have traditionally been called 'conversion symptoms'. According to Freud's theory, ANXIETY unconsciously repressed is converted into a symptom. This is said to represent whatever was the anxiety-provoking conflict in the patient's infancy. (This is very similar to the psychodynamic explanation of PHOBIAS.) One problem with this theory is that despite the postulated 'conversion', most sufferers remain highly anxious – the anxiety has not been transformed.

A different manifestation of hysteria is the 'dissociative state'. Amnesia is a typical example – the person remains conscious, but may state that he remembers nothing at all about his past. There is no physical explanation for this, and the amnesia differs in some ways from that produced by head injuries and so on. Again, this condition has been explained as a way for the person to deal with anxiety he is repressing – with total amnesia he is blocking out his entire past life. Very rarely a dissociative state involves the person adopting another personality. This is the split personality disorder often confused with SCHIZOPHRENIA which is a totally different condition.

These are the two most usual forms of hysteria, both held to be unconsciously motivated behaviour. The person is causing the symptoms to appear, but is unaware of doing so. It has been said that this is what distinguishes the hysterical patient from the malingerer – the latter is deliberately inventing his symptoms to avoid some situation. With hysteria, there is also held to be some motive, but the person does not realise it. Perhaps the symptom arouses sympathy in a partner, or illustrates to others how much the person is suffering with DEPRESSION. Some doctors include 'parasuicide' – attempted SUICIDE which is a 'cry for help' – as a form of hysteria. The person would therefore not think 'I will do this to show how bad I feel', but would harm herself with full suicidal intent. However, if the hysteria theory is correct, her unconscious motive would be a plea for attention, rather than a wish to die.

Recently some psychiatrists have rejected this view of hysteria. Their learning theory postulates that the sufferer learns that it is advantageous for him to be a 'sick' person, and so continues in this role. For example, he may avoid having to go out to work. The learning theory of hysteria is not concerned with whether someone deliberately or unconsciously develops a symptom, but simply states that the symptom is perpetuated because the person finds this preferable to the stressful situation he is avoiding.

Related to the two main forms of hysteria is mass hysteria, which usually occurs in groups living at close quarters. Large numbers succumb to the same symptoms, although there is no physical transmission of an illness. 'Folie à deux' is where someone 'develops' the symptoms of a sick person with whom he has a close relationship, although he does not actually have the illness.

Illness suffered by someone known to the person with hysteria is one factor determining which symptoms develop. Another is the person's own experience of the symptom – for example, people with EPILEPSY sometimes also suffer hysterical fits which have no physical cause.

There is a link between having a hysterical personality and developing hysterical symptoms: sufferers frequently show certain personality traits. For instance, they tend to have dramatic mood swings – from tears to laughter – but no mood lasts for long. They like to be the centre of attention and some display a dramatic jealousy.

What can be done
Hysteria can be just a temporary condition. If a specific incident triggered the symptom, the person should recover when the situation returns to normal. When it persists for a long time, perhaps involving a multitude of physical complaints, hysteria should be treated.

The chosen treatment will depend on how the psychiatrist conceives of hysteria. If he takes a psychodynamic view, his aim will be to uncover the repressed conflict causing the anxiety which is being 'converted' into the symptom. ABREACTION or HYPNOTHERAPY might be used. Other forms of PSYCHOTHERAPY may be used to discover what is currently causing the patient such anxiety that he cannot live a healthy life. Those who favour the learning theory will seek to help the patient see that a sickly existence is not really an advantage at all. A patient suffering from hysterical paralysis who is caught in a house-fire realises this and immediately recovers the ability to run. The therapist hopes that his patient will reach the same conclusion less dramatically. For minor symptoms such as a tremor it is harder for the patient to appreciate the disadvantages. Psychotherapy will also help the patient to see the advantages of being healthy. Other ways are learnt of coping with the situations which the patient has previously avoided by being ill. FAMILY THERAPY may be a necessary part of the treatment. BEHAVIOUR THERAPY may also be used, with operant conditioning to reward the desired behaviour.

Mania

The mild form of mania is hypomania, but cases are generally treated quickly now so tend not to develop beyond the stage of what was once called hypomania. There is no clear dividing line between the two conditions, and it is easier to think in terms of early or mild symptoms, and more serious symptoms, of mania. People rarely suffer only attacks of mania and it occurs more commonly as part of MANIC-DEPRESSION.

The first signs are that the person becomes over-active and over-excited. He speaks more rapidly, often boasting about his achievements and plans. Though a ready wit is common and may at first make him good company, he is irritated, even hostile, if someone tries to interrupt or contradict him. He begins to sleep less and never rests or relaxes – he is too busy with new schemes and ideas which become increasingly reckless. He loses his inhibitions and may start to spend money extravagantly, drink heavily, gamble, shoplift, or become more active sexually. His personal appearance may be neglected.

As it becomes more serious, mania impairs the sufferer's judgement and he has delusions, often of grandeur, but sometimes of being persecuted. His speech eventually becomes incomprehensible as his mind jumps from one idea to the next. He may experience visual hallucinations. In extreme, untreated cases, the person collapses through sheer exhaustion having neither eaten nor slept for days. Mania is a PSYCH-OSIS (see Chapter 3) because the sufferer loses touch with reality and does not know how seriously ill he is.

The causes of mania are discussed under MANIC-DEPRESSION. It may appear that the stress of working too hard has been the cause. Sometimes this is the trigger for an attack of mania (though probably not the sole cause). However, it can also be the first sign of mania developing.

Mania has also been observed as an adverse reaction to certain DRUG treatments – for example, for PARKINSON'S DISEASE or DEPRESSION. It has been suggested that if an antidepressant triggers an attack of mania, it is likely to be because the sufferer was predisposed to manic-depression.

What can be done
When mania reaches the stage of affecting the person's ability to run his affairs competently, he begins to commit acts which have serious repercussions for himself and for his family. Treatment is essential, but the person feels extremely well and will angrily dismiss any suggestion that he is ill and needs help. Compulsory admission (see Chapter 12) may be necessary. However, if he has had an attack of mania before, he may recognise that he needs to be admitted to hospital.

Two types of DRUG are used, depending on the severity of the symptoms. For mild cases lithium salts alone are used and generally control the symptoms. In more severe cases lithium and a neuroleptic drug (as prescribed for SCHIZOPHRENIA) may be given together. The lithium takes about ten days to work, but the neuroleptic controls the over-activity, excitement and any aggression much more quickly. If drugs alone cannot subdue the patient's excessive activity, ECT is occasionally used.

The most important use of lithium is for long-term maintenance treatment for patients who have recurrent episodes. Lithium prevents these, or at least reduces their frequency. This is discussed further under MANIC-DEPRESSION.

While the patient is receiving lithium, COUNSELLING may be used and attending a group of fellow-sufferers may encourage him to continue taking the drug when he is feeling well. FAMILY THERAPY may be necessary, especially if the patient's behaviour while he was ill has seriously strained relationships at home.

Manic-depression

The classification of DEPRESSION has posed difficulties which are still unresolved, and this extends to the definition of manic-depression. As the term is commonly used, manic-depression refers to bouts of depression alternating with bouts of MANIA. This is also called a 'bipolar disorder' because it involves two extremes of mood and behaviour. Recurrent mania and recurrent depression are known as unipolar disorders. However, because mania so rarely occurs on its own, it is sometimes classified as a bipolar disorder – on the assumption that the other 'pole' of depression will eventually follow. The situation is further complicated by the fact that in some definitions 'manic-depressive psychosis' refers to all these conditions, and not just to an alternation between depression and mania. Thus, someone who suffers from only recurrent depression would be said to have 'manic-depressive psychosis, depressed type'. There is also 'manic type' and 'circular type'. This last category is described in this section.

Generally, sufferers do not swing from one extreme to the other, but have a period of 'normality' in between. The cycle may occur every few years or months, or even more frequently. The attacks of depression or mania do not seem to have any external cause, and may occur suddenly or develop gradually. They may last from a few weeks to a few years if untreated, but on average are about seven months long. A few sufferers experience both mania and depression during one attack.

The causes of manic-depression are still unclear. There is almost certainly a genetic component because mood disorders are more common among the relatives of those with a bipolar disorder (including mania) than among the relatives of people who suffer only depression.

Research on the brain's chemical messenger systems has failed to confirm what might be expected – namely that the imbalance is in opposite directions during episodes of depression and of mania. The suggestion is that the imbalance may even be quite similar in both cases.

One theory is that mania is actually a worsening of the same illness which causes depression.

There is a personality disorder called cyclothymia connected with manic-depression, in which the person's mood tends to vary from depressed to elated. This is too mild to classify as an illness, but in some such people manic-depression later develops. Some sufferers have had 'affective' personalities characterised by mood swings only to depression or to elation, from time to time.

A further classification problem is a disorder which includes many symptoms of SCHIZOPHRENIA and of the mood disorders, depression and mania. This has been called atypical schizophrenia or schizo-affective disorder (or psychosis). For a long time it was thought to be a form of schizophrenia, but the tendency now is to consider it as an affective (or mood) disorder. Schizo-affective disorder sufferers seem to have more in common with those with mood disorders, than with those who have schizophrenia. For example, mood disorders are suffered more often than schizophrenia by the relatives of those with schizo-affective disorder. There is usually a complete recovery after an attack, as in the mood disorders, but a recurrence is likely. Sufferers are typically aged 22 to 35 when they first develop the condition.

What can be done

Treatment for an attack of DEPRESSION or MANIA is described elsewhere. The risks of either SUICIDE or serious repercussions from manic extravagance may necessitate hospital admission.

Lithium salts may be prescribed as maintenance treatment for sufferers who have had at least two attacks in the past few years. Most find either that they have no further attacks, or if they do, that these are less severe and less frequent. The drug must be taken continuously and may have adverse effects if the necessary precautions are not followed. In excessive doses (which are little greater than those required for a therapeutic effect), lithium can affect the thyroid gland and kidneys. Patients are therefore asked to have the level of lithium in their blood monitored – about once a week initially and then less frequently. They are also given thyroid checks every six to nine months. These tests are carried out at lithium clinics; it is very important to attend as frequently as requested so that any adverse effects can be quickly spotted. Side-effects of taking lithium may include drowsiness, sickness and diarrhoea, and tremor (which can be corrected by another drug).

Some patients find the side-effects unacceptable and do not wish to continue with preventive treatment. This means that they are likely to continue suffering from manic-depression. If arrangements can be agreed for prompt treatment at the first warning signs, it may be possible to end the maintenance treatment.

Schizo-affective disorder also responds to lithium maintenance treatment to prevent recurrences.

The **Manic Depression Fellowship** has a network of local self-help groups for sufferers and their relatives and friends. Groups have also been set up under the **Scottish Association for Mental Health**.

'Nervous breakdown'

This is not a mental illness, but it is sometimes used as a colloquial expression for the observable effects of an episode of mental illness. It means that the person has become – usually quite rapidly or dramatically – too ill to cope at all with his everyday life. He is probably being treated with DRUGS, bed-rest and perhaps a short stay in hospital. It is not a very meaningful expression because it says nothing about the causes or nature of the person's problem, and it is often used as a euphemism.

The cause of the 'nervous breakdown' is usually DEPRESSION, ANXIETY or a combination of the two. Often the term is used for someone who has become increasingly tense and exhausted, under continual STRESS, until one incident – possibly something quite minor with which he would otherwise have coped – is the final straw. The 'breakdown' prevents him from facing any further demands, and rest becomes unavoidable.

To some people a 'nervous breakdown' is signalled by an outburst of violent, uncontrollable behaviour – screaming and crying, with possibly even a SUICIDE attempt.

The term may also be used when someone has been admitted to hospital because of the sudden onset of a more serious illness – SCHIZOPHRENIA or MANIA, for instance.

Obsessive disorders

Two types of obsessive disorder are described here – see also COMPULSIONS. The first is an irresistible urge to do something which has no rational function, to perform a ritual. The second disorder is an inability to block out persistent thoughts which keep coming into the sufferer's mind. In both cases the person is aware of the compulsion, realises that his actions or thoughts are ridiculous and almost invariably fights to avoid them – but he never succeeds. The struggle arouses terrible ANXIETY, but this does not totally subside even when he is performing the compulsive action.

Obsessive rituals may take many forms. Perhaps the most familiar is compulsive handwashing. A sufferer might feel compelled to wash his hands dozens of times a day, fearing that they have been infected by something he has touched, or that he is spreading germs. A fear of contamination is commonly connected with obsessive rituals. Counting is often involved – the sufferer might always be compelled to count to a certain number before entering the house. Another form of compulsive action which is familiar to many people is safety-checking. Most people need to check the window-catches and door-locks only once before leaving the house; someone with an obsessive disorder may have to complete a two-hour series of checks. Not surprisingly rituals can take up a great deal of time and can severely disrupt family life.

Obsessive thoughts may also take a number of forms. Some sufferers cannot prevent themselves turning over in their minds such questions as 'Is there life after death?' or 'How many stars are in the sky?' Others are distressed by frightening thoughts about what might happen, often with a sexual or aggressive theme: 'What if I feel compelled to stab someone?' They never perform these acts, but are obsessed by the thought of such an urge developing in the future.

Why some people should develop such disorders is not at all clear. ANXIETY certainly appears to be a key feature, although this does not explain why a minority of severely anxious people perform compulsive rituals. Most sufferers also have DEPRESSION, but again this is not a satisfactory explanation of the cause of obsessive disorders. Doctors sometimes describe patients as 'insecure' and certainly sufferers do tend to have a sense of foreboding compelling them to perform a ritual to ward off danger. To the psychoanalyst, the obsession has its roots in anxiety repressed since the person's infancy, and has a symbolic meaning which he then sets out to interpret.

There is a type of personality described as obsessive. Such people are typically concerned with detail and neatness; they like to complete one task before starting another, and are not flexible when unforeseen situations arise. People with this personality sometimes develop an obsessive disorder, anxiety or depression, but there is no close link between obsessive personalities and disorders.

What can be done

There is no need to worry about a child who has a 'going-to-bed' ritual – the teddy must be one side of the bed not the other. Nor does a superstition about not walking under ladders count as an obsessive disorder. The person who needs help has his whole life disrupted by the condition. It controls how he spends his time – he cannot 'choose' to leave the house in a dash because he is late: the checking ritual *must* be performed.

There is nothing to be gained by telling a sufferer to pull himself together, and such a lack of understanding of his distress will be destructive. PSYCHOTHERAPY can be helpful – either supportive or interpretive if it is suspected that there is an underlying cause for the anxiety. However, there is not a lot of evidence for the success of PSYCHOANALYSIS. Another use of psychotherapy is to encourage the person to find more productive ways of spending the time left free as obsessive rituals are reduced. RELAXATION may also help with anxiety.

DRUGS have been tried – one of the antidepressants is claimed to be effective in decreasing rituals and ruminations. Some experts dispute this, saying that it works only by relieving the depression which caused the obsessive behaviour. However, treatment for depression does not always remove compulsive thoughts and actions. Drugs and psychotherapy may be used together, and prove as successful as ECT.

BEHAVIOUR THERAPY is probably more successful with rituals than obsessive thoughts. For example, the patient might watch and copy the therapist washing a piece of fruit only once before eating it – when the patient normally does it seven times. Desensitisation would involve the patient gradually reducing the washing ritual from seven times to one; flooding would require him to brave his fear of contamination by abandoning the ritual immediately.

Paradoxical intention can be used for ruminations – the person is instructed to bring his obsessive thoughts to mind, to imagine even more fearful possibilities, and to continue thinking in this way. Another technique with obsessive thoughts, if they occur during the therapy session, is for the therapist to interrupt them – for instance, by hitting the table with his hand to make the patient jump. The person is then instructed how to do this for himself, so that he can 'snap' himself out of a rumination.

FAMILY THERAPY may be required, either to help with relationship difficulties caused by the obsessive disorder, or to teach relatives how to participate in the patient's treatment – particularly if a behavioural approach is being used.

If every other treatment fails, and the obsessive disorder is intolerable for the patient, PSYCHOSURGERY may be considered.

Paranoid disorders

Several mental illnesses can be described as paranoid disorders. SCHIZOPHRENIA, in which paranoid delusions can be a key feature, is described later in the book.

Late paraphrenia is usually classified as a type of schizophrenia. Sufferers are elderly, usually living alone. They often have poor hearing or sight and appear to lead isolated, lonely lives – although this may have been their choice for many years. They have not generally suffered a mental illness before, and their mental health is unexceptional apart from one paranoid delusion (see SCHIZOPHRENIA), which generally causes them ANXIETY. Two delusions are common: one is that other people want the person to leave his home, and are plotting ways to achieve this (neighbours are often blamed). The other delusion is that someone is making sexual advances – the sufferer is usually an elderly woman in this case. Auditory hallucinations (hearing voices) are common experiences.

Paranoid PSYCHOSIS (see Chapter 3) may develop in someone with a paranoid personality. Such a person is suspicious and tends to interpret experiences as criticisms or attacks. His lack of trust causes him to live a socially isolated life. A psychosis may gradually develop from this personality, although it is far from inevitable. It takes the form of a delusion, usually of being persecuted in some way. Sufferers are generally middle-aged, and may appear angry and irritable, perhaps depressed.

Paranoid psychosis can be caused by DRUGS – including those prescribed for heart disease, PARKINSON'S DISEASE and for various infections. Illicit drug use as described under DRUG DEPENDENCE can produce a psychotic reaction which is very like schizophrenia.

Paranoid states are more symptoms than definite conditions. The term is used for people who are suffering from a delusion – usually of being persecuted. Heavy drinkers with ALCOHOL DEPENDENCE sometimes suffer paranoid states in which they are convinced that their partner has been unfaithful. Paranoid ideas may develop into an affective (mood) disorder. Sometimes a paranoid state develops into schizophrenia, or it can be a feature of DEMENTIA. The reaction to drugs described above could be called a paranoid state. However, it may so closely resemble schizophrenia that it is generally referred to as a psychosis. SURGERY and infections can also occasionally produce a paranoid state.

What can be done

The treatment is generally the same as for SCHIZOPHRENIA – neuroleptic drugs. In the case of paranoid psychosis, antidepressants may also be necessary. As with schizophrenia, the sufferer may need to take the drugs continuously to prevent the condition re-appearing.

Elderly people with late paraphrenia are sometimes admitted to hospital where the delusion may diminish, but without treatment it will re-appear when the patient returns home.

Parkinson's disease

This is a disease affecting the brain, as a certain group of nerve cells deteriorate. Three-quarters of all patients develop the disease between the ages of 50 and 65, but one in seven are in their thirties or forties when it begins. The early symptoms may be of feeling a little shaky or tired, perhaps a bit depressed. These are experienced by many elderly people, but those developing Parkinson's disease may well have an expressionless face and a quiet monotonous voice. Sufferers find their movements becoming increasingly slow and clumsy, often affecting how they walk. They may find it difficult to speak, and most have a tremor and stiff muscles (rigidity). A sufferer's body does not do what he wants it to. The symptoms may be mild for many years, but they tend to increase gradually.

The term Parkinsonism is used for patients who have developed symptoms very similar to these, but not because of a spontaneous deterioration in their brain cells. Parkinsonism is a possible side-effect of the neuroleptic DRUGS prescribed for SCHIZOPHRENIA.

Studies have shown that heredity is not a factor in Parkinson's disease.

Parkinson's disease can affect the sufferer's ability to drive – see DRIVING in Chapter 13.

What can be done
There is, as yet, no cure for this condition and its cause is still unknown. DRUG therapy can, however, often alleviate the symptoms. Research has shown that sufferers have a deficiency of one of the chemical messengers described in Chapter 2 under CHANGES IN THE BRAIN. Drugs such as L-dopa are therefore given to make up for this lack, and probably about four out of five sufferers improve with this treatment. Patients may be prescribed a number of other types of drug which work in different ways. Some sufferers find that the beneficial effects of L-dopa decrease after a number of years, while side-effects become more troublesome. L-dopa is therefore normally combined with an additive which increases its beneficial effects and reduces the likelihood of side-effects. Some recently-introduced drugs can also help to avoid the side-effects of L-dopa, and are sometimes prescribed with it. With all the drugs prescribed for Parkinson's disease, adjustment of the dosage under medical supervision can usually reduce side-effects. New medicines with fewer side-effects can be expected in the future.

If the sufferer develops DEPRESSION or ANXIETY, drugs may be prescribed for these conditions.

Treatment is also aimed at keeping the person mobile and fit for as long as possible. PHYSIOTHERAPY in a hospital department should be followed by practising at home the exercises demonstrated. As he becomes more physically disabled, aids will help to make his life easier – occupational therapists from the social services department (or equivalent) will advise on these.

SPEECH THERAPY can be very helpful.

Cell transplants to replace the damaged nerve cells have been tried in a couple of Swedish patients, but this experiment does not appear to be an encouraging way forward.

Alternative therapies such as HOMOEOPATHY and acupuncture have been tried, but not scientifically evaluated.

Sufferers and their families will find the **Parkinson's Disease Society** a source of helpful advice and literature. There are over 100 branches in the UK, which act as self-help groups providing support, welfare, social activities and funds for research.

Phobias

A phobia is an intense fear which the sufferer cannot control and which cannot be reduced by someone else reassuring him. It is out of all proportion to the object or situation causing it, and usually leads to the sufferer avoiding that object or situation at all costs. The inconvenience of this, or the level of anxiety involved, interferes with the person's daily life. A phobia of dogs for example would limit the sufferer's ability to visit both public places and private homes. If someone with this phobia sees a dog, or even a picture of one, he has a panic attack. This is described under ANXIETY. An important feature of phobias is that the fear is not only of a particular object, but frequently extends to related subjects. Thus someone with a phobia of birds may be just as panic-stricken by a feather.

Why some people develop phobias has been the subject of much speculation but so far research has not uncovered a definite answer. Among the proposed factors are personality, a predisposition to anxiety, incidents during childhood, traumatic experiences and their meaning (real or imagined) for the person, emotional and mood disorders, attitudes of those close to the person, and so on. Phobias other than AGORAPHOBIA commonly start in childhood or adolescence. Even if a specific event can be pinpointed as the time at which the phobia originated, this still does not explain why it did so. One child bitten by a dog may develop zoophobia (a fear of animals), but another after an identical experience still love animals.

The psychodynamic view (see PSYCHOANALYSIS) is that the phobia is an expression of the 'real' fear which is buried in the person's subconscious. The object of his phobia represents what he is really frightened of. This theory suggests that someone suffering from acrophobia (a fear of heights) is actually afraid of moving upwards in an abstract sense – of taking extra responsibilities, for instance.

Specific phobias occasionally develop in children with a relative who has this fear. For example, a parent's phobic fear of dentists might be passed on to a child. Therefore learning may well be involved in the development of some phobias.

Over 375 phobias have been recorded. The commonest, AGORAPHOBIA, is described at the beginning of this chapter. Other frequent phobias are discussed overleaf:

Claustrophobia – this is a fear of enclosed spaces and may be experienced as a fear of lifts, underground trains, crowded shops and so on. If it is extended the person may become unable to go into very small rooms, or those with low, sloping ceilings. The fear is of being trapped, and sufferers need to work out an 'escape route' from any new situation. In addition to the typical symptoms of panic, they may experience a suffocating or choking sensation.

Social phobias – these are a related group of fears which share some characteristics with AGORAPHOBIA. They are not fears of being away from home, but of being with people in certain situations – such as eating or talking in public, or meeting strangers. The result may be that the person is confined to his home, but unlike the agoraphobic sufferer, he wants to be alone, rather than fearing this. Specific fears may be involved – such as of blushing or of spilling food when eating in public. These people often suffer from generalised ANXIETY and low self-confidence and have serious difficulties in forming relationships. These problems need to be tackled in dealing with the phobias.

School phobia – there is some disagreement about the validity of this concept. Some argue that the children classified as experiencing this are either truanting, or suffering from other emotional disorders which affect their willingness to leave home – or even that they are justly afraid of a particular teacher. Cases of truancy are easily separated because they involve no anxiety. Very often such children set off happily for school, but never arrive there. Parents of a child who is frightened of going to school are in no doubt of his anxiety. Any of the common anxiety and panic symptoms, together with vomiting, may be suffered – at least until it is too late to get to school on time. This probably happens to many children occasionally, especially if the day involves an unpleasant event such as an exam. If it is an activity, such as a feared sport, which is causing the problem, parents and teachers can often find a solution. The child's fear may be based on an exaggeration of the danger or a fear of being laughed at.

The child requiring treatment as soon as possible is the one who suddenly or gradually develops an anxiety reaction every schoolday morning, but who seems at least reasonably contented at other times. Any of the child mental health services (see Chapter 11) can be contacted for this.

Illness phobias – these are suffered by healthy people whose lives are dominated by fear of a particular disease or illness. Sufferers do everything they can think of (including making up their own theories) to avoid this illness. Simply giving up smoking would not be enough for someone with cancerophobia, for example. The trigger for an illness phobia to develop (which is not to say the sole cause), is often a close friend or relative developing the condition. See also HYPOCHONDRIA.

What can be done

BEHAVIOUR THERAPY is the most widely used treatment, either as individual or GROUP THERAPY. Sufferers tend not to ask for treatment until the condition is seriously affecting their lives, but behaviour therapy can be effective even if the phobia is not one of long standing. Treating a phobia of spiders illustrates the use of behavioural techniques:

- desensitisation – while relaxed, the person is first shown a picture, held at a distance, of a small spider, graduating to holding a photograph of a larger one, then a model, and finally holding a real spider. Each step is practised at several therapy sessions until it causes no anxiety, before the next item is tackled
- flooding – with his agreement, the person is presented with a real spider and encouraged to tolerate the resulting anxiety and panic. Having survived the situation once, he finds it easier to repeat until the phobia disappears or is at least reduced. This method seems to be the most successful, used either initially or after a desensitisation course. The exercise may be carried out in the patient's imagination, although this may be less effective, at least in the short-term
- modelling – the person watches someone else handling a spider
- paradoxical intention – the person is given a spider, perhaps in a clear box, and told to feel as much anxiety as possible. When a phobia has to be overcome quickly this may be the best method of treatment.

COGNITIVE THERAPY may be used for treating phobias. For example, the therapist might teach the person certain phrases to repeat to help reduce the feelings of anxiety as he touches the spider.

Minor tranquilliser DRUGS are sometimes used in conjunction with behaviour therapy, particularly with flooding. They enable the person to confront the object of his phobia in the initial stages of treatment if he refuses to attempt it otherwise. However, he must learn to manage without antianxiety drugs, and to master the anxiety himself.

RELAXATION techniques are an important aspect of behaviour therapy and may include HYPNOTHERAPY. They help the patient to face the feared situation and must be learnt by the sufferer so that he does not need anyone to help him relax. Relaxation on its own, however, will probably not remove a phobia.

COUNSELLING and PSYCHOTHERAPY may be used if the therapist feels that other emotional problems are connected with the person's phobia. He may discuss personality problems or relationship difficulties if these are relevant. If the therapist holds a psychodynamic view of the origins of the phobia, he will use a form of psychotherapy related to PSYCHOANALYSIS. Even if this is used, the therapist is likely to encourage the person to confront the object or situation he fears, although behavioural techniques would probably not be employed.

Sufferers from social phobias in some places are able to attend training courses in social behaviour. They are taught to deal with the social situations they may have to face. Various behavioural methods may be used, such as modelling, social skills training and assertiveness training.

Self-help programmes have been produced and are worth trying, although as with any treatment, success cannot be guaranteed. They are available as books, leaflets and cassette tapes.

A number of organisations exist for sufferers of phobias in general. The **Phobics Society** is the largest of these. Practical help is given wherever possible to those who are isolated by their phobia, and self-help literature is provided to members. Branches around the country encourage sufferers to meet.

Psychopathic disorder

As described in Chapter 3, this is a personality disorder, not a mental illness. It warrants inclusion in this chapter because it is one of the mental disorders specifically mentioned in the Mental Health Act 1983, although not in the equivalent legislation in Scotland and Northern Ireland (see Chapter 12). The alternative name of sociopathy is being adopted in the USA and may become more common in this country.

The Act defines a psychopathic disorder as 'a persistent disorder or disability of mind . . . which results in abnormally aggressive or seriously irresponsible conduct'. The term has been given a variety of definitions, and to the general public a psychopath is often someone who commits hideous crimes with pleasure, or at least with no remorse. Such a person might well have a psychopathic disorder, but this is evident in many other types of antisocial behaviour.

By no means all antisocial behaviour is psychopathic. The determining factor is the person's attitude to his behaviour, his feelings about society and moral responsibility. The young person who rebels against authority, steals out of greed and so on is probably well aware that he is transgressing from 'right' to 'wrong' behaviour. He may be pleased to do so, proud of the admiration from other members of his gang, or he may feel remorse. The important point is that he knows what he has done. Someone who has a psychopathic disorder has no social or moral conscience. If he commits a crime it is because he wanted to act in that particular way and did not resist his instincts – it would not have occurred to him to do so. He did not set out to 'commit an offence', because that implies an awareness of 'right' and 'wrong' which the person lacks. Psychopathic behaviour may not actually break any laws, but simply offend social values. He might, for example, lack any feeling for the people he knows, showing a callous disregard for their emotions. He may consistently arrange to meet friends, but never turn up, or borrow their possessions without asking permission first.

This type of psychopathic behaviour raises difficult questions about the boundary between normal and abnormal, acceptable and unacceptable behaviour. Social judgements are to a certain extent subjective.

ALCOHOL DEPENDENCE and DRUG DEPENDENCE are often additional problems of psychopaths but they are not considered to be psychopathic disorders themselves.

Psychopaths are usually male and may be described as grossly immature. Like young children they are impulsive and cannot defer any pleasures – whatever they want must be obtained immediately. Carefully planned, premeditated murder may therefore not be the act of a psychopath, despite the layman's definition.

As described under DELINQUENCY, some children and adolescents show antisocial behaviour. By no means all will become psychopaths and this label would probably not be used for someone under about 25 years. Psychopaths have, however, invariably exhibited behaviour problems as a child.

What can be done

Punishment seems to have no effect on psychopathic behaviour. DRUGS are occasionally helpful in the case of aggressive psychopathy. Personality disorders are very hard to remedy, and only limited successes have been claimed for helping psychopaths. If any change is to be achieved it must be by instilling a sense of guilt for aggressive or seriously irresponsible behaviour – that is, the person must develop a conscience. Any form of PSYCHOTHERAPY requires the patient's active co-operation. A psychopath is unlikely to feel that he requires help and so will resist the therapist's efforts. GROUP THERAPY may be used, and experiments are being conducted using therapeutic communities (see ACCOMMODATION in Chapter 13). It may be best for such people to live somewhere providing quite strict discipline which they do not apply to themselves.

Schizophrenia

The title of this section should really be 'schizophrenias' because it is a group of similar and related mental illnesses, rather than a single disorder. The term is therefore used when a combination of certain symptoms occur together. Schizophrenia is not a 'split personality'. That is a very rare disorder described under HYSTERIA. There is no dramatic split in schizophrenia, but rather a crumbling of certain divisions – between reality and fantasy, and between the self and the rest of the world. Someone suffering from schizophrenia finds these distinctions difficult to make.

No sufferer has all the possible symptoms of this type of mental illness, but thought disorder is the key feature of schizophrenia. In a severe case the sufferer may feel that thoughts are being inserted into or withdrawn from his mind by some external force. He may believe that others know his thoughts, and he may hear these thoughts being spoken – perhaps before he thinks them. He may hear a voice describing what he is doing, commenting on his thoughts and actions, often in a critical or threatening manner. These auditory hallucinations are sometimes accompanied by visual ones. Some sufferers feel as if their emotions and actions are determined by an external force, that they are not in control of their own body or will.

Sufferers do not know that their experiences are not real, but the product of their illness – that is, they are suffering from a PSYCHOSIS (see Chapter 3). They are often frightened by these experiences, although this may subside when they 'realise the explanation'. This is actually a delusion – another key symptom in schizophrenia. A delusion is an unshakable conviction, maintained despite evidence which is obvious to everyone else, that the belief is entirely false. The sufferer may believe that witchcraft is responsible for the thoughts being plucked out of his head, or that rays from the television set are putting thoughts into his mind. Delusions sometimes follow a perfectly ordinary incident – the television newscaster's red tie has a special significance, being a secret message from an organisation meant for the sufferer. Often the delusions are of being extremely important – even convictions of being God or Christ – but they are more commonly of being persecuted (see PARANOID DISORDERS). Occasionally these cause the sufferer to be violent, as he believes others are about to attack or harm him.

These thought disorders inevitably affect the content of the sufferer's speech. He may go from one subject to the next showing a strange association of ideas – looking at an apple makes him think of the planet earth, for example, both being spherical. He may use long words which he has made up, or suddenly stop talking in mid-sentence.

The effect on the sufferer's mood is generally to cause a loss of emotion so that he appears apathetic. He has no interests or enthusiasm, and finds it difficult to make even a small decision. From time to time his mood will suddenly change without warning, and he becomes irritable or highly excited. Some sufferers become very depressed and there is a risk of SUICIDE. Sometimes emotions are completely inappropriate to the situation – a person with schizophrenia might become terribly upset at good news, for example.

All these symptoms come and go, and sufferers generally have periods when they are not experiencing schizophrenic symptoms, although they may still think of them. Other less common features may appear, such as smelling, feeling or tasting things which are not really there. Some believe that their bodies are changing (see HYPOCHONDRIA).

Schizophrenia poses many problems for those who live with a sufferer. Sometimes the features of the illness do not seem like symptoms at all, but irritating habits which can cause tension within the family. Relatives often find the person's lack of activity and of conversation difficult to live with. Sufferers sleep a lot and cannot entertain themselves in any way, but will sit motionless for hours. They may make no effort to look after themselves. An apparent lack of sociability may be deceptive. The sufferer may well appreciate having company in the house, and hearing all the conversations, but he simply shows no sign of this. A less common problem is that of socially embarrassing behaviour, perhaps making offensive remarks to visitors, or talking to himself (responding to auditory hallucinations). A severely ill patient may come to dominate an entire family, and his behaviour, and the stigma of the illness, may seriously restrict their social life.

Most cases of schizophrenia begin when the sufferer is between 17 and 30, and it is rarely diagnosed in someone older than 50. The related condition of late paraphrenia (see PARANOID DISORDERS) is diagnosed in older people. Schizophrenia may develop suddenly or so gradually that it is impossible to say when it began. When it starts during the person's late teens the first signs may be attributed to adolescence. These signs include a change in personality, loss of self-confidence and of interest in life, becoming less active and sociable, or becoming restless and agitated. Relatives may notice odd habits, such as collecting rubbish, or peculiar speech. The person may be anxious and insecure. The major symptoms described above may develop from these initial signs.

The cause of schizophrenia has been a controversial subject, especially since one theory was proposed that the early relationship between the sufferer and his mother was to blame. Schizophrenia is not caused by a bad upbringing and probably all psychiatrists have abandoned this theory by now.

The chemical messenger systems of the brain appear to be disturbed in schizophrenia, and neuroleptic DRUGS which affect these biochemicals bring an improvement in many symptoms. Less certain is the role of this postulated imbalance in causing schizophrenia – it could be a result of some other causal factor.

Food allergy or intolerance (see DIET in Chapter 2) has also been proposed as a cause in some instances of schizophrenia. A faulty digestive system may result in an inability to digest wheat correctly or a sensitivity to several food components. These factors could in turn affect the functioning of the brain. Conversely, rather than being a cause of schizophrenia, these factors may be a result of a biochemical imbalance. These theories are still being investigated.

There is almost certainly a genetic component to schizophrenia, although the exact size of this is disputed. Among the general population the chances of anyone developing schizophrenia are just under one in a hundred – far more common than most people think. Close relatives of sufferers stand a significantly higher chance of developing the illness. It seems that about half those who have an identical twin with schizophrenia will themselves become sufferers. However, as there is only a 50 per cent risk even when all genes are shared, heredity is far from being the whole explanation.

If genetic factors and abnormalities in the brain's chemical messenger systems produce a predisposition to schizophrenia, it may be that the person's experiences form the trigger. Some form of stress or crisis may precipitate the attack. This might be a fairly minor event which someone not predisposed to the illness would have tackled with little difficulty. The strain of university exams is an example.

Some research has shown that certain social environments can trigger a further acute attack of schizophrenia in sufferers. These occur in families where there is hostility or excessive criticism of the sufferer, or where he is over-protected in an intense emotional atmosphere. It appears that many sufferers find it impossible to cope with too much emotional involvement with their relations. The research does not show that excessive emotion, whether critical or protective, is related to the initial development of schizophrenia, but in some cases it can trigger a relapse.

Physical conditions linked with schizophrenia include EPILEPSY in a particular part of the brain which sometimes precedes the development of schizophrenia. Some women have an attack after giving birth, but in this case childbirth appears to be a source of stress triggering an episode in a sufferer or in someone already predisposed to schizophrenia.

A schizoid personality is evident in between a third and half of those who later develop schizophrenia. These people are shy, withdrawn, with few social contacts. They are very sensitive to criticism and are suspicious, and so avoid relationships which could upset them.

It has been suggested that a virus triggers the development of schizophrenia in people who have inherited a predisposition to the disorder. This has yet to be proven.

The disagreement over the causes of schizophrenic disorders is paralleled by debates as to how they should be classified.

Of the many classifications which have been proposed, one of the most widely used was the division into simple, hebephrenic, paranoid and catatonic schizophrenia. Each disorder was held to have different characteristics. For example, silly and inappropriate behaviour typified hebephrenic schizophrenia and a tendency to adopt statue-like poses, as if in a stupor, typified the catatonic type. However, it was discovered that a sufferer might well exhibit the characteristic symptoms of all the categories at different times, and that the age at which he developed schizophrenia was also a critical factor determining the symptoms suffered. The four categories therefore have come to be regarded as of little value.

One alternative classification has 19 sub-categories; but a far simpler division is into Type I and Type II schizophrenia. Type I involves symptoms which could be said to be 'additional' to the person's previous behaviour – hallucinations and delusions, for instance. Type II involves symptoms which could be described as a 'loss' of behaviour – reduced self-confidence, activity, social contact and so on. Some sufferers may have Type II schizophrenia with episodes of Type I. Others suffer only one type. Such a distinction has some relevance because the neuroleptic DRUGS described below generally affect only Type I symptoms.

Atypical schizophrenia or schizo-affective disorder is now generally classified as a form of affective (mood) disorder, and is described under MANIC-DEPRESSION.

What can be done
The outcome of a first attack of schizophrenia can be anything from a complete recovery to a steady deterioration in the sufferer's mental health, to the point that he cannot leave hospital. About 50 per cent of sufferers will fall somewhere in between. The prospects are better for certain types of sufferer than others: for example, those who do not have a family history of schizophrenia, nor a previous personality disorder. A relatively sudden onset of schizophrenia after a stressful event, and prompt treatment, are usually associated with good recovery. If the sufferer does not lose all interest in life, nor the ability to experience various emotions, his prospects are brighter. Sufferers with only Type I symptoms have the best prospects for complete recovery.

Schizophrenia always requires professional attention. As soon as you notice symptoms in a relative which worry you, ask him to see a GP, or contact a doctor yourself. If the GP does not think that there is a problem, but the symptoms continue, contact him again describing precisely what you have noticed. If he is still not worried, ask for a referral to a psychiatrist.

Some hospital admission is necessary, at least for a short stay while DRUG treatment is begun. Once the more severe symptoms have been controlled the patient is usually able to return home, although re-admission may be necessary for another acute attack. Some families find that their relative's behaviour, even when he is taking drugs, demands more care than they can give at home, but that hospital or hostel admission is not offered either. There is no easy answer to this problem, but relatives in this situation may be helped by the advice and support of the specialist self-help organisations.

The drugs used for schizophrenia are neuroleptics. These are effective for the Type I symptoms – hallucinations, delusions and thought disorder. They do not cure schizophrenia, but the improvement they produce may enable the sufferer to lead a relatively ordinary occupational and family life. Other sufferers are at least able to live at home, even if they are dependent on their relatives. When treatment is started there is never an immediate improvement, and it may be several weeks before the symptoms begin to fade. When the maximum improvement has been achieved, the treatment is continued to prevent reappearance of the symptoms.

Some sufferers forget to take their pills, or refuse to do so because they feel well. Relatives can sometimes help with this, but long-acting injections are also used for these reasons. This alternative is usually chosen only if the schizophrenia developed very gradually (and therefore the chances of a good recovery are reduced), or if there has been more than one attack. The injections are given once every one to eight weeks, depending on the drug used.

Unfortunately, neuroleptic drugs have unwanted effects as well, some minor and avoidable, others more serious. It is sometimes necessary to make a choice between the side-effects and the chance of severe schizophrenic symptoms reappearing. Schizophrenia is usually said to be worse than the neuroleptic side-effects, but this view is questioned by some.

Any side-effects noticed initially may disappear after a few weeks. These include drowsiness, dry mouth, tremor, no facial expression, but spasms of the muscles around the mouth. This is called Parkinsonism and is produced as described under DRUGS in Chapter 4. The remedy is to reduce the dose of neuroleptic, or to change to a different drug, or to give the drugs prescribed for Parkinson's disease. The disadvantage of the latter remedy is that it seems to increase the likelihood of a more serious side-effect from taking neuroleptics. This is called tardive dyskinesia and is seen as disjointed movements, such as grimaces or fidgeting. At its most serious it may cause the limbs to jerk uncontrollably. Drugs to control the tardive dyskinesia do not have a long-lasting effect, and it is normally irreversible. It is more common in elderly people. At one time it was thought that taking regular two-week breaks from the neuroleptics would reduce the risk of tardive dyskinesia, but this does not appear to be so.

ECT is not widely used for schizophrenia, although it may be helpful if the patient also has severe DEPRESSION, or tends to develop a statue-like immobility.

Following the theory of food intolerances being linked to schizophrenia, special diets have been advocated – typically excluding grain and milk. Multivitamin treatments have also been proposed, although there is not widespread support for this.

PSYCHOTHERAPY is not generally used in this country for schizophrenia. COUNSELLING and perhaps supportive psychotherapy may help the patient to learn how he may avoid future attacks by identifying the stresses which precipitate them.

Many books have been written on schizophrenia, and the specialist organisations listed below produce their own literature. Relatives may find reading such material of enormous help in learning how to cope with the demands of living with a sufferer. The sort of advice given is to provide a structure to the sufferer's day – requiring selected small tasks to be completed, and arranging for a few hours occupation (ideally at a day centre). Relatives should neither contradict delusions, nor go along with them. Reducing emotional tension is difficult to achieve, but when this is necessary FAMILY THERAPY or COUNSELLING may be available.

Learning from published literature does not replace information from the psychiatrist in charge of the sufferer's care, but some families find that despite requests, they do not receive as much advice as they would like. Doctors sometimes feel that relatives do not wish to discuss the patient's diagnosis and would be upset by pessimistic predictions for his recovery. If you do want more information, even if it is not very encouraging, let the psychiatrist know, and talk to other staff involved in your relative's care – such as the hospital nurses, psychiatric social worker and community psychiatric nurse.

Relatives who would like advice on the genetic aspect of schizophrenia may ask a GP or psychiatrist to refer them to a genetic counsellor, though few specialise in counselling on schizophrenia. It is important to bear in mind that only a predisposition to schizophrenia is inherited – and it is far from inevitable that the children of schizophrenic parents will themselves develop the disease.

The **National Schizophrenia Fellowship** actively campaigns to increase public understanding of the illness and has many local groups providing information and support for sufferers and their relatives. Literature is produced, and in some areas the Fellowship runs hostels and day and 'drop-in' centres for sufferers and their relatives. Its affiliated body, the **Northern Schizophrenia Fellowship**, is also setting up hostels and sheltered workshops.

The closely linked **National Schizophrenia Fellowships of Scotland** and of **Northern Ireland** have local groups and contacts.

The **Schizophrenia Association of Great Britain** is concerned with schizophrenia as a medical problem, rather than a social one. Advice and information are available by phone or letter to sufferers and their relatives. Callers may visit the Centre for Schizophrenia in North Wales where there are clinic facilities and a day centre. Any nutritional advice given is seen as a supplement to medication and not an alternative. Local groups of the Association are being planned.

Suicide

This is not a mental illness, nor inevitably caused by one. However, at least half of those who commit suicide have been suffering from DE-PRESSION (though only a minority of severely depressed people kill themselves). Others have been suffering from ALCOHOL DEPENDENCE or DRUG DEPENDENCE, or – less commonly – SCHIZOPHRENIA and other PARANOID DISORDERS. EATING DISORDERS occasionally result in suicide. Severe MARITAL PROBLEMS, losing one's job (see UNEM-PLOYMENT) and being seriously ill with a physical disorder sometimes precede a suicide.

Twice as many men as women commit suicide, and the risk increases with age and among those who have isolated, lonely lives (see LONELI-NESS). Those who are single, divorced or separated are much more likely to commit suicide than married people of the same age and sex. BEREAVEMENT also increases the risk of suicide, but this may be because of a combination of previous mental ill-health and losing a spouse. The bereavement is then the 'final straw' which leads the widower to take his own life.

It is not true that those who talk about suicide never do it. Most people who commit suicide have previously given some indication of their intentions. Those whose attempts fail may ultimately kill themselves, although there are two categories of attempted suicide, one being more serious.

A minority of suicide attempts can be thought of as 'failed suicides'. The same serious intention to die is shown, and plans are devised to make rescue unlikely. As with those who die from suicide, these attempts are more likely to be made by older men who have been severely mentally ill. The chances of suicide are increased for someone who has made this kind of attempt.

The second type of suicide attempt is far more common. It is usually made by females – typically adolescents and young adults. In contrast to the serious attempts, these are not carefully planned to maximise the chances of dying. The attempt may be made in a place where she is likely to be found – even in front of someone. Her reason for attempting suicide is not a long-considered desire to end her life, but an impulsive reaction to anger or despair. A distressing incident in a relationship may provoke her into taking an overdose of tablets. She may want to make her partner regret a quarrel, or to show him or others how badly she

116

feels. Some people who attempt suicide in this way have been living under continual stress – perhaps in poor conditions and with an unsatisfactory relationship. They may react to a sudden crisis with a suicide attempt, finding no other way to cope with the situation. (See earlier in this chapter for a discussion of the theory that this type of suicide is a manifestation of HYSTERIA.)

People making this second type of suicide attempt may make further attempts, and there is a risk of their ultimately committing suicide. However, even if they do not fully intend to take their own lives, a relatively small overdose or injury can prove fatal in chance circumstances.

In the classification of suicide attempts a number of terms have been used, sometimes applied in different ways. Some doctors call all suicide attempts 'parasuicides', but most psychiatrists seem to use this term for the more common and less serious type described above. Other doctors do not talk of 'attempts' at all, but refer to deliberate self-poisoning or self-injury, depending on the method chosen. This avoids having to make a distinction between a serious intention to die and an impulsive gesture of despair.

What can be done

Because suicide is so often connected with serious mental illness, it is very important to treat any disorder promptly. Severe DEPRESSION, for example, may call for ECT, rather than risking a two- to three-week wait for antidepressants to have an effect. Hospital admission may well be necessary for someone who is seriously suicidal. Some research with suicidal men dependent on alcohol did not, however, show an increased benefit from very persistent efforts to prevent suicide. It seems that someone who is really determined to take his own life may perhaps resist all attempts to stop him. This is not to say that efforts to help suicidal people are a waste of time. But if everything possible has been done, relatives and professionals should not feel guilty if they fail to prevent a suicide.

Someone who tries but fails to commit suicide, may be amenable to treatment – especially if it was not a serious attempt. COUNSELLING is needed in all cases, and PSYCHOTHERAPY in some although this may not always be automatically arranged, in view of the large numbers admitted every day from deliberate self-poisoning. The therapist will try to discover what provoked the attempt, and to help the person find other ways of coping with crises and relationship difficulties. FAMILY THERAPY may be relevant. If ANXIETY or DEPRESSION is involved drug treatments may be used, although a relative would probably be given responsibility for administering the pills – at least until psychotherapy had made some progress.

117

People who feel suicidal should discuss it with someone. This should be any mental health professional with whom they are already in contact, or a friend, relative, or the **Samaritans**. This is a 24-hour emergency befriending service (see COUNSELLING). Volunteers are available seven days a week to listen to anyone who telephones at any time, or visits one of their 180 centres during the day or evening. The service is free and you do not have to give your name. They do not impose any religious or philosophical views on dealing with life, but offer a sympathetic ear, and when relevant, suggestions of which other agencies may be able to help with problems. If you wish they may make the first contact for you.

Chapter 14 discusses the problems of living with someone who threatens to commit suicide. As suggested there, you may contact the Samaritans if you are in such a situation and wish to discuss it. (You should also obtain a doctor's advice.) The Samaritan volunteer might consider contacting your relative to offer his help as a sympathetic listener.

There are self-help groups in a few areas for people who feel suicidal. Ask your GP or local Samaritans centre if there is one in your area.

6

Emotional problems

There are many experiences in life which may affect mental health. Reduced psychological well-being may be experienced as feelings of depression, anxiety or general dissatisfaction, low self-confidence and less ability to cope with difficulties. Sometimes this state of poor mental health develops into mental illness, or it may trigger episodes of mental or physical illness which have a combination of causes. Those who had suffered a mental illness before, or were dependent on alcohol or drugs, are more likely to develop a psychiatric disorder.

The experiences which are most likely to cause emotional problems are described in this chapter. In each case advice is given on what can be done to improve psychological well-being afterwards.

Bereavement

Only in a minority of cases will the natural grief following a bereavement turn to mental illness. However, many people fear that they are developing such an illness because of the disturbing experiences which are a part of grief. Bereavement is probably the most traumatic experience anyone suffers and being widowed heads the list of life's STRESSES. It has been said that the death of a child is an even more traumatic event, and the strain can cause MARITAL PROBLEMS adding to the parents' misery.

Grief can be thought of as having four stages, although bereaved people do not usually experience them in strict succession and according to a precise timescale. Nevertheless most people who mourn a loved person and then accept the inevitable changes in their lives, will have gone through these stages:

1 The first reaction is shock, disbelief and numbness – an inability to feel anything. Bereaved people cannot talk about their grief, or take in what is said to them. They are not even aware of their actions, but may behave as if in a trance. This state may last from a few hours to several

days. The bereaved person then begins to acknowledge the death, and more open grief replaces the numbness.

2 As grief is more openly expressed, the bereaved feel great distress, longing and crying out for the dead person. They may want to look for him although they realise that the person has gone – they may even believe that they see or hear him. These experiences should not be mistaken for psychotic hallucinations. This is a very painful stage, during which the bereaved may find it equally distressing to look at photographs, for example, and to resist doing so. It may be a time of restlessness, irritability and obsession with the loss – an inability to concentrate on anything else. Insomnia and ANXIETY are common. Bereaved people often try to find a reason for the death, refusing to accept the inevitability of a terminal illness or that an accident was unavoidable. They may want to blame someone or something – doctors, God, fate, themselves – even the dead person. Guilt is often felt – at things said or done while the person was alive, or at not having saved his life, even though this is rarely realistic. The bereaved may continue to feel that the dead person is close, or imagines seeing him among a crowd.

3 The next stage is depression and apathy. This may alternate with the more acute grief for a time, but gradually the pining abates. The person may feel defeated, unable to make an effort at any necessary task, exhausted by grief, and still feeling angry and bitter.

4 Finally they begin to accept the loss of the loved person, and that life must continue. It will be different, but they begin to realise that it can still be contented and fulfilling. Appetite and the ability to sleep return; they become more interested in meeting people again.

Children generally express grief in a different way, as an alteration in their behaviour. They may be aggressive, angry, start wetting their beds again and find it difficult to concentrate at school. They may feel frightened and guilty, especially if they somehow feel responsible for the death.

It is impossible to say how long mourning will take, and most people underestimate the time, believing that the person should be coming to terms with the death in a few weeks. Some people are recovering after six months, others take a year or longer. A minority do not make this natural recovery and may need specialist help. Some develop DEPRESSION as a mental illness, rather than as a stage of mourning. This may be because they have refused to acknowledge and express their grief. Children can sometimes find it hard to express their grief, and may not show any emotion for months or even years.

When bereavement causes depression this is sometimes accompanied by suicidal attempts, and treatment is then urgently required. It is generally people who have suffered from serious problems before the bereavement who react in this way, and a small number will commit SUICIDE.

Another abnormal reaction is chronic grief – a failure to reach the final stage of the normal process. This grief is usually more severe and sometimes involves an excessive amount of self-blame. Some feel that they must mourn for ever to show their love for the dead person. Others find the grief overwhelming and insurmountable. These more severe reactions may be caused if the bereaved person was excessively dependent on the dead relative, or felt a mixture of love and hate for him.

Grief may lead a bereaved person to drink heavily or rely on drugs, but as described under ALCOHOL DEPENDENCE, this does not relieve feelings of depression, and can instead block natural grieving.

Some forms of death bring special problems:

- suicide – the bereaved may feel angry because death was avoidable, rejected and guilty for not having prevented it
- stillbirth or neonatal death – the parents have not had the chance to get to know the lost baby and the mother especially may feel guilty about not having produced a healthy child. Some couples experience MARITAL PROBLEMS. Miscarriage may have similar effects
- cot death or sudden infant death – the shock of finding their baby dead after the relatively recent joy at the birth leaves parents devastated. They may wonder whether something they did or failed to do caused their baby's death. This worry may be increased during the enquiry to establish that the death was natural (as is required for all unexpected deaths)
- death after long illness – especially if this has been distressing and exhausting for the relative, there may be relief at the death and yet guilt about this reaction. Life can seem empty and lacking purpose now that the person has died.

What can be done

Grief cannot be avoided if the bereaved person is to recover and find a new life. Trying to fight it indefinitely can be harmful, though many people delay their grief until the funeral provides a transition between the first and second stages described above. Supporting someone in their mourning, especially if you are affected by the death yourself, is very difficult and many people feel awkward and inadequate. The most helpful reaction is to encourage bereaved people to express their grief – to cry, to talk about the dead person and the plans they had made. Many bereaved people find that others are sympathetic for a while, but then avoid them in their embarrassment and unwillingness to talk about death. As they become depressed, bereaved people may be harder to

121

approach and reject offers of company. The most helpful attitude then is to show that you are available, still sympathetic and willing to listen when the person wants to talk.

Children must also be encouraged to grieve especially if they seem to be repressing their feelings – a GP or health visitor may be able to give advice. Some misbehave after a death in the family and it is important to see this as an expression of grief or as a plea for attention which they have been temporarily denied.

Some bereaved people feel that they have no one to whom they can turn in their grief, and for them bereavement COUNSELLING may be a source of support. This normally involves someone visiting the bereaved as often as necessary, listening sympathetically, accepting his need to cry and reminisce. Some services are run by professionals; others use trained volunteers although professionals may be involved in the service. Cruse (the National Organisation for the Widowed and their Children) offers individual and group counselling and practical advice and information. They run social groups for widowed people, which helps with LONELI-NESS. Bereaved people may use the service whenever they need support, not only immediately after a death. Leaflets and books are produced, and there are over 100 local branches throughout Britain.

The National Association for Widows has branches in many parts of the country offering support, befriending (see COUNSELLING) and a social life. The Widows Advisory Service gives help with practical and emotional problems. Volunteers visit widows where requested and run a telephone helpline. Leaflets and books are produced.

Age Concern and the National Marriage Guidance Council (see MARITAL PROBLEMS) run support groups in some areas.

Parents who have suffered a stillbirth may find that it helps to name the baby, to hold him if possible and perhaps to have a photograph, so that a 'real' person can be properly mourned. After losing a baby or child some parents wish to have another baby as soon as possible. It is generally better to wait until the death has been accepted and the parents have begun to come to terms with it. A number of organisations help parents to cope with the loss of a baby or child:

The Compassionate Friends offer a befriending service to bereaved parents by telephone, letter or personal visits. Regional branches arrange for local members to meet and books on child bereavement can be borrowed. Leaflets are produced.

The Foundation for the Study of Infant Deaths gives personal support and offers to put parents who have suffered a cot death in touch with their nearest group or individual parents in the area who have had the same experience. This befriending, and support from the Foundation by telephone or letter, continues for as long as necessary.

The Stillbirth and Neonatal Death Society has many local support groups providing befriending individually or at group meetings. Books on the subject may be borrowed and leaflets are produced.

The **Miscarriage Association** provides information and support to women who have miscarried. They produce leaflets and have a network of support groups.

Professional help is needed for abnormal grief reactions, such as delayed or prolonged grief. Techniques may be used to induce the process of grieving, or to encourage the person to emerge from his grief and begin a new life. DRUGS are sometimes needed for short periods in the initial stages of grief, or if depressive illness develops. However, they are not necessary in most cases of bereavement.

RELAXATION helps some people to cope with their experience, enabling them to replace ANXIETY with a more peaceful state and to lessen the overwhelming fatigue that the shock brings. **Relaxation for Living**, for example, produces a leaflet on 'Easing Grief for Oneself and Other People'.

Cancer and terminal illness

These two subjects are dealt with together for convenience, because terminal illness is often due to cancer. However, by no means all cases of cancer are terminal and research suggests that it is important to be hopeful about the future if cancer is diagnosed. Everyone experiences shock and probably fear on being told he has cancer – many remember little else that the doctor says on that occasion. A wide range of emotions may ensue. One is 'denial' which involves the patient rejecting the diagnosis and the feelings he would have about it. He may continue to act and feel just as if he had not heard the information, or he may block the thought of cancer out of his mind but be a little less successful in carrying on as if nothing had happened. This may seem an unhealthy attitude, but in fact it can protect the patient from the intensity of the shock he would feel. Later he will accept the diagnosis and the illness can be discussed. However denial entails two possible dangers. One is that the denial may not fully protect the patient from the shock and fear he would normally experience. The other danger is that he will refuse all treatment because he denies being ill. Denial before hearing a diagnosis – for example, that a breast lump could be a tumour – prevents the person even seeking advice.

After the initial shock some sufferers see their diagnosis of cancer as a challenge. They become determined not to succumb to a life of illness, but to fight and beat the tumour. Some research suggests that these people are likely to have more cancer-free years after the diagnosis than other sufferers. Those who show denial are a little more likely to develop cancer again after successful treatment for the first episode. Submitting to the disease, either by a stoic acceptance of it, or worst of all by a complete loss of hope, seems to be associated with a recurrence of cancer. Such research is not conclusive proof that attitudes to cancer determine future health. However, there is a strong suggestion that hope, optimism and an active determination to be well, are better than despair. Some sufferers actually find that their lives are happier and richer after an episode of cancer, because they re-assess their priorities and decide to lead more fulfilling lives.

Despite its prevalence cancer is still very much a taboo subject, and some people find it extremely difficult to talk about. This can place a tremendous burden on the sufferer who needs to discuss the nature of his illness, what it will mean in the future and his feelings about it. Being unable to do so could make him anxious or depressed.

Some researchers are interested in the possible effect of previous mental well-being on the development of cancer. It is very unlikely that someone's psychological state could be a sole cause of cancer, but it might be a contributory factor in some cases. One theory is that such cases are preceded by a severe emotional trauma. Another is that sufferers tend to be the sort of people who instinctively contain, rather than express, strong emotions such as anger. Such theories are still being investigated and sufferers should not look back on their lives wondering if their own behaviour led to their present illness. Looking forward to the future is much more important.

When it is known that an illness is going to be terminal in a relatively short time, it is better for the patient not to continue fighting, but to reach a calm acceptance of the situation. If he cannot, he may suffer ANXIETY or DEPRESSION. Sometimes depression is caused by bottled-up anger about his illness, which may eventually be directed at his family, nurses or doctors. Relatives, themselves sad and worried, may find this hard to bear. Some feel less inclined to visit the patient and bitterly regret this after his death. It may be the patient himself who requests fewer visits at the end of his life, finding it easier to move gradually towards the inevitable separation. Again the family should not be hurt by this.

Relatives may wonder how much to discuss the seriousness of the illness with the patient and the rest of the family. Much depends on the people involved, but it seems that it is often better to be honest than to keep secret what everyone has guessed at, unless the patient indicates his wish not to know. Despite many parents' reluctance to involve them, children may handle such distressing information more easily than would be imagined.

When it is a child who has the terminal illness, the strain on the parents may lead to MARITAL PROBLEMS, but others find that their relationship is strengthened.

What can be done

Many people with cancer and their relatives find that they would like more information than even the most willing doctors and nurses have time to give. **CancerLink** will answer questions on types of cancer and of treatment, and on services available. It has six mutual support groups in and around London and one in Oxford and provides help and advice for other self-help groups around the country (they will tell you where your nearest one is). Some groups provide practical help, as well as information and emotional support.

A number of methods have been proposed for improving the mental well-being of people with cancer who find their illness difficult to accept. Some people do feel better – for example, if they have been finding the side-effects of medical treatment unpleasant. RELAXATION by various methods such as meditation, hypnosis or using biofeedback is recommended. Some people use HOMOEOPATHY, acupuncture or healing; others follow special diets. Visualisation involves keeping a healing image or scene in mind, under instruction from a therapist, while in a relaxed state. Practice enables the person to use the technique at will so that he can create peaceful imagery for himself. COUNSELLING also helps patients to discuss their feelings. The **Cancer Help Centre** offers many of these techniques as a complement to medical treatment, although a few people attending the Centre have rejected surgery, drugs and radiotherapy. A patient may stay for one or two weeks, or attend for just a day. A close relative is encouraged to accompany him and to receive counselling. In cases of financial difficulty help with the fees is available. A number of self-help leaflets and a relaxation cassette tape are produced.

Terminally ill patients may remain in hospital or be transferred to a hospice where psychiatrists and psychologists are able to help sufferers and relatives with their emotional problems. Sometimes a patient may need to be encouraged to discuss the anxiety or depression which he is obviously experiencing, and DRUGS are used if necessary. Counselling and PSYCHOTHERAPY can help him to accept the situation while retaining his self-esteem. The sufferer will in turn be able to support his partner in preparing to assume a new role. Thus the processes involved in BEREAVEMENT are begun before the person dies, and this can help the surviving partner.

Some patients prefer to return home before they die, and are then under the care of their GP. In addition to the NHS, two charitable services provide nurses specifically for terminally ill cancer patients. Macmillan home care nurses are trained to advise on pain and symptom control and to give emotional support to patients and their relatives. They are provided at no charge to the patient but are funded by the **National Society for Cancer Relief** or by health authorities. Cancer Relief also gives grants to families in financial difficulty. In some areas bereavement counselling is arranged. Marie Curie nurses are provided by the **Marie Curie Memorial Foundation,** again at no charge to the patient. They provide nursing care by day or more usually by night: this is as much to support caring relatives or friends as to look after patients. The Foundation also provides counsel, advice and information to cancer patients and their carers, and maintains eleven in-patient units.

Crime victims

In addition to the shock of the crime, victims also sometimes feel that they are neglected during the processes of investigation and possible prosecution. The emotional aspects of being a crime victim are gradually being given more consideration. Some victims are left feeling a bitterness which is connected more with legal procedures after the incident than with the crime itself.

In many cases of violent crime, the victim has had a very bad relationship with the offender for some time. This, in addition to the actual offence, will have affected the victim's mental health.

The typical reactions of men and women to having their homes burgled seem to be different. Some people lose their confidence in being able to protect themselves, their families and their possessions after a robbery or an attack. It is not only victims who suffer, but also their relatives – perhaps especially their parents or partner.

Rape usually has the most serious effects on a woman's mental well-being. Her feelings about herself and men are understandably altered and she may suffer DEPRESSION or ANXIETY. Her partner and men in her family may well have as many psychological problems after the rape as the victim.

The effect of sexual abuse of children requires more research. Some children hide their feelings of fear and even guilt, although it seems that others who are showing no emotions are actually not very disturbed by the incident. In these cases the parents' reactions of anger and disgust may be more of a problem. It appears that depression, anxiety, fear and perhaps EATING DISORDERS are suffered later as a result of such crimes.

What can be done

The **National Association of Victims Support Schemes** is the umbrella organisation for schemes in nearly 260 areas. Victims are usually referred to the schemes by the police. Trained volunteers offer advice and support, and can give practical help, referring victims to local agencies if long-term care is necessary. Leaflets are produced. An equivalent organisation in Scotland is the **Scottish Association of Victims Support Schemes.**

Rape crisis centres have telephone helplines for COUNSELLING and advice. Some provide a female volunteer to go with the victim when she reports the crime or has a medical examination.

The **Matthew Trust** helps crime victims by providing advice on applying for compensation, and legal and medical assistance.

Divorce

Like BEREAVEMENT, divorce involves the loss of a partner who may then be mourned. It is thought to cause less STRESS than being widowed, but in some ways the grief is harder to bear because of the additional emotions of regret, guilt, failure, humiliation, resentment and shame. Some divorced people begin to drink heavily or develop mental illnesses such as DEPRESSION, which can be severe enough to lead to SUICIDE. Chronic grief, as experienced in bereavement, occurs sometimes. Some people cannot accept the finality of the divorce and desperately believe that their partner will return.

The greater incidence of depression and other minor mental illnesses among divorced and separated people can be explained in two ways. People who have repeated episodes of such disorders may be more likely to have MARITAL PROBLEMS. Or the lack of an intimate, supportive partner in whom to confide may make them more susceptible to mental illness in the face of adverse experiences.

Divorce can have other long-term implications, especially if ill-judged decisions are made during the stressful period before the divorce. The partners may have lost the ability to communicate rationally and poor decisions affecting the children and finances may have serious consequences.

The mental well-being of children is affected by severe marital problems and divorce, some research suggesting that boys are more seriously affected than girls. Their behaviour and moods may be disturbed and they may learn more slowly to speak and write. Some children are naughty, attempting to bring their parents closer together; others become aggressive.

What can be done

Conciliation services help couples who have decided to live apart or divorce, with specific problems arising from their separation – commonly concerning their children. They help the couple to reduce their conflicts and instead to reach considered decisions which are the least damaging for all concerned. Some such services are attached to the courts, others act as voluntary services. Family Conciliation Services operate in many areas and will help separating couples who have not been married. A fee is charged, but Legal Aid may be available.

Couples are referred by their solicitors or approach the service themselves.

Reconciliation services are rather different in that they aim to help the couple save their marriage. Divorce COUNSELLING also differs from conciliation in that it concentrates less on legal and practical issues, and more on the emotional aspects of the divorce. Sympathetic support is provided to one or both partners, for as long as it is needed as they readjust to their new lives. **Marriage Guidance Councils** (see MARITAL PROBLEMS) help couples who have decided to divorce, and some counsellors work as conciliators. A few Councils run groups for divorced people.

The **National Council for the Divorced and Separated** has local branches which provide opportunities for meeting other people in the same situation. Most have a Welfare Officer to advise on practical issues.

Hysterectomy

Among the various reasons for SURGERY to remove the uterus (womb) is CANCER, so there may be several factors which can affect the woman's mental well-being. Even if she no longer wants or could have children, the removal of part of the reproductive system can cause her grief. She may feel 'less of a woman' because of this, and occasionally partners of women who require hysterectomies have the same attitude. However, there is no need for the operation to cause SEXUAL PROBLEMS. If it is necessary to relieve a condition which has been painful, the woman may even enjoy a better sex life.

Hysterectomy has generally been thought to increase the chances of a woman experiencing DEPRESSION. One study, though, suggests that the operation does not often cause ANXIETY or depression, but that the conditions may well have been present before the hysterectomy, possibly as a result of the disorder in the uterus. By relieving a physical condition, the operation may result in a feeling of improved mental well-being.

If the ovaries have to be removed during the hysterectomy and the woman had not yet reached the MENOPAUSE, the operation usually causes menopausal symptoms.

What can be done
Many worries and queries can be cleared up by discussing the operation with the gynaecologist who has recommended it. The specialist may be willing to see the woman and her partner together, so that he too can discuss his feelings about the operation. Some women feel needless anxiety that the operation will change their personality or lessen their femininity.

The **Hysterectomy Support Group** provides information and comfort to those who have had a hysterectomy, or are about to undergo the operation. Support is offered to women and their partners by letter, phone and at group meetings.

Loneliness

Loneliness appears to be linked to DEPRESSION and thus to SUICIDE. People who feel that they have no one to turn to may be especially vulnerable to the effects of stressful events in their lives.

There are many causes of loneliness apart from the isolation of living a long way from friends and relatives. Elderly people have decreasing contact with people, as those they know become ill and die. Their own physical inability to leave their homes may also isolate them. Occasionally, elderly people who appear lonely are not discontented but have always preferred a life with little social contact.

People may feel emotionally isolated, even if there are others around them, because of BEREAVEMENT, DIVORCE or mental illnesses such as depression or PHOBIAS. Others may lack the social skills necessary to form satisfying relationships. One piece of research found that in some cases people who say that they are lonely are with friends for as long as people who are not lonely. But the lonely people did not reveal their thoughts, emotions, personalities and so on to their friends – they would not let the other person 'under their skin'. Some were not able to make the other person feel 'rewarded', so that the relationship was not satisfying for either party.

Another reason for loneliness can be the isolation imposed by motherhood. Some mothers find the change from a busy work and social life, to being at home with the baby, very difficult. Together with worry about looking after the baby and perhaps exhaustion from sleepless nights, this loneliness may be a factor in post-natal depression.

Social isolation – being away from close relatives and in a situation where it is hard to make new friends – has been found to be an important factor in child abuse. Many types of STRESS combine to drive a parent to harm a child, but the lack of anyone to provide support and comfort may be a decisive factor.

What can be done

The **Samaritans** offer befriending (see COUNSELLING) not only to those contemplating SUICIDE, but to anyone who is in despair and has no one else to talk to. Social workers and voluntary schemes provide company for elderly people who cannot leave their homes, or encourage them to attend clubs and day centres.

Social skills training (see BEHAVIOUR THERAPY) has been advocated for people who have difficulty making and maintaining relationships which would stop them feeling lonely. This might be available if the lonely person were also suffering from a mental illness.

The **Outsiders Club** is for people who feel isolated and lonely as a result of some form of emotional or physical disability. The Club suggests which other members they should get in touch with by letter, telephone or in person. Social events are organised, and there is a library of relevant books, magazines and articles. Counselling is not offered but the Club produces a booklet of self-help ideas and will suggest sources of help. The affiliated Social Habilitation and Integration Trust for Disabled People offers counselling in SEXUAL PROBLEMS.

The **Meet-A-Mum-Association** has local groups to help mothers who feel lonely and isolated after their baby is born. The groups meet and organise social events, and where possible offer more personal support to mothers who have specific problems.

The **National Childbirth Trust** has branches and groups throughout the country offering post-natal support to provide friendship and prevent isolation and loneliness.

The NSPCC is trying to reduce the risks of socially isolated parents harming their children by introducing them to playgroups and day centres as part of a network of 60 Child Protection Teams. Teams offer COUNSELLING and advice. The NSPCC is contacted by many parents who feel that they are on the verge of taking out their despair on their children.

The **Family Welfare Association** runs several support groups in London for young mothers who feel isolated and under other forms of STRESS.

Marital problems

There are conflicts and arguments in probably every marriage but these are not a problem if they are resolved. However, the poor communication between some couples makes resolving problems increasingly difficult. Hostility, criticism and indifference may characterise the way in which they speak to each other. They may make general criticisms of each other based on one incident which has upset or annoyed them. Each tends to find the other more hostile than that person intended to be. Their communication becomes progressively less rewarding so that neither makes the other feel good, for example by showing understanding, interest or acknowledgement of the other's worth. This breakdown in communication makes it harder to resolve other problems which affect the couple. For instance, a SEXUAL PROBLEM may become a greater source of STRESS in such an atmosphere than it would within a better relationship.

There are many other possible stresses in marriage, such as ALCOHOL

DEPENDENCE or child BEREAVEMENT and mental illnesses such as MANIA and MANIC-DEPRESSION. It is very difficult to forgive a partner who has had an affair or spent the family's savings, even when it is appreciated that an illness caused this behaviour. The MENOPAUSE, and equivalent part of a man's life, can be a time of marital strain. Twenty per cent of DIVORCES occur after 20 or more years of marriage.

As well as the possibility of separation or divorce, marital problems may cause sexual problems or DEPRESSION. A lack of support from a woman's partner may be one factor in post-natal depression. The effect of severe marital conflict on children is discussed under DIVORCE.

What can be done
Marital therapy may involve COUNSELLING, PSYCHOTHERAPY and BEHAVIOUR THERAPY especially using contracts. The couple agree a written contract which aims to decrease the negative aspects of their communication and to increase the positive factors. They each agree to do things which the other expects and wants, and their progress is discussed with the marital therapist(s) at the next session. Other behavioural methods are assertiveness training, modelling and learning better ways of communicating with each other. As with all therapy, both partners must want to achieve an improvement in their marriage.

Behaviour therapy assumes that changing certain behaviour will relieve tension and frustration in the relationship. Some complex marital problems may require interpretive psychotherapy. Psychodynamic therapy (see PSYCHOANALYSIS) aims to help both partners change, resolving the psychological problems which they are assumed to have, in order to restore the balance in their relationship.

Marriage Guidance Councils provide COUNSELLING at over 160 centres in the UK (apart from Scotland). The **Scottish Marriage Guidance Council** is an independent body but operates in a similar way. The Councils help couples or individuals with relationship problems before, during and after marriage. Appointments are made, by telephone or letter usually, for confidential interviews which last about an hour. These are held weekly at the counselling centre for as long as help is needed. The trained volunteers offer mainly sympathetic counselling, but will also give practical advice or suggest sources of specialised help. Those who use this service are asked to contribute towards the cost of it, but charges are waived in cases of financial difficulty. Booklists and books are available. Some counsellors work with social work teams or in GPs' surgeries and health centres.

Organisations offering marital counselling include the **Jewish Marriage Council**, and the **Catholic Marriage Advisory Council** who are happy to see people of any, or no, religious denomination. **Family Service Units** provide a variety of services for couples with children.

Mastectomy

SURGERY to remove a breast is generally necessary because of CANCER, which adds to the problems of coming to terms with the loss of a part of the body so closely associated with the woman's femininity. Perhaps more than in the case of HYSTERECTOMY she may feel 'less of a woman' and be anxious as to her partner's reaction. Research suggests that ANXIETY, DEPRESSION and SEXUAL PROBLEMS are suffered by at least a quarter of patients. Some women feel ashamed that they have been unable to adapt and so do not admit this or other emotional difficulties to the medical staff after the operation.

What can be done

If a woman is having difficulty in accepting her new body-image, feels anxious or depressed, COUNSELLING, PSYCHOTHERAPY (including BEHAVIOUR or COGNITIVE THERAPY and PSYCHOANALYSIS) or anti-depressant DRUGS can all be used. Her partner may also need counselling, so that their relationship can continue as before. BEHAVIOUR THERAPY using desensitisation has been used to help couples accept the result of a mastectomy – see SURGERY. If there are sexual problems, therapy will first concentrate on getting the woman and her partner used to looking at the scar comfortably.

Reconstructive surgery is possible in some cases, either at the time of the mastectomy or later, to build an artificial breast. This has practical advantages over the prosthesis or breast-form which is worn otherwise. In a study to investigate the psychological advantages, researchers found that mental problems were reduced for women who had an immediate reconstruction after the mastectomy. However, this was mainly among women who had unhappy marriages and were thus more vulnerable to psychiatric problems. Few women ask for a reconstruction after they have left hospital, and this is thought to be because they are not sufficiently worried about their changed appearance to undergo another operation. There are problems with reconstructive surgery and it should not be imagined as the perfect solution to the loss of a breast.

The **Mastectomy Association** will give information and put women in touch with others who have had a mastectomy if they would like someone to talk to. They can tell you if there is a Mastectomy Group in your area and provide guidelines on how to set one up.

Menopause

This term actually means the cessation of menstrual periods. The time of life commonly referred to as the menopause is properly called the climacteric. Hormonal changes can cause physical and mental symptoms, although some women experience hardly any. One of the physical changes may cause SEXUAL PROBLEMS because vaginal dryness may make intercourse difficult. The mental symptoms are generally an exaggeration of those experienced as PRE-MENSTRUAL TENSION – for example, DEPRESSION, ANXIETY, irritability and an inability to concentrate. However, it is often wrong to attribute reduced mental well-being solely to hormonal changes. For instance, depression at this time may be related to previous bouts of the illness or to family difficulties, MARITAL PROBLEMS, and financial and job worries.

This period of a woman's life around the age of 50 brings other problems. It is sometimes said that men, too, experience a 'mid-life crisis' which causes similar features of depression, self-doubts, regrets and fears of growing old. The validity of this as a defined mental condition is debatable, but some men and women do find this period of their lives difficult. Parents whose children have left home may feel unwanted, those who have not reached as high a professional position as they had wanted may feel that their working years have been wasted. Some people regret their lost youth and those looking after sick, elderly parents may find this a forceful reminder of what is in store. For some people these negative attitudes may result in depression, heavy drinking, GAMBLING, anxiety or some dramatic change in their lives – a change of job or an extra-marital affair.

What can be done

Any symptoms worrying a woman should be discussed with her GP and they may be unrelated to the menopause. In some places there are NHS and private menopause clinics to which a GP can refer patients; otherwise gynaecologists treat menopausal problems. Oestrogen-progestogen treatment, commonly called hormone replacement therapy (HRT), can be prescribed. It helps physical problems such as hot flushes and vaginal dryness. Whether it helps the mental symptoms has not been established, although curing the physical problems may achieve this indirectly.

RELAXATION may help men and women to achieve greater mental well-being. More serious dissatisfaction with their lives may respond to COUNSELLING or PSYCHOTHERAPY. The aim will be an acceptance of their present situation with plans and optimism for the future, rather than fear and regrets.

Women's Health Concern publishes information on the menopause including details about where there are menopause clinics. A GP's referral is necessary to attend these.

Pre-menstrual tension

This is often abbreviated to PMT and is sometimes used as a synonym for pre-menstrual syndrome (PMS). Strictly speaking, PMS is a collection of physical and mental symptoms which occur for a few days to a fortnight before a period and stop when the period begins. The mental symptoms are collectively known as pre-menstrual tension. They may include DEPRESSION and even suicidal feelings, ANXIETY and panic attacks, irritability, sudden mood changes, low self-confidence, crying without reason, impaired concentration and judgement. Some women feel as if their whole personality changes, others that they are 'going mad'. In the minority who suffer severe PMT their lives at home and at work may be seriously affected. The symptoms may worsen as the woman gets older, particularly after having children. Taking the contraceptive pill seems to cause a PMT-like condition in a few cases, although it alleviates symptoms in others. Some cases in young girls may be dismissed as 'adolescent moodiness'.

Pre-menstrual tension causes some women to drink more alcohol, and can exacerbate various conditions. One of the physical symptoms of PMS is a craving for certain (usually sweet) types of food.

The levels of hormones fluctuate in every woman during the menstrual cycle. It seems, however, that the level of progesterone, one of the hormones produced by the ovary, may be abnormal in some women, resulting in the worsening of PMT symptoms. Another theory, not yet confirmed, is that the cause of PMT is closely linked to deficiencies in certain vitamins and minerals – either because the DIET (see Chapter 2) is unbalanced or because it does not correct existing deficiencies. One extreme view is that at least some symptoms are experienced because the woman expects them, or that she attributes feelings due to unrelated causes to PMT.

What can be done

Women who believe that they are suffering from PMT should record their symptoms, the dates on which they occur and the dates of their periods for three months. This will help the GP to determine whether the condition is caused by PMT. If the patient needs a specialist opinion, there are a few clinics for pre-menstrual problems, but the GP is more likely to refer her to a gynaecologist.

Some experts recommend the pill (if the woman anyway wants this method of contraception), others believe that this makes the symptoms worse. Some doctors prescribe one of the hormones (progestogen) contained in the pill. Tranquillisers are sometimes prescribed for the sufferer to take on the days when her anxiety is worst. Some women find that RELAXATION helps, others have tried COUNSELLING or supportive

PSYCHOTHERAPY. A counsellor may help the woman to re-organise her life according to the predictable changes in her mental well-being. Her family may be more understanding if she explains PMT to them.

Dietary changes have been recommended and Vitamin B6 and evening primrose oil are successfully used by some sufferers. Both can be bought in health food shops, but it is important to obtain expert advice on the correct dose.

Women's Health Concern organises counselling sessions and publishes literature on Premenstrual Syndrome and on its treatments with vitamin B_6 and evening primrose oil. It will recommend suitable clinics and consultants.

The **Pre-Menstrual Tension Advisory Service** does not recommend hormonal supplements, but advocates dietary change for the relief of PMT. After completing a questionnaire, the woman receives advice on how to change her diet and what nutritional supplements to take. A fee is charged for this service. A booklet of general dietary changes is also available and these may be adequate for mild cases.

The **National Association for Premenstrual Syndrome** provides dietary advice of a different kind, and is also in favour in some cases of progestogen as a treatment for PMS. Local support groups offer sympathy and understanding and a booklet and reading list are produced.

Sexual problems

Two types of problem are discussed in this section: difficulties in an existing sexual relationship, and sexual deviations or perversions.

The terms frigidity and impotence have been abandoned by some doctors and replaced by more precise descriptions of the problems. The female problems are orgasmic dysfunction (sexual pleasure, but no orgasm) and general sexual dysfunction (little or no sexual pleasure). The male problems are erectile dysfunction and absent or premature ejaculation. The latter is diagnosed not according to a time scale, but is based on both partners' dissatisfaction. Libido is the sex drive and a significant decrease in this causes sexual problems. Vaginismus in women is a muscle spasm preventing penetration. Vaginal dryness is a possible symptom of the MENOPAUSE and can make intercourse difficult.

The sexual response being a combination of physical and emotional factors, difficulties of either type can impair sexual functioning. Any of the sexual problems may have a physical cause and certain types of SURGERY, illnesses and DRUG treatments can affect sexual functioning. However, it is often the reaction to a problem which is the most significant factor. For example, erectile dysfunction to a small degree may cause a man such anxiety that he becomes incapable of any sexual response. A woman who is very anxious about delayed orgasm becomes less likely to experience orgasm at all.

A decreased interest in sex may be caused by PRE-MENSTRUAL TENSION, DEPRESSION, ANXIETY, ALCOHOL DEPENDENCE, increased age, MARITAL PROBLEMS and SURGERY which has altered the appearance of either partner. Sometimes ignorance about sexual functioning causes difficulties. Guilt can be involved in sexual problems – for instance, if one partner feels that he should not want sex after a recent BEREAVEMENT, when his partner is ill, or 'at his age'. Some people feel guilty about past sexual experiences, or are embarrassed about displaying their feelings during sex.

Homosexuals may experience any of these difficulties and some find living in a society in which heterosexuality is the norm an additional problem.

Sexual deviations are much less common than these problems. Fetishism is where an object, rather than intercourse, fulfils the person's sexual desires. Transvestism is the wearing of clothes normally worn by the opposite sex, and may be a form of fetishism. Transvestites are not necessarily homosexual. Transsexuals feel themselves to be the opposite sex and if they seek treatment it is usually surgery to change their anatomy. Sado-masochism is a desire to be cruelly aggressive, or to suffer pain or humiliation, during sex.

Sexual offences include exhibitionism (indecent exposure), paedophilia (wishing to have sex with children and thus abusing them) and rape (usually committed by men with PSYCHOPATHIC DISORDER). Exhibitionism is sometimes a compulsion, and in these cases the offender may have a type of OBSESSIVE DISORDER. One element of a tendency to commit sex offences may be an inability to satisfy sexual desires normally. It is believed that some offenders may be unable to form more appropriate relationships. However, this is far from being a full explanation of why some people develop deviant sexual interests.

What can be done

Some GPs have a special interest in sexual problems and treat patients themselves. Others refer them to NHS sexual dysfunction or psychosexual clinics. There are also private clinics, but a doctor's referral is still advisable – anyone can claim to be a sex therapist without having proper training. Some women's groups offer help with sexual problems. The **Family Planning Association** can advise on where therapy may be obtained. Other sources of help include those **Marriage Guidance Councils** (see MARITAL PROBLEMS) with a counsellor who has specialist training in sexual problems. Therapy here is available only to couples who have a good relationship – others are advised to have marital COUNSELLING first. An organisation called the **Association to Aid the**

Sexual and Personal Relationships of People with a Disability (SPOD) offers advice and counselling in interviews or by letter. They can help whatever the disability – being elderly, having EPILEPSY or after SURGERY, for example. See also LONELINESS.

Some physical causes of sexual problems can be treated or reversed – for instance when a drug causing reduced libido is no longer needed. Treating depression, however, does not invariably restore libido to its former level. If the reason for the sexual problem is not so much illness, its treatment or an operation, but either partner's reaction to one of these, discussing anxieties with a doctor may improve matters considerably.

Counselling, BEHAVIOUR THERAPY and PSYCHOTHERAPY are used for sexual problems. There are two main forms of therapy, although many variations are used. The aim is for both partners to enjoy a sexual relationship and not to meet any set criterion, such as frequency of intercourse. The more behavioural method is based on the Masters and Johnson approach. This can involve a two- or three-week residential course with two therapists per couple, but may also be used with out-patients and only one therapist. The Marriage Guidance Council uses this non-residential adaptation. The couple are given graded tasks to carry out at home or in privacy if on a course. These are increasingly intimate and the therapist discusses their feelings and difficulties at the next session. Counselling and psychotherapy are used as necessary.

Another method involves simply counselling or psychotherapy, and sex education when appropriate. The therapist helps the couple to change their anxious feelings or unrealistic attitudes about sex.

With any kind of treatment, once the couple begin to enjoy their sexual relationship, they feel more confident and at ease and this adds to the improvement.

Therapy for homosexuals depends on their problem. If they are unhappy about their sexual feelings, counselling is aimed at helping them to sort out what they want and to adjust to this preference. Therapists do not try to alter homosexuality unless the person specifically asks for help to regain a heterosexual lifestyle. Psychotherapy and behaviour therapy are used to deal with anxiety preventing the person having a heterosexual relationship.

Psychotherapy and behaviour therapy are also used with sexual deviations, generally with very limited success. In many cases the person does not want to change his sexual habits, but has been persuaded by others to seek treatment. It may be possible using counselling, marital and sexual therapy to improve the normal sexual relationship between the patient and his partner, so that the deviant interest fades. If there is no such relationship the therapist's task is much harder. With sexual offences, a first conviction is often effective in deterring the person from committing the crime again. Behavioural methods have been used, including social skills training to help them form conventional relationships. Aversion therapy has been used, associating a small electric shock or nauseating drug with the perversion. Drugs to control the sex drive are available, but may have side-effects.

Stress

This is so closely linked with mental health that references to stress are made throughout this book – see the Index. Most of the topics in this chapter are events which can cause stress and so affect mental well-being. Stress as a cause of mental illness is discussed in Chapter 2, and the section on ANXIETY in Chapter 5 also deals with this subject.

People's ability to withstand stress varies enormously. In part it is determined by their personality, but it also depends on the number and degree of stresses coming at the same time or close together. Some people are said to 'thrive on stress' and an addiction to adrenalin produced by the body is believed to occur, causing these people to keep themselves under pressure.

While it is usually too much stress which affects mental health, too little can also be a problem leading to boredom and lethargy. Some may seek out unproductive ways of increasing the excitement in their lives, perhaps resulting in ALCOHOL or DRUG DEPENDENCE, GAMBLING or crime.

The warning signs that someone is suffering from the effects of too much stress include irritability, changes in sleeping and eating patterns, difficulty concentrating and making decisions, worrying or getting angry about trivial matters and so on. The person feels swept along, rather than in charge of his own life; there is too much to do and too little time in which to do it. Being unable to relax, the sufferer becomes increasingly tired until, as described under 'NERVOUS BREAKDOWN', he reaches the point where he can no longer cope at all and rest is unavoidable.

What can be done
When the level of stress in someone's life ceases to make him more efficient and alert, and begins to affect his performance adversely, either in his personal or professional life, the problem should be dealt with. If it is recognised quickly enough, he can choose one or more methods of RELAXATION and combat the problem. If ANXIETY has developed, a doctor's help may be needed, although even then tranquillisers are not the inevitable answer. They may be prescribed for a short initial period, to break the cycle of stress and unproductive activity – in effect, forcing the person to begin to relax. Once he begins to feel calmer, other methods of relaxation, COUNSELLING or PSYCHOTHERAPY may be used.

Surgery

Surgery which is for CANCER can affect mental well-being because of the distress this diagnosis can cause. In addition the operation may remove a part of the body or affect its functioning in ways that may be upsetting. If the surgery is to remove the uterus or a breast, the problems described under HYSTERECTOMY and MASTECTOMY may be experienced. An operation to remove the colon (colostomy) requires the patient to adapt to wearing an external appliance in place of his bowel. Sometimes this operation also causes SEXUAL PROBLEMS.

Surgery to the lung can result in DEPRESSION, as can an amputation. It has been said that losing part of one's body is similar to losing a loved person – a form of BEREAVEMENT leading to grief. Patients react to amputation in many ways – some feel depressed and useless, others are angry and resentful. They may feel bitter or ashamed if they can no longer be independent, and there are practical difficulties in learning to use an artificial limb. Sexual problems may result if the patient or his partner cannot come to terms with how his body now looks. Pain after an amputation can be made worse by depression or ANXIETY.

It should not be imagined that any of these mental or emotional problems is inevitable after surgery. Research suggests that between a quarter and half of patients having this sort of operation suffer depression, anxiety or sexual problems to some degree. Certain factors make it more likely that a patient will have problems. These include having had a mental illness before, knowing someone who has had a bad experience of a similar illness or operation, a lack of support and of someone with whom to discuss worries about the operation, complications after surgery and being unable to come to terms with it. Some people add to their problems by feeling ashamed that they have not coped better with the situation, imagining that everyone else takes such surgery in their stride. A few patients develop a PARANOID state after surgery.

What can be done

Advice and information about the operation should make it easier to adjust to a new body-image or altered functioning. Whether it reduces the incidence of mental illness has not been established. Nevertheless, by removing doubts and misconceptions it should improve mental well-being. Patients should put questions to the doctors and nurses caring for them – some hospitals have nurses and social workers who specialise in providing such information. Volunteers who have had the same operation sometimes visit patients who would like to discuss its implications.

Voluntary organisations to help patients come to terms with specific types of surgery include the **Hysterectomy Support Group** and the **Mastectomy Association**. Representatives of the **Colostomy Welfare**

Group will visit patients to help overcome the psychological and practical difficulties.

Some patients need 'permission' to express the emotions they have bottled up. They feel that to cry and complain about the effects of the operation is unacceptable. Nurses and relatives can reassure them that it is far better to express these feelings, and that it is not a sign of weakness. When the patient returns home relatives can play an important role in helping him to adjust to the effects of his operation. They should find a middle course between treating him as a total invalid (unless this is really the case) and expecting him to return to his former self immediately. Sympathetic encouragement probably sums up the correct attitude.

Those patients who do not make a good readjustment may require help from a psychiatrist or psychologist. For example, BEHAVIOUR THERAPY using desensitisation can reduce anxiety about the lost body part or function. Gradually, in his imagination or by looking at the scar or stump, the patient comes to accept his altered body. Until this stage is reached any SEXUAL PROBLEMS cannot be tackled.

Unemployment

Employment plays a very important part in many people's lives for several reasons. It brings income, activity and interest, status or a position in society, and companionship. Research, mainly in men, has shown that mental well-being suffers during unemployment. Some may initially feel relieved if there has been a period of doubt – threatened redundancy, for example – because uncertainty can be a source of STRESS. A minority of people actually feel good about unemployment because of the pressure they experienced in their jobs. For most, however, unemployment brings a progressive decline in psychological well-being. Their mood is depressed, they feel strained and anxious, and later hopeless. Unemployed people tend to feel that they do not have any control over their lives – unemployment and rejection at job interviews are experienced as things happening to them over which they have no power. Their days no longer have a structure. They are more likely to think negatively about themselves than employed men, and more likely to suffer psychiatric illness. SUICIDE is more common among unemployed men. It is important not to over-estimate the cause-and-effect relationship. With some men, their poor mental health may have led to them losing their jobs, rather than vice versa. This same factor may lead some to commit suicide – that is, the link between unemployment and suicide is only indirect. Nevertheless, research does seem to show a direct causal link for many men between being unemployed and having low psychological health.

The despair of unemployment may cause MARITAL PROBLEMS and

LONELINESS. If the person reduces his contact with others he is less likely to hear about job vacancies 'on the grapevine'.

Perhaps the major reason for unemployment having these effects is its financial implications, but the loss of all the other benefits of work described at the beginning of this section also plays an important part. The person does not just lose his role as an employee, and acquire the much less desirable role of being unemployed – his other roles in life may also be affected. He may lose his position as the major earner in the family. If his wife goes to work he may assume a domestic role for the first time.

From the research that has been carried out it appears that women suffer similar problems if they are single and have thus been supporting themselves, or if theirs was the couple's main source of income.

What can be done

Some people cope well with unemployment by devoting their time and energy to an interest such as politics, voluntary work or further education. Although this may not bring any income, it may fulfil the person's other psychological needs sufficiently to compensate for this.

For those who find it especially difficult to come to terms with unemployment COUNSELLING is sometimes available – this is probably more likely in areas of high unemployment. **National Marriage Guidance Council** centres offer help to couples whose problems are due to the strain of unemployment.

Obviously the best treatment is a new job and it is worth remembering that many are obtained not through advertisements, but by listening for mentions of local vacancies and applying quickly. It is therefore wise not to lose touch with people who might know of work becoming available.

7

Mental handicap and mental illness

These are two quite distinct forms of mental disorder. This book is primarily concerned with mental illness. This affects previously healthy people, either temporarily or, with varying intensity, for very long periods – perhaps even the rest of their lives. It can be treated, though total cures are not always possible.

Mental handicap is usually present from birth, and at the moment there is no chance of curing it. The lives of mentally handicapped people can, however, be improved by special training to make the most of their abilities. Occasionally mental handicap is the result of an accident which has caused severe brain damage, and although it is by and large irreversible, research is being carried out into ways of reducing the effects of such damage.

Mental handicap is an impairment of brain functioning which causes the person's intellectual ability to be lower than would otherwise have been the case. Mental illness may reduce a sufferer's performance, but this is usually only temporary. The causes are often apathy, lack of confidence, inability to concentrate and so on. Once the illness is treated these symptoms disappear and the person is as 'bright' as he was before. Mentally handicapped people do not have this prospect. The exception to this distinction is mental illness which is caused by irreversible ORGANIC damage (see Chapter 3) – for example, DEMENTIA. Because of their slow onset, without any external cause of damage to the brain such as an accident, these disorders are usually referred to as mental illnesses and so are covered in Chapter 5. Their effect, however, resembles mental handicap – irreversible impairment of intellectual ability. AUTISM is another disorder described in Chapter 5 which also has links with mental handicap, because over half the children who develop it are severely mentally retarded.

The rest of this chapter is concerned with the fact that mentally handicapped people are more susceptible than the rest of the population to mental illness. This is partly attributable to their brain abnormalities. These people are also subject to a variety of social stresses – such as failure at school, rejection by society, feelings of being different from brothers and sisters, and perhaps perception of their parents' frustration, anger or guilt.

It is especially important to diagnose mental illness in mentally handicapped people quickly and accurately so that their already reduced quality of life is not further impaired by treatable illness. The problems facing psychiatrists, however, are that illnesses may take a slightly different form in these patients, and the mental handicap also reduces the patient's ability to communicate. It is always important in the diagnosis of mental illness to compare the patient's current mental state with the way he previously felt, thought and behaved. Certain assumptions are made with non-handicapped patients about their previous functioning, though diagnosis should always include an investigation about this. However, it is particularly necessary to determine the previous abilities of mentally handicapped patients.

SCHIZOPHRENIA and PARANOID DISORDERS: mentally handicapped people have less fluent speech and this is reflected in the way they experience and describe some of the symptoms of these PSYCHOSES. Symptoms of thought disorder and delusions, for example, cannot be reliably diagnosed in those with IQs of less than about 45. Some mentally handicapped people have rich fantasy lives which are not the same as delusional beliefs. A paranoid state can be a first indication that the person is developing DEMENTIA. However, it can also be a reaction to stress in mentally handicapped people, and does not necessarily indicate a psychotic illness.

DEPRESSION: even if the patient cannot describe his mood, it is often possible to diagnose depression. With more severely handicapped people the observations of those who know them well may be necessary to confirm the diagnosis. Depression may be indicated by regressed (childlike) behaviour in adults. Mentally handicapped people in general may be more susceptible to depression and MANIA than others, and this certainly seems to be the case with Down's syndrome sufferers (Mongols). With these affective disorders, the depressed or elated mood may not be maintained for as long as in patients who are not handicapped. The disorders may also develop at an earlier age than among the general population.

MANIA: if the elation does not last long it is followed by excitement, restlessness and irritability. Sufferers who are not handicapped often exhibit an engaging wit, but mentally handicapped patients may not be sufficiently fluent to show humour.

ANXIETY: excessive, unwarranted anxiety is more common than the full anxiety state described in Chapter 5. This is easy to spot, even if there are language difficulties.

PHOBIAS: these are also a more likely expression of tension and stress than ANXIETY neurosis.

HYSTERIA: mentally handicapped people show an increased tendency to exhibit dramatic, hysterical symptoms.

OBSESSIVE DISORDER: this can probably be diagnosed only in mildly retarded patients.

CONDUCT DISORDERS: these are perhaps more common than NEUROSES in Down's syndrome sufferers. With severely mentally handicapped patients it may not be possible to diagnose neurosis at all, and a conduct disorder would be a more likely diagnosis.

PERSONALITY DISORDERS: it would be very difficult to describe a mentally handicapped person as having such a disorder. The description of PSYCHOPATHIC could justifiably be used only if the degree of handicap was mild.

DEMENTIA: sufferers from Down's syndrome are more vulnerable than the rest of the population to ALZHEIMER'S DISEASE at a relatively young age. The risk increases as they get older.

SUICIDE: attempts are not unknown, but self-inflicted injuries in mentally handicapped people do not always signify deliberate attempts to end their own lives. Some handicapped people seem not to experience pain normally and so self-inflicted injury is made easier. It may represent a CONDUCT DISORDER rather than a suicide attempt. However, in cases of DEPRESSION, self-injury may be a plea for help or a true suicide attempt.

Mentally handicapped patients with mental illness are generally treated within the psychiatric services available for all patients. As described above, there are problems for psychiatrists with little or no experience of such patients. A few psychiatrists have specialised in the treatment of mentally handicapped patients, and there are also some psychiatric units within mental handicap hospitals.

As might be expected, treatment of mental illness requires some modifications for mentally handicapped sufferers. DRUGS, for example, sometimes have unusual effects on these patients, and may lead to cases of DELIRIUM. Mentally handicapped patients cannot always tolerate the full recommended dose of the drugs. ECT must be prescribed with caution. COUNSELLING and supportive PSYCHOTHERAPY, particularly as GROUP or FAMILY THERAPY, are possible with mildly retarded patients. However, BEHAVIOUR THERAPY is much more widely used.

8

Professional mental health workers

The following chapters describe the services provided by many people trained in mental health problems who work for the health and social services, for voluntary organisations, or in private practice. Many of the names sound similar and it is important to recognise the difference between, for example, psychiatrists and psychologists. This chapter describes briefly the occupations you are likely to come across. References are given to longer descriptions of some of the professions elsewhere in this book.

- **General practitioner** (GP) – the family doctor, and usually the 'entry' to other NHS services. His training includes an introduction to mental illness, but not usually specialist training. Under the vocational training scheme, now compulsory for new GPs, more emphasis is being placed on helping patients to handle their emotional problems.

- **Psychiatrist** – a doctor who has completed five or more years of specialist training in mental illness after his general medical training. Consultant psychiatrists are usually Fellows or Members of the **Royal College of Psychiatrists**, the body which sets standards for doctors training in psychiatry. The consultant psychiatrist, like hospital consultants in other specialties, works with a team of doctors who are training in psychiatry. The grades of doctor most often found are registrar, senior house officer, and senior registrar (in the final stage of training). A psychiatrist may be a general psychiatrist or specialise in a particular area such as child psychiatry, mental handicap, or the psychiatry of old age, for example. Some have also undertaken training courses in PSYCHOTHERAPY.

- **Psychogeriatrician** – a psychiatrist who specialises in mental illnesses in old age. However, not all psychiatrists with a special interest in the mental illness of old age call themselves psychogeriatricians. They all treat such conditions as DEMENTIA, and symptoms such as

CONFUSION, in elderly people. See SERVICES FOR ELDERLY
PEOPLE in Chapter 11.

- **Neurologist** – a doctor who specialises in nervous system disorders.
  His opinion may be required if the cause of a mental disorder seems
  to be ORGANIC (see Chapter 3).

- **Psychotherapist** – see Chapter 4 for a definition of PSYCHOTHER-
  APY. Qualified therapists have trained for several years, and have
  usually undergone a form of psychotherapy themselves (especially if
  they practise a psychodynamic therapy). Before training as therapists they have often attained qualifications in another area – such as
  social work, psychology, nursing, education or medicine.

- **Psychoanalyst** – a therapist who uses PSYCHOANALYSIS – a particularly intensive form of psychotherapy. Many analysts are doctors
  who have then trained in psychoanalysis. They are always required
  to undergo analysis themselves.

- **Behaviour therapist** – as described in Chapter 4, BEHAVIOUR
  THERAPY is a form of psychotherapy. These therapists are often
  psychologists, but may be nurses, social workers or psychiatrists.

- **Psychologist** – psychology is the study of how the mind works, of
  how people think and behave. A first degree in psychology usually
  concentrates on the workings of the normal mind. Post-graduate
  courses in **clinical psychology** apply this knowledge to mental health
  problems. Clinical psychologists may be involved in a diagnosis if a
  psychiatrist asks them to administer tests. They also help in decisions over the best form of treatment for a patient. Psychologists
  may lead GROUP THERAPY sessions or provide BEHAVIOUR THER-
  APY. They may be involved in REHABILITATION (see Chapter 13).
  Most clinical psychologists work in the NHS, though a few are
  employed by social services departments (or the equivalent).
  Another route to becoming a psychologist is to qualify and work as
  a teacher and then take a post-graduate course in **educational
  psychology**. These psychologists are employed by education authorities and some work in child guidance clinics. Their job is to assess
  the problems faced by children with emotional and educational
  difficulties, and to find ways of helping them. Psychologists of any
  kind who have the title of 'Dr' are not usually medically qualified,
  but have attained a PhD for a thesis on an aspect of psychology.

- **Counsellor** – as explained in Chapter 4, COUNSELLING is provided
  by several of the professions listed here, as well as by counsellors,
  such as Marriage Guidance Counsellors (see MARITAL PROBLEMS),

most of whom will also provide counselling for other types of emotional problem.

- **Psychiatric nurse** – nurses in mental hospitals and psychiatric units of general hospitals are usually Registered Mental Nurses, which means that their training has been specially geared towards this type of work. They are commonly called psychiatric nurses. They spend more time than the doctors with patients in hospital, and their observations on each person's progress are therefore valuable. Increasingly, they are responsible for arranging an individual treatment plan for each patient. They lead GROUP THERAPY sessions and, like all nurses, give patients their prescribed medicines.

- **Nurse therapist** or **nurse behavioural psychotherapist** – these are psychiatric nurses who have also been trained in a form of PSYCHOTHERAPY. They work with a GP or psychiatrist who retains overall responsibility for the patient and monitors his progress.

- **Community psychiatric nurse** (CPN) – as the name implies, these nurses look after mentally ill patients who are not in hospital. The patients may be living at home, or in various types of other accommodation (see Chapter 13). All CPNs are Registered Mental Nurses and some have taken a special course in community psychiatric nursing. CPNs generally work in teams, about half of which are currently based in hospitals. Some are attached to the psychiatric department of the hospital and continue to see patients discharged from these wards, helping them to readjust to life outside the hospital. Other CPNs see a wider variety of patients – such as residents at local hostels and referrals from GPs. They may give the GP their opinion as to how he should treat these patients, or they may provide care themselves. They are trained and experienced in COUNSELLING and various forms of PSYCHOTHERAPY. If a patient has been prescribed long-acting injections (see DRUGS in Chapter 4 and SCHIZOPHRENIA in Chapter 5), a CPN often administers these. CPNs are equally concerned with the welfare of families of mentally ill people, and can offer support and advice to relatives. They may arrange for various services to be provided, perhaps in collaboration with a social worker. Some CPNs specialise in particular types of problem – for example, ALCOHOL or DRUG DEPENDENCE, the problems of elderly mentally ill people, or crisis management.

- **Social worker** – the professional qualification is the Certificate of Qualification in Social Work; it is usually obtained after a full-time course. The Certificate in Social Service is obtained while the social services worker continues in his job. A few social workers have neither of these qualifications. Social workers are usually employed either by the local authority (the Health and Social Services Board in Northern Ireland) or by the voluntary sector. Most work in the social services department (or equivalent), though some are based in child guidance clinics. Another local authority service employing social workers is the education welfare service. There is also the probation service. (In Scotland these are not separate services, but come under the social work department.) Social workers can help mentally ill people and their families in a variety of ways. Their main concerns are the personal and social effects of the person's illness, rather than the medical problem. Because they are employed by the local authority they can often help with housing, arrange any necessary social services, such as home helps, and arrange attendance at a day centre. Social workers can advise on financial benefits and are often more aware of the voluntary help available locally than health workers. They are also concerned with the welfare of children if one of the parents is mentally ill. Social workers may provide PSYCHO-THERAPY and sometimes lead GROUP and FAMILY THERAPY sessions. They work with people suffering mental and emotional problems who do not need a stay in hospital, and with those who have been discharged following in-patient treatment. Social workers who specialise in helping mentally ill people are sometimes called **psychiatric social workers**, and have undergone specialist training in this field. Some social workers are based in hospitals, although they too are employed by the local authority. Their broad functions are those of any other social worker, but they also help with the special difficulties of in-patients. For example, they can help with family problems arising because the patient is away from home, and they are also involved in preparations for his discharge. **Approved social workers** (in Scotland, mental health officers) have special training and are appointed to discharge powers and duties regarding the compulsory detention of certain patients, particularly to ensure that alternatives are considered – see Chapter 12.

- **Occupational therapist** – the use of OCCUPATIONAL THERAPY is described in Chapter 4. While most such therapists work in hospitals, others see patients in the community. Some social services departments (or the equivalent) employ occupational therapists. Another role of occupational therapists is to assess the needs of people with physical disabilities and arrange for aids to be provided and for modifications to be made to the home.

- **Music, art, drama, dance and movement therapists** – specialist therapists whose work is described in the section in Chapter 4 on OCCUPATIONAL AND RELATED THERAPIES.

- **Health visitors** – nurses who have taken a further specialist course. Much of their work is with children under five and elderly people. They are also concerned with family health and welfare, both of which may be damaged by mental or emotional problems.

The work of the remaining therapists, usually based in hospitals, is described in Chapter 4 under the relevant therapy:

- **Industrial therapist**
- **Physiotherapist** and, less commonly, **remedial gymnast**
- **Speech therapist.**

9

Getting help for yourself

If your mental state is causing you concern or distress, you should seek help as soon as possible. If you are suffering from a mental illness, the sooner treatment starts, the better. If you are not ill, your GP can reassure you that there is no mental problem. Any symptoms may, however, have a physical cause, which should be dealt with promptly. When worries come into the category of emotional problems, sharing them with someone who has professional or voluntary experience of such difficulties can make an enormous difference. Unless you are sure that all you need is someone to talk to, it is always wise to see your GP first.

So how can you tell if you have a mental problem? The single most important factor is *change*. Sleeping for four hours a night is not a warning sign, unless you used to sleep solidly for eight hours and now find it difficult to go to sleep and stay asleep until the alarm wakes you. Some people naturally worry more than others, but if you are worrying increasingly about minor problems that would not have concerned you before, then seek your doctor's advice. As a general guide the following signs might indicate the onset of mental illness:

- becoming less active, finding it difficult to get out of bed, or up from an armchair at the weekend
- changes in work or school behaviour, becoming less or more industrious
- changes in sleeping habits
- changes in appetite
- changes in sexual behaviour
- changes in mood, feeling constantly weepy, becoming more shy or aggressive
- increasing periods of feeling uneasy or nervous
- a fear that you will lose control, 'go berserk' (the chances of this are actually remote)
- new feelings of guilt about past events
- being unable to understand your own feelings, bewilderment at what is happening to your thoughts or mood.

It is sadly still true that people are sometimes afraid of being told that they are mentally ill, and so delay seeking help. They continue to worry about what might be wrong with them, and resist the nagging feeling that it would perhaps be best to 'get it over with' by seeing a doctor. This adds to the strain of being mentally ill or emotionally distressed, and can only make matters worse. Some people even try to deny to themselves that there is anything amiss, rejecting all attempts by family or friends to sympathise and offer support. It is very difficult to admit that something strange is happening to your thoughts and feelings which you are unable to control. But acknowledging it, first to someone close to you, and then to someone qualified to help, is the best thing you can do.

Going to the GP

Some people feel embarrassed about consulting their GPs for emotional or mental complaints, feeling that only physical disorders should be discussed with doctors. They may therefore describe physical symptoms, such as difficulty in sleeping, aches and pains, but not mention their suspicions that stress, an emotional upset or an inexplicable mental problem might be linked to the symptoms. A good GP should be able to spot that there is more to his patient's problems than the physical symptoms, but it is a great deal easier if the patient is frank in the first place. Your time with a GP is better spent discussing all aspects of your problem and ways of tackling it, than secretly hoping that the GP will guess that you feel depressed and ask you about it.

When you make an appointment with your GP ask the receptionist if it is possible to book a longer or double appointment because you have something to discuss with the doctor which will take more than a few minutes. If she says this is not possible, make an ordinary appointment. When you see the GP tell him what you wish to discuss and that you would like to see him for a longer session to explain the details. He may be willing to extend the appointment if other patients are not waiting to see him, or tell you how to book a longer appointment. This may be with himself or with someone else at the surgery or health centre who specialises in your type of problem – see Chapter 11.

When you have fully explained your problem to the GP, he will decide on the best course of action, ideally discussing any alternatives with you. If the problem seems to require diagnosis and/or treatment by a psychiatrist, the GP will refer you – see Chapter 11. He may provide DRUGS and/or COUNSELLING himself, or refer you to a counselling service (see later in this chapter). Unfortunately there is sometimes a third alternative which is that the GP will take no interest in your problem. This is very unlikely to be the case if you are suffering from a mental illness, as a GP could be disciplined for failing to treat or refer a patient in such circumstances. It might, however, happen if you have a GP who has no particular interest in dealing with emotional problems. He should then advise you where to go for help. If your GP does not do this, you will have to use the other sources of information listed at the end of this chapter.

If you cannot even contemplate discussing a mental or emotional problem with your own doctor, it is worth considering registering with a different one. Advice on this is given in the Consumers' Association/Patients Association book *A Patient's Guide to the National Health Service*. Bear in mind that if you are registered with a group practice you can normally see any of the GPs – not just the one with whom you are registered. (See also 'Self-referral services' opposite.)

Prescriptions

Whenever DRUGS are prescribed there are a few points which patients should clarify. You should be sure you understand why the doctor is prescribing a medicine. Sometimes this is obvious, but with minor mental illnesses drugs are not always necessary, and you should discuss the alternatives with the doctor. He may, for example, suggest you also see a counsellor while you take a short course of drugs, and then continue with just the COUNSELLING for a while.

Ask how often you should take the medicine, at what time of day, and whether you should avoid alcohol, any foods or driving (especially if the drug is for ANXIETY or DEPRESSION). If you are pregnant or are likely to become pregnant, discuss this with your doctor. Before leaving, find out when you should come back for the doctor to review your progress. You may be offered a repeat prescription facility, so that you do not need to see the doctor for a new prescription. But do not take any drug for longer than six months without seeing the doctor to check that you still need the same dose – or even need the medicine at all.

Ask the doctor what side-effects you might experience and whether you should make an appointment to see him if these develop. If the drug seems to be causing a side-effect which you were not warned about, see the GP as soon as possible.

Seeing a homoeopath

As described in Chapter 4, HOMOEOPATHY is a form of complementary medicine. If you prefer this type of treatment to orthodox medicine you will probably already know a practitioner. A few GPs give homoeopathic treatment on the NHS, but you must register with them to receive this. There are also a few NHS hospitals where you can ask to be treated homoeopathically, such as the **Royal London Homoeopathic Hospital**. You must be referred by a GP for treatment. The alternative is to go privately. Lists of doctors who practise homoeopathy are available from the **British Homoeopathic Association**.

Self-referral services

There are an increasing number of self-referral or direct-access services for people with mental or emotional problems, meaning that you can use them without being referred by a GP. Some are run by the NHS, perhaps in conjunction with the local authority social services department (or equivalent). Centres which involve NHS staff are often called community mental health centres or centres for community mental health. Not all have a self-referral service, but if they offer a 'walk-in' or 'drop-in' service you do not even need to make an appointment before visiting the centre. Some will strongly advise you to see your GP first, especially if they suspect that you do have a problem which needs medical treatment. Your GP would then refer you back to the centre, if the required treatment was available there.

If you have a reason for not wishing to go to your GP, discuss it at the centre. They may be able to reassure you that your fears are unfounded. They can also advise you on how to approach the discussion with your GP, and may even offer to hold a practice interview. You can then rehearse describing your symptoms succinctly, and should therefore feel more confident about seeing your GP. If you really feel that you cannot contemplate discussing your problem with him, some centres will agree to see you, provided you give them permission to tell your GP that you are attending the centre.

In some areas you can contact an NHS clinical psychologist directly, perhaps to discuss what sort of treatment is available for your problem. Telephone the information department of the local health authority and ask if it is possible to speak to someone in the District Psychology Department or Service. More rarely you can arrange to see the psychologist without being referred by your GP, but the psychologist would then inform him of the treatment you were receiving.

One service offering direct access to a clinical psychologist is a 'walk-in' clinic in South Tees, the **Woodlands Road Clinic**.

In some areas it is possible to contact a community psychiatric nurse directly.

If you would like to talk to a social worker, ring the local authority social services department (or equivalent).

Some walk-in centres are not connected with the health service and cannot offer treatment, though some may provide COUNSELLING. The centres chiefly provide information on services available locally and help with practical problems, such as financial benefits and accommodation (see also Chapter 13). If a visit to the GP is recommended they can offer advice on how to approach this.

This chapter describes some of the many services in the UK which offer help for mental illness and emotional problems in general, for which a GP's referral is not always necessary (though it may be advisable). The

'What can be done' sections in Chapters 5 and 6 list others which specialise in individual types of illness or problem. Advice is given at the end of this chapter on how to find out what services are available in your area.

Examples of two types of self-referral service are:

- Emergency Clinic at the **Maudsley Hospital** in London – open 24 hours a day, seven days a week. Anyone urgently requiring psychiatric help may go directly to the Clinic without obtaining an appointment. There may be a wait of anything up to four hours at the Clinic – especially if people misuse the service by attending with non-urgent problems for which they could have consulted a GP. A psychiatrist at the Clinic writes to the GP of every patient seen there, to inform him of the patient's treatment

- Advice and Resource Centre run by LINK: **Glasgow Association for Mental Health** – offers free confidential help in welfare, housing, legal and mental health matters, as well as counselling

- Mental Health Advice Service of the **Northern Ireland Association for Mental Health.**

Counselling and psychotherapy services – free
There are a number of free COUNSELLING services provided either under the NHS, or more commonly as a voluntary service. They vary in whether or not they prefer you to see your GP first. They are suitable for emotional problems and minor mental illnesses such as ANXIETY, which are not so severe that they require medical treatment. Some call their service purely counselling, others also offer PSYCHOTHERAPY. For example:

- the **Isis Centre** in Oxford is run by the NHS and offers individual, group and marital therapy for people suffering from such problems as ANXIETY, DEPRESSION, severe relationship problems and difficulties in coping with crises or everyday life. There may be a short waiting list

- the **Family Welfare Association** has 12 centres in London, Milton Keynes and Northampton where their social workers provide counselling for individuals, couples and families in distress. They can refer people to other services which may help to alleviate their problems – though not to specialist NHS services. The counsellors strongly encourage people to see their GPs if they have a health problem, and will discuss any reservations they may have about making an appointment

- the **Andover Crisis and Support Centre** offers counselling in person or over the telephone 24 hours a day, seven days a week. Emergency accommodation for those who have problems apart from nowhere to live is also available for stays of up to three weeks; there is a charge for this but it may be met by the DHSS

- **Simpson House, Family Counselling Centre** in Edinburgh is one of a number of centres run by the **Board of Social Responsibility of the Church of Scotland**, offering counselling and support to families and individuals.

Some free counselling services are provided specifically for young people. Examples are:

- the Young People's Counselling Service at the **Tavistock Clinic** (NHS) in London is a self-referral service for those in the age range of 16 to 30. It offers short-term counselling using a psychodynamic approach based on a shared assessment of the young person's problems. Appointments are made in advance by telephone, and there can be up to four meetings each of about an hour (see PSYCHOANALYSIS)
- **Brent Consultation Centre** offers a service to young people aged 16 to 23 where their problems can be confidentially discussed with trained interviewers. Individual psychotherapy using a psychodynamic approach may be available for those who live, work or study in the London Borough of Brent. The Centre will try to arrange appropriate help for those living elsewhere
- **Brook Advisory Centres** around the country offer counselling on emotional and SEXUAL PROBLEMS mainly for people under 25
- the **London Youth Advisory Centre** offers counselling and psychotherapy to young people aged 13 to 25. Individual psychotherapy and counselling use a psychodynamic approach. Parents may also attend alone or with their adolescent children if family conflicts are the problem. The Centre additionally provides information on a wide range of topics relating to young people
- **Contact** in Belfast provides a 'walk-in' and telephone counselling service for adolescents and young adults.

Counselling and psychotherapy services – fees charged
Some counselling and psychotherapy services which can be approached directly charge a fee for each session, though this is sometimes negotiable, with reduced fees for those in financial difficulty. As with the free counselling services, they vary in whether or not they wish GPs to be informed before therapy begins. For example:

- the **Norwich Centre** offers individual counselling (for a negotiable fee) and also sometimes convenes counselling groups
- the **London Centre for Psychotherapy** accepts self-referrals, but will ask permission to inform your GP if you are accepted for therapy

155

They will also accept referrals made by your doctor or others. The individual or GROUP THERAPY is analytically orientated (see PSYCHOANALYSIS) and counselling is also available

- **Westminster Pastoral Foundation** in London offers counselling for people with personal, marital or family problems. It has its origins in the Church but people in need, regardless of their religious views or affiliations, are welcomed for counselling. Counselling is offered individually, in groups, couples or families. Clients are expected to pay what they can afford but no one is ever refused help for lack of money. The Foundation can provide information on affiliated centres in England and Wales
- the **Arbours Association** runs a psychotherapy clinic for people in emotional distress. They also offer long- and short-term accommodation in therapeutic communities (see Chapter 13). Therapists at the Arbours Centre will answer telephone calls from people who need to talk for a while about their distress. Application forms for psychotherapy are available from the Association. A psychodynamic approach is taken, and the Association stresses the importance of supporting the whole family, not only the person experiencing the crisis
- the **Institute of Group Analysis** accepts requests and referrals for this type of therapy (see GROUP THERAPY and PSYCHOANALYSIS)
- the **British Association of Psychotherapists** offers a clinical service for those who wish to have analytical psychotherapy. They prefer you to inform your GP if therapy is undertaken
- the **Institute of Behaviour Therapy** offers individual treatment by qualified psychologists. They treat problems such as ANXIETY, OBSESSIVE DISORDERS, DEPRESSION and EATING DISORDERS.

It is important to remember that anyone can call himself a counsellor, psychotherapist or hypnotherapist even if he has had no training or experience. The services listed above all use trained staff, but if you intend going directly to any other private therapist it is always advisable to check first that he is qualified. Probably the easiest way of doing this is to find a therapist who is a member of a professional organisation. Some of these are mentioned above, and training courses are obligatory for membership.

If your GP refers you, you can be confident that the counsellor or therapist has satisfactory credentials. (Referrals by GPs are covered in Chapter 11.)

When making a direct arrangement with a private counsellor or therapist use the first appointment to agree the terms of your treatment. Find out how long and how frequent the sessions will be, and how many you are likely to need. Discuss the cost – this is often negotiable. Find out whether the counsellor or therapist requires your GP to know about the therapy, and if so, agree which of you is going to inform him. Ask also whether the counsellor or therapist wishes to see any members of your family. If so, and there are some matters you do not wish to be mentioned at these group sessions, make this clear. Or if he believes such discussions are fundamental to helping you, the counsellor or therapist may make them a condition of accepting your case.

Self-help

You may be looking not for treatment, but for the companionship of fellow-sufferers, and the encouragement of those who have recovered from the condition or survived a similar crisis. This type of support can complement treatment from professionals, or may be the only form of help you need at the moment. Realising how many people have gone through the same experiences can help you put your own into perspective. There are hundreds of self-help organisations, for almost every conceivable mental and emotional problem. They range from groups of local sufferers meeting once a fortnight, to national organisations with professional advisers and dozens of local associations. Some of these self-help groups and organisations are listed in Chapters 5 and 6 under the individual mental illness or emotional problem. Other ways of finding out whether a relevant group exists are given at the end of this chapter.

While a self-help group may be an invaluable source of support and practical advice, there may be a risk of meetings becoming little more than 'symptom-swapping sessions'. While telling others how bad you feel can provide some release, it has no long-term benefit and some people may find they feel more depressed for hearing other members' troubles. If the group takes a more positive attitude, however, it can be a lifeline for those who feel isolated by their illness or problem.

A variation of the self-help group is co-counselling. This is where a number of people, all of whom have emotional problems, undergo a training course in COUNSELLING skills. They are then available to help each other, taking the role both of counsellor and of client at different times.

If you would like to set up a self-help group because there is no appropriate group near you, a 'Self-Help Group Starter Pack' is available at a small charge from the **Self-Help Team** in Nottingham. You can also get advice from the **Mind Your Self Project** in Leeds. The **Association of Self-Help and Community Groups** runs courses for those who wish to set up and run self-help groups.

Self-help need not involve joining a group, which does not appeal to everyone. Mental illness requires professional advice, but there are emotional problems which can sometimes be improved or overcome solely by your own efforts. If tension is your problem, one of the

RELAXATION methods may be all you need, rather than tranquillisers. If LONELINESS or feeling discontented with life is the problem, there are clubs and many publications which aim to help you see life in a different light. Examples of the organisations selling self-help books and cassette tapes are:

- **LifeSkills Ltd** – books, tapes and seminars on handling stress problems using behavioural psychology techniques (see BEHAVIOUR THERAPY)
- **Relaxation for Living** – leaflets, tapes and day or evening classes around the country run by trained teachers
- the **Proudfoot School of Hypnosis and Psychotherapy** – books, tapes and seminars on hypnosis and self-help techniques.

Finding out what is available

Going to your GP is the best way of finding out what is available locally under the NHS. He can then provide any necessary referrals. GPs may also know about local social services and voluntary organisations.

Other ways of finding out about local mental health services and general information are:

- ask at your Citizens Advice Bureau (CAB), library or Community Health Council (CHC). To find the address of the CHC look under 'Community' in the telephone directory or under the name of the CHC if you know it – this may well be the name of the District Health Authority. Some CHCs advertise in local newspapers. You could also ask at your GP's surgery or at a local hospital. Or contact the **Association of Community Health Councils for England and Wales.** (The equivalents of CHCs are Local Health Councils in Scotland and District Committees in Northern Ireland. The two bodies concerned are the **Association of Scottish Local Health Councils** and the **Association of Northern Ireland District Committees**)
- ask at a local association for mental health affiliated to MIND (the National Association for Mental Health) if you live in England or Wales. You can also contact MIND's Advice, Information and Rights Unit at their headquarters. They publish a list of organisations which offer psychotherapy, mainly in the London area. MIND Regional Resource Centres in Gateshead, Leeds, Preston, Sheffield and Cardiff can supply information on psychotherapy elsewhere
- if you live in Scotland ask at a local association affiliated to the **Scottish Association for Mental Health,** or contact the headquarters
- if you live in Northern Ireland contact the **Northern Ireland Association for Mental Health**

- contact the local authority social services department (or equivalent)
- contact **Good Practices in Mental Health**, with details of the sort of service you are interested in. For a small charge they will send you photocopies of any information sheets they have on that type of service in your area or elsewhere. Local studies have been carried out under the Project in many parts of the UK to identify mental health services which work well. The studies are published locally as directories of services or information packs. Good Practices in Mental Health will tell you whether a survey has been carried out in your area and how to obtain a copy. Or contact your local mental health association or CHC
- the **College of Health** is an organisation for members of the public who are interested in learning more about health. Members receive its magazine *Self Health*, which has articles on physical and mental health. The College also holds a register of over 1,000 caring and self-help organisations. Members may contact the College to ask whether there is one relevant to their problem.

  The College of Health also has a telephone information service called Healthline which has over 150 tapes on a wide range of health subjects including aspects of mental health. The service is free except for the cost of the telephone call and is open to anyone whether or not they are a member of the College. You can get a directory of the tapes from the College or ring the Healthline on 01-980 4848 between 6pm and 10pm (seven days a week) to ask if there is a tape on the subject you need
- the **Patients Association** is an independent organisation offering advice to patients and representing their interests. The Association produces information leaflets and a directory of self-help health organisations and will answer queries by letter or telephone on NHS or private medicine problems
- the **Mental Health Foundation** has produced a book listing 10,000 self-help and community groups in the UK (and the Republic of Ireland) offering support to people with 'coping problems'. It is called *The Mental Health Foundation's Someone to Talk To Directory 1986* and may be available at your library, CAB, CHC etc for you to consult. (The directory may also be bought at bookshops or directly from the publishers, Routledge and Kegan Paul)
- the **British Association for Counselling** publishes directories of *Individual Counsellors* and *Counselling Agencies and Organisations*. They also offer a telephone information service for people wanting to find a counsellor
- two feminist organisations supplying information on women's health and self-help groups are the **Women's Health Information Centre** and the **Women's Information Referral and Enquiry Service**

- the **National Association of Young People's Counselling and Advisory Services** will give details of such services in your area
- the **Churches' Council for Health and Healing** coordinates the Churches' healing ministry and is a resource and information centre.

10

Getting help for someone else

It may be that you are worried not about your own mental health, but that of a relative, friend or work colleague. Before suggesting that he might benefit from seeing a doctor, think carefully about whether your relative or friend is really showing signs of mental illness. 'Strange' behaviour may have a perfectly logical explanation. Someone who is emotionally distressed following a very upsetting event may require nothing more than a concerned person to offer support and sympathy.

The common signs of the onset of mental illness are described in Chapter 9. You may spot several of these in someone close to you, or other signs which are less obvious to the person himself:

- becoming hostile, defensive and guarded
- appearing confused or distressed, and 'cold' in response to efforts to comfort him
- seeming to lack any emotion, or showing excessive emotion when it is not warranted – perhaps even in totally inappropriate situations (eg laughing at sad news)
- becoming withdrawn, unwilling to mix with family and friends or to join in activities
- expressing unwarranted suspicions about people or circumstances
- reacting to sights or sounds which do not exist (hallucinations).

If the person you are concerned about makes no attempt to seek help himself, put the suggestion to him calmly, but quite firmly, that you think it would be a good idea for him to explain his feelings to the doctor. Hearing that someone else is worried about his health may be all that is needed to persuade him to contact his GP. He may, however, be feeling so depressed or apathetic that he cannot make the effort to call the surgery. You can offer to do this, and then ensure that he keeps the appointment. It is helpful anyway to accompany the person to his first appointment for 'moral support'. He may ask you to go into the surgery with him, and the GP is unlikely to object to this. Let him do the talking, though, and add only any important details which he does not mention.

Your relative or friend may be more resistant than this to the idea of seeing a doctor. If he has specific fears you may be able to answer them – for example, by reassuring him that a stay in hospital will probably not be necessary. He may fear being forcibly admitted – even that you are trying to have him committed. Explain that this is extremely rare, and that no one is going to do anything without first explaining it and asking for his agreement. His fears may be concerned with what you and others will think of him if he is diagnosed as mentally ill. You will have to judge how best to reassure him that your relationship will not be affected by this.

If the person is still afraid to see a doctor, he may agree to a social worker visiting him at home. The social worker might persuade him to go to his GP, or may be able to arrange some other form of help as a temporary measure.

If all your efforts fail to persuade the person to accept help, and you feel that a doctor's opinion is vital, make an appointment to see the GP yourself. This is, of course, warranted only in a serious case – you cannot go to someone's GP telling him that his patient has felt depressed for a couple of days, and has difficulty sleeping. You are, however, quite justified in contacting the GP of someone who has become increasingly depressed over a couple of weeks, no longer gets out of bed, talks only of 'ending it all' and has not eaten for three days. Describe to the doctor all the symptoms that are worrying you. He will probably not say much to you about what he thinks – a GP must always keep confidential any information about his patient. It would therefore be unethical for him to comment in detail to you on what he thinks may be the problem. The GP will probably agree to visit, or if he thinks a specialist opinion is urgently needed, he can arrange for a psychiatrist to visit.

Some of the services described in Chapter 9 may be able to help you if you are worried about the mental health of a relative or friend – for example 'walk-in' advice centres and local mental health associations.

Emergency help

Very occasionally people suffer 'psychiatric emergencies'. Usually this is not a sudden onset of severe mental illness, but a serious deterioration in someone who is already ill. He might, for example, have SCHIZOPHRE- NIA, and suffer another attack after a relatively symptom-free period. If you live with such a person you will probably know what to do in such an emergency. If you do not know this, ask the person's doctor whom you should contact if the need arises or the local social services depart- ment (or equivalent) – it is much better to know in advance what to do.

A few places have crisis intervention teams (perhaps working from a local hospital) who deal with psychiatric emergencies. They can visit a patient quickly and arrange whatever treatment and help is needed. It is often the patient's GP or social worker who contacts the team and asks them to visit. You should be able to reach your GP (or his colleague or a deputising service) at any time by telephone. If you cannot contact him in an emergency, or a social worker or community psychiatric nurse, call the nearest hospital and ask their advice or that of the local social services department (or equivalent), or take the person to the nearest Accident and Emergency (casualty) department and ask for the duty psychiatrist. A psychiatric emergency does sometimes require an admission to hospital. Patients are always asked first to agree to this, but in rare cases compulsory admissions cannot be avoided – see Chapter 12.

If you live in London you could take the person to the Emergency Clinic at the **Maudsley Hospital** described in Chapter 9 under 'self-referral services'.

II

Getting
specialist help

Chapter 9 looked at the services which you can approach as a first step to getting help for mental illness. Often this is all that is needed. In most cases a GP can treat the illness himself, or a few COUNSELLING sessions may help you to deal with an emotional problem. Sometimes, however, patients seeing GPs for mental problems are referred to specialist services – at the surgery or health centre, a community mental health centre, or more commonly at a hospital. This chapter looks at all the specialist services to which patients are referred by GPs. Some of these can also be approached directly as already described.

Services in the community

These are services which are not provided in hospitals but in other settings, although hospital staff might be involved. Some services to which GPs refer patients are available at their own surgeries or health centres. Various health and social workers who specialise in mental and emotional problems provide the services. They may not work permanently at the GP's premises, but have appointments there for a few hours a week. Usually they are said to be 'attached' to the GP's practice; they do not work for him, but with him at his premises. However, some practices do directly employ counsellors. Sometimes these health and social workers are based at health centre premises but not attached to a particular group practice there. They see not only patients registered with GPs who work at the health centre but also those of other local GPs.

Clinical psychologists are working increasingly with GPs rather than solely as hospital services. A growing but still small number work at surgeries and health centres, and occasionally a visit by a clinical psychologist to a patient's home can be arranged. The patients they see are typically suffering from ANXIETY, PHOBIAS, OBSESSIVE DISORDERS, EATING DISORDERS, MARITAL and SEXUAL PROBLEMS and ALCOHOL DEPENDENCE.

Social workers sometimes spend part of the week at a surgery or health centre, as well as visiting patients of the GPs with whom they work. GPs may refer to them patients with NEUROSES or relationship problems. The social workers can give support and reassurance, and have longer to listen to problems than the GP.

Community psychiatric nurses are receiving an increasing number of referrals from GPs. They may see patients at surgeries or health centres, or visit them at home. The patients might have any type of mental and emotional problem, and are frequently patients whom the GP feels need more specialist attention than he can provide, but not a full psychiatric investigation.

Counsellors who come from the **National Marriage Guidance Council** to provide COUNSELLING at a GP's premises normally charge those patients who are able to pay (see MARITAL PROBLEMS). This fee may, however, be waived. Other counsellors, who do not have another professional title (such as social worker or psychologist), work with GPs either as volunteers or as private practitioners. The latter may be paid by the GPs in the practice to offer the service. The only way private counsellors could work from the premises and charge their clients fees would be if they rented a room in a health centre outside surgery hours.

If your GP does not have any 'attached' professionals at his premises he may refer you for their services elsewhere. In the case of social workers and community psychiatric nurses he will probably contact them, provide some details of your case, and ask them to visit you. For counselling, he would probably tell you where to contact a counsellor. If he recommends your seeing a psychologist this would probably be a hospital out-patient appointment. GPs can sometimes make direct referrals to psychologists. Otherwise patients have to see a psychiatrist first.

If there is a local community mental health centre, the GP can refer you there for a specialist opinion on your problem. Psychiatrists are usually connected with these centres, though they do not work at them every day. When it is felt that a psychiatrist's opinion is needed for a patient, an arrangement is made for the person to see one at his next appointment.

Out-patients appointments

At your first appointment with the GP he may suggest that you see a psychiatrist, or less commonly a psychologist, as an out-patient. (This means that you visit the hospital only for the appointment and do not stay overnight as an in-patient.) If your problem does not seem too serious or complicated the GP may recommend some initial treatment and ask you to see him regularly to report how you are getting on. If your condition does not improve he might then refer you for a specialist opinion.

You may have some ideas about the sort of specialist treatment you would like, and therefore wish to ask your GP to refer you for that kind of therapy. Most doctors want their patients to take an active interest in their treatment, and to regard it positively. If you do have a preference you could say that you have heard of a particular type of therapy and would like to know if it is available locally. Demanding that your GP refer you to, say, a psychoanalyst is not, however, going to improve your relationship with him. There may be good reasons why a particular form of therapy would not be suitable for you, and it may not even be available locally on the NHS (almost certainly not in the case of PSYCHOANALYSIS). Your best course of action is to show your GP that you would like to discuss the alternatives, which in some parts of the country will be limited anyway. If the one you agree upon does not lead to the hoped-for improvements, you can go back to your GP and ask to be referred somewhere else. Bear in mind that your commitment to recovery may be just as important as the actual treatment used. Occasionally GPs offer patients a choice of the psychiatrist to whom they would like to be referred, perhaps explaining the different approaches used by the psychiatrists.

Seeing a psychiatrist

An out-patient appointment with a psychiatrist will usually be at a mental illness hospital, day hospital, or the psychiatric unit or department in a general hospital. (These hospitals are described later in this chapter.) A few psychiatrists hold out-patient consultations at health centres. In certain circumstances the GP will arrange for the psychiatrist to visit you at home.

Various methods of arranging appointments are used – be sure you understand what, if anything, you are supposed to do. A common system is for the hospital to send you a card notifying you of an appointment date and time. If it is impossible for you to attend, telephone the consultant's secretary or the hospital appointments department to arrange another appointment. As you may have to wait some time after seeing your GP for this first appointment, it is wise to make every effort to attend the appointment you are offered. Always let the hospital know if you cannot keep an appointment, even if you cannot give them much notice, so that they can offer it to someone else on the waiting list.

Despite the appointment system you may still have some time to pass in the hospital waiting room, so you may want to ask someone to go with you for company.

Your GP will have referred you to a consultant psychiatrist, but the doctor you actually see might be the psychiatric registrar who will later discuss your case with the consultant. The psychiatrist may do what is called a Mental State Examination. This consists of a series of questions which helps to tell the psychiatrist what sort of mental illness you are suffering from, if any. He will also ask about your personal and medical history. Although some of these questions may seem embarrassing, it is important to answer honestly, so that the psychiatrist is able to make an accurate diagnosis of your condition. He will certainly ask when you first began to have problems, and what prompted you to see your GP, so it helps to think in advance about this. To discover whether there is a physical cause for your symptoms, which would require a different type of treatment, the psychiatrist may examine you and arrange for various laboratory tests to be carried out.

You may ask the person who accompanied you to the hospital to go into the appointment with you; the psychiatrist may even request this. A social worker sometimes interviews the patient's relative during the patient's appointment with the psychiatrist. A psychiatrist may ask to see you alone first, then your relative or close friend alone to ask what changes he has noticed in you, and then the two of you together. You can tell the psychiatrist that you do not want anyone who knows you to talk to him, or that you will not leave the room during their discussion. This may, however, handicap the psychiatrist in investigating your problem – even possibly to the extent that he does not wish to continue with your case, and will ask your GP to refer you elsewhere. An advantage of having someone else present at the end of the appointment is that your relative or friend also hears the psychiatrist's opinion, advice and recommendations for further treatment. It is sometimes difficult to take in all this information, and two of you together are more likely to remember all the important points.

Going privately

There are few psychiatrists who offer only private consultations, though some work in the NHS and also have private patients. They almost always require a GP's referral before seeing a patient. However, as in the NHS, if you have a very good reason for not seeing your GP first, a psychiatrist might see you – provided you give him permission to inform your GP of the situation. A very small number of psychologists see patients privately, too.

You might wish to consider seeing a psychiatrist privately for one of several reasons:

- you do not want to attend a hospital out-patient department – psychiatrists are seen privately at their own consulting rooms or at your home
- your GP will not refer you for an NHS appointment. This will be because he does not consider a specialist opinion to be necessary. If

you disagree, and cannot convince him that an appointment would put your mind at rest, you can either ask him to refer you to a psychiatrist privately, or change GPs

- you are on the waiting list for several months, very worried about your problem, and despite asking your GP to persuade the consultant to see you more quickly, you do not get an appointment for the near future

- your GP will not, or cannot, refer you for NHS treatment of the type you want. Bear in mind the information earlier in this chapter about choosing your treatment. It is unlikely that you would want to consult a psychiatrist privately for this reason, but it may be the only way of obtaining a particular kind of PSYCHOTHERAPY. For example, if you want PSYCHOANALYSIS you will almost certainly have to go privately. Usually if you want HYPNOTHERAPY private treatment is the only option. It is always best to ask your GP for a referral in this situation. He is responsible for referring you to a qualified practitioner. If you do go directly to a therapist, follow the advice at the end of Chapter 9.

The psychiatrist's opinion

After your first discussion with the psychiatrist, which might take an hour, he may ask you to come back for further, probably shorter, appointments. Alternatively, he may ask you to go back to your GP, and he will write to the GP with his diagnosis and suggestions for your treatment. A third possibility is a referral to someone who specialises in the type of treatment you need. This might be a psychotherapist or a clinical psychologist, in which case you would remain under the care of the psychiatrist whom you first saw, and your progress would be monitored by him or he may refer you to another psychiatrist with special expertise. With any of these options the psychiatrist might also write you a prescription – see the advice on PRESCRIPTIONS in Chapter 9.

When the psychiatrist gives you his diagnosis and recommendations, he will not necessarily explain these in detail – ask if there is anything else you want to know. After seeing you, the psychiatrist will write to your GP with his conclusions and you can then make an appointment to discuss the situation with your GP.

In a minority of the cases he sees, a psychiatrist will recommend a stay in hospital as part of the treatment.

Going into hospital

Admission to hospital may be arranged in an emergency by a GP or psychiatrist visiting the patient's home. A social worker may also have been asked to visit if an emergency admission is predicted. If the patient refuses to agree to go into hospital, compulsory admission may be necessary (see Chapter 12), but this is rare. It is much more likely that if admission to hospital is suggested, this will be during a hospital out-patient appointment with a psychiatrist. If it is an urgent case there should be little delay; non-urgent cases are generally put on a waiting list.

These days, psychiatrists try to avoid admitting patients to hospital if they can continue to live at home and be cared for with their family's help or perhaps as a day patient. However, in some cases, hospital admission is essential, for example where there is a danger of SUICIDE attempts, or a refusal to eat or drink, or the patient's symptoms and behaviour make it likely that he will be a danger to himself or members of his family.

If the patient is admitted, arrangements will have to be made with friends, relatives or the local social services department (or equivalent) for looking after any children and the house, which might not be the case if the patient remained at home. It may also be advisable to have a break from a particularly distressing relationship which is aggravating the patient's problem.

Which hospital?

There are three types of hospital for mentally ill patients:

Mental illness or **psychiatric hospitals** are often some distance from the nearest town. Some of the larger ones are being closed down and the patients moved to other hospitals or residential facilities. Although the buildings may be old these hospitals sometimes have better facilities than other hospitals for OCCUPATIONAL and INDUSTRIAL THERAPY, and for leisure activities.

Psychiatric units are being created in an increasing number of general hospitals, including teaching hospitals. They are more likely to be used for short stays than for patients requiring several years of hospital care.

Day hospitals are really an intermediate point beween out-patient and in-patient care. They may be attached to other hospitals. Patients do not stay overnight, but the daily routine in the ward is much the same as in the two other types of hospital. According to the patient's needs regarding treatment and his home situation, he may attend every day from about 9 am until sometime in the afternoon, or just one full day a week, or for only half-days. Transport is sometimes provided; otherwise patients have to make their own arrangements. Day hospitals are most often used as an alternative to admission as an in-patient, enabling the patient to sleep at home. They can also be used for discharged patients who still need to receive treatment during the day while they settle back into life away from the hospital. (Sometimes such patients continue to attend the same ward during the day where they used to be an in-patient.) A third use of day hospitals is to provide more long-term support for patients who do not need in-patient care, but require hospital treatment on at least several days a week. Elderly mentally ill people are particularly likely to come into this category, and some day hospitals are specifically for elderly patients. Additional facilities may be provided – chiropody or supervised bathing, for example. Finally, day hospitals may be used by patients who are staying in a ward of a nearby hospital.

Day hospitals have some similarities with day centres which are run by local authorities (see Chapter 13). However, day hospitals are primarily concerned with medical treatment and OCCUPATIONAL THERAPY, while day centres and voluntary day facilities are geared more towards social and occupational activities.

There is not always a choice of hospital when admission is required – there may be only one local possibility. A patient who has been attending an out-patient clinic at a mental illness hospital would probably be admitted to a bed there. If the out-patient appointments have been at a general hospital, admission will be to that psychiatric unit, provided it has beds available, and the patient's case is suitable. Some units, particularly at teaching hospitals, accept only certain types of case. Most hospitals have 'catchment areas', meaning that they admit patients from only a limited geographical area around the hospital. These rules are sometimes waived if a patient who lives outside the area, or his psychiatrist, has special reasons for requesting admission to that particular hospital.

Being in hospital

Most patients now have far shorter stays in hospital than was the case in the late 1960s. More than half the patients admitted to hospital are discharged within one month, and well over ninety per cent within a year. The aim is for patients to spend as short a time as possible away from their home environment, returning to hospital if necessary at a later date.

Those who have been in hospital for over two years are said to be 'long-stay' patients. Many such patients have been moved from mental illness hospitals to the other forms of accommodation described in Chapter 13. Some had been in hospital for such a long time that it had become their home; it is hoped to avoid this happening in the future for so many people. A small proportion of mentally ill people may always require long stays in hospital, but other long-term provisions are planned for those dependent patients who do not need constant hospital care.

Hospitals and psychiatric units often have a number of special wards where certain types of patient are grouped together. A common sort is the acute admission ward, for new patients who will probably stay only a short time. Some hospitals have wards for patients being treated for ALCOHOL or DRUG DEPENDENCE. The few available mother and baby wards are particularly useful for severe cases of post-natal DEPRESSION. Adolescent and children's wards, and psychogeriatric wards, are discussed later in this chapter. In rehabilitation and self-care wards, patients who have been in hospital for some time are helped to prepare for a new life outside the hospital ward. Such patients may also be in 'token economy' (see BEHAVIOUR THERAPY) or therapeutic community wards. Some voluntary organisation ACCOMMODATION schemes are run as therapeutic communities; this is discussed in more detail in Chapter 13. The rationale is that certain types of social environment are a form of therapy in themselves. The ward functions as a community in which everyone is important, and is expected to contribute – for example, by helping with chores and organising activities. The boundaries between staff and patients are reduced (frequently the staff are not in uniform) and discussion is encouraged. There may be a morning meeting of all staff and patients in the ward, and other smaller group discussions during the day. Token economy therapy (rewarding patients for particular types of behaviour) may also be used to encourage communication in the ward.

Most wards have no locked doors, but some hospitals have one or more 'special', security or locked wards. These are for some disruptive patients who are compulsorily detained (see Chapter 12). Special provisions are sometimes made for those patients with DEMENTIA who wander and may get lost.

Wards are often mixed, but sleeping areas are segregated and separate from the communal day area. Every patient should have a cupboard for his personal belongings. Patients are asked to bring their own clothes, but long-stay patients are given hospital clothes to wear if they do not have their own.

Most social security benefits are reduced when a patient has been in hospital for a period that varies with the particular benefit. You should notify the social security office when you are admitted. Leaflet NI.9 'Going into hospital?' from this office gives details. The benefits are described briefly in Chapter 13. A very small proportion of older long-stay patients are not entitled to any social security benefits and the health authority provides them with 'pocket money'. Patients in some hospitals can also receive 'therapeutic earnings', without affecting their entitlement to benefits (see Chapter 13). This might be for tending hospital gardens, for example, or working in the INDUSTRIAL THERAPY unit.

If a patient is unable to handle his own affairs, and there is no relative or friend to do this for him, the health authority can be appointed to act for him. Social security payments must be saved for him by the health authority and used only for his personal benefit. In certain circumstances social security payments can be reduced or withheld if they 'cannot be used by or on behalf of the patient for his personal comfort or enjoyment'.

If you are in hospital and would like advice on any financial problems, contact the social worker. He can also help with other problems which arise from your being in hospital. If legal proceedings are involved he can arrange for you to receive specialist advice, and representation if necessary. Citizens Advice Bureaux have been set up in a few psychiatric hospitals. A free Advice and Legal Representation Project has been set up within one London hospital, and others may follow. The legal department at MIND can also help with queries.

Problems about your illness and treatment will be answered by the doctors and nurses, or you may wish to talk to the social worker. If you would like to discuss a problem with a doctor you will find that the registrar is more available than the consultant psychiatrist. The nurse in charge of your ward will arrange a meeting for you. Consultants vary in how often they routinely see their patients. Some make only a brief weekly 'ward-round' – seeing the consultant in his office is the usual practice.

Case conferences provide another opportunity for asking questions, but you may prefer not to discuss your problem with so many staff present. The conferences involve nurses, psychologists, social workers, therapists, as well as the doctors in the consultant's firm. When their individual cases are being discussed, patients are sometimes invited to attend for part of the meeting.

Another type of conference you may be told about is a teaching conference. A doctor may ask your permission to discuss your case at a meeting of nurses and doctors or other staff in training.

In some wards a member of staff is 'allocated' to each new patient to take the lead in arranging with others how the patient will spend his time while in hospital. This programme will be reviewed, and your personal 'therapist' is the person to see if you would like to discuss any possible changes. In addition to other parts of the programme, adult education classes may also be available. Some hospitals have amenities such as sports facilities and beauty salons.

Visitors and visits home

Visits from relatives and close friends are normally a great help to patients. A patient who is reluctant to enter hospital for the first time will be reassured by frequent visits that he has not been 'abandoned'. Visitors can often come at any reasonable time, though it is a good idea if they arrange this in advance in case the patient will be having treatment or OCCUPATIONAL THERAPY at that time. When they are not having meals or therapy, patients are not obliged to stay in the ward, and can go for a walk in the grounds or into the town, with their visitors. The nurse in charge of the ward should always be told before patients leave, however.

The psychiatrist may well suggest that a patient goes home for the odd day or at weekends, to see how he manages. If the visit does not go well, both the patient and his family should discuss it with a nurse, doctor or social worker, who may be able to make suggestions for the next occasion. One unsuccessful visit does not rule out the possibility of further breaks at home.

Voting

Informal patients who are in hospital temporarily can be included on the electoral registration form completed by the householder at their usual address. Patients who are 'resident' (that is, staying for at least several months) in the psychiatric unit of a general hospital, in a nursing home or in a hostel, may use this as their address, and thus be included on the electoral register.

Mental illness hospitals and mental nursing homes may not be used as addresses for this purpose. Patients here must be told that they need to make a 'patient's declaration' if they wish to vote. This involves the patient giving the address at which he would be living if he were not in hospital. If he has no other home he may give any UK address (even if it no longer exists), at which he lived before entering the mental illness hospital. He must declare, without assistance, that he is an informal mental patient, and may then be given any necessary help to complete the form. His name is thus entered on the electoral register.

The system in Northern Ireland is different – contact the **Chief Electoral Officer** in Belfast for details.

Discharge from hospital

After a short stay in hospital a patient may be discharged to receive further treatment at a day hospital, as an out-patient or from his GP. These are all options for long-stay patients, too, but their future needs may also be for accommodation and social support – especially if they have few or no relatives to help them (see Chapter 13).

Any patient who is not compulsorily detained (see Chapter 12) is free to leave whenever he chooses. If hospital treatment is recommended by a psychiatrist this will be in the patient's interest – doctors are aware that in-patient treatment is expensive and are unlikely to recommend it lightly. It is therefore inadvisable to leave hospital against the advice of a psychiatrist, and far better first to discuss with him your dislike of being an in-patient. It may be possible, for example, for you to become a day patient instead.

If a seriously ill patient entered hospital voluntarily, but then tried to discharge himself, the staff could in certain circumstances detain him for a limited period (see Chapter 12).

Complaints

Unless you wish to complain about your clinical treatment, negligence by a medical practitioner or unprofessional conduct (see below), your first step should be to complain to a ward sister or the senior nurse on duty. If the matter cannot be sorted out (or if you prefer) write to the hospital administrator. If you get no reply to your complaint or are not satisfied with the explanation, you may wish to make a more formal complaint. This may be to a senior officer at the hospital, a hospital administrator or the district administrator. If you are still dissatisfied, you may then complain to the **Health Service Commissioner**, sometimes called the Health Ombudsman. There are Commissioners for England, Scotland and Wales; the equivalent Ombudsman in Northern Ireland is the **Commissioner for Complaints**. There is a procedure for obtaining a second opinion if you are dissatisfied with the doctor's clinical judgement. If the complaint refers to the ethical, personal or professional conduct of a doctor, write to the **General Medical Council**. Your Community Health Council can advise you on making a complaint. More details will be found in *A Patient's Guide to the National Health Service* (published by Consumers' Association/Patients Association).

Private in-patient care

Some of the private facilities – usually called clinics or (mental) nursing homes – are specifically for treating ALCOHOL and DRUG DEPENDENCE. Psychogeriatric patients (see later in this chapter) are accepted at some clinics.

There are private clinics for general psychiatric care, such as **Woodbourne Clinic**, one of the Community Psychiatric Centres chain. Patients must be referred by a GP or consultant and remain under the care of that consultant, or that of one of the clinic psychiatrists. NHS hospitals do not generally accept psychiatric patients in their private wards.

Private medical insurance schemes do not always cover psychiatric care, and an in-patient stay can be very expensive. Discuss the likely cost with the doctor who is referring you, and check your insurance policy.

Services for elderly people

Some elderly in-patients have been in hospital for so many years that they cannot live independently, even though hospital treatment may no longer be necessary for their condition. Alternative accommodation with nursing care is being found for some of these patients, but others will spend the rest of their lives in mental illness hospitals.

Psychogeriatricians (see page 145) are psychiatrists with special responsibility for treating mental illness in elderly people, though some work only part-time in this role and see younger mentally ill patients, too. The number of such doctors is increasing, but they are still not available everywhere. Scotland and south-east England are better served with psychogeriatric services than the rest of the UK. If there is no specialist, these patients are seen by psychiatrists, geriatricians or physicians.

An elderly mentally ill person may be referred by his GP to a hospital assessment unit involving both psychiatrists and geriatricians (and sometimes social workers). Psychogeriatric teams or DEMENTIA services are based at some hospitals. Typically these services include consultants, community psychiatric nurses (CPNs) and social workers, although help from many other sources may be co-ordinated to help elderly patients and their families. A similar role is played by community dementia teams based at health centres. A CPN, social worker, volunteer and someone from the hospital-based service help local sufferers living at home.

An accurate diagnosis is the first step and this may be reached by an assessment in the elderly person's home, as a day patient or out-patient, or during a short stay in hospital. Most consultants prefer to see the person at home, at least initially, to get a realistic impression of how he behaves in familiar surroundings. It is also easier to interview relatives, friends, neighbours and any other helpers there. The consultant will want to know about the elderly person's memory, ability to look after himself, moods, awareness of what is going on around him, and so on. The facilities available at the hospital may be needed to complete the assessment, and a physical examination is important in reaching the correct diagnosis. It is just as important for a close relative or friend to be available at a hospital assessment, to answer questions about the elderly person, and to reassure him. If the consultant feels it important for nurses to observe the patient's behaviour at night as well, admission to the hospital will be arranged. This may be to a ward which forms part of a specialist unit.

When the specialist has reached his conclusions about the patient's condition, further care will be arranged. If the person can no longer live at home, he can be admitted to a ward for elderly mentally ill patients. This may be a long-stay ward, but some units have new patients who are being assessed and long-term patients in the same ward.

If the patient's condition is less serious he may attend a day hospital for a while, and then a day centre. The psychogeriatric team will co-ordinate any necessary services to help the patient, and perhaps the family, to cope at home. This may be the job of the social worker who liaises with relevant local authority departments, and with voluntary organisations. Services vary around the country – more details are given under DEMENTIA and in Chapters 13 and 14. Sometimes a referral from the psychogeriatrician is necessary to obtain a service. Nursing care can be provided by a CPN or district nurse and advice by a health visitor.

If the elderly person cannot be looked after at home, but does not require hospital care either, admission to local authority, voluntary or private accommodation may be arranged. Some local authority homes specialise in the needs of elderly mentally ill people. Others allocate up to half their rooms for such residents.

Services for children

Among those providing services specifically for young people are child psychiatrists, educational and some clinical psychologists (who may be known as child psychologists), child psychotherapists and, increasingly, occupational therapists. Child psychiatric services usually involve only out-patient care, although hospital admission is sometimes necessary for a small number of young people.

Children are generally referred for behaviour problems such as bed-wetting or HYPERACTIVITY, or for NEUROSES, such as PHOBIAS. PSYCHOSES are very rare in children. Adolescents are also more likely to be referred for behaviour problems than for serious mental illnesses. Educational difficulties are commonly involved in children over five. The emotional and behavioural difficulties experienced by young people are often referred to as psychiatric disorders, rather than mental illness. As discussed in Chapter 3, CONDUCT DISORDERS are not properly classified as mental illnesses. If they are severe or persistent enough to affect the child's life, they require specialist help.

Children and adolescents may be referred for this help by many people concerned with their welfare – parents, teachers, GPs, and health visitors in the case of pre-school children. Young people do not often refer themselves for help, although a few adolescent clinics do offer a direct 'walk-in' service. There are also some COUNSELLING services which can be contacted directly by young people – see Chapter 9. If teachers are aware of the problem they may refer the young person to the school psychological service, school counsellor, education welfare officer or educational psychologist – according to the local availability of such services. Some children require special educational facilities; it is the responsibility of the local education authority to assess these needs, with the advice of educational psychologists. A clinical psychologist at a hospital paediatric department may be asked to help in this assessment – particularly if the child is under five.

If a GP refers a young person for specialist advice, he is more likely to use health service facilities, such as child psychiatry departments in hospitals. Psychiatrists and clinical psychologists, as well as nurses, social workers, psychotherapists and perhaps community psychiatric nurses, work in these departments. There are also day hospitals which children with psychiatric disorders attend with their mothers.

Another source of specialist help is the child guidance clinic which may be run by the health service or by the local authority. These clinics are staffed by various combinations of the professions already mentioned, and a child will not necessarily be seen by a psychiatrist.

Child and adolescent psychiatry departments and units, and child guidance clinics, usually have catchment areas. However, this is not always a strictly enforced rule.

A young child may require considerable reassurance if he is aware that he is seeing a 'doctor' because of his behaviour, but is too young to understand why. However, help for young people with psychiatric disorders is moving away from direct contact between the child and a psychiatrist or psychologist. Increasingly, these professionals are advising those who are responsible for the young person's welfare – such as parents, teachers and staff at residential homes for children. In the case of teachers, this advice may well be from an educational psychologist. Parents taking a child to a child guidance clinic might spend several sessions alone with a psychiatrist, clinical psychologist or social worker learning how to cope with the behaviour problems. Community psychiatric nurses who are based at child psychiatry departments may visit families at home. With the emphasis moving away from treating children and adolescents individually, the use of FAMILY THERAPY is becoming more widespread. The department or clinic may ask all the family to attend with the young person, for at least one appointment.

Occasionally in-patient treatment is necessary, and special facilities are available for those under 17 years old. An adolescent unit might admit young people aged 12 to 17, or there might be one unit for teenagers aged up to 16 and another for those over 16 for whom educational facilities are not compulsory. A psychiatrist may refer an adolescent to a young people's unit as an in-patient for five days a week during term-time. Teachers are responsible for the patients' education, in co-operation with health and social workers who devise a therapeutic programme for their behaviour problems.

Special children's units provide beds for those under 12 or 13. These are in general hospitals, rather than mental illness hospitals.

Before being admitted to an in-patient unit it is often possible for the

177

young person to spend a day there. He can then discuss with his parents and the psychiatrist any worries he may have about the unit. After admission, parents are invited to attend the unit for group discussions during the child's stay.

Special residential care – disturbed and disruptive behaviour can sometimes lead a young person to the courts. This is not necessarily because he has committed a crime, although that is a common reason. There are a number of facilities specifically for young offenders – for example, detention centres and borstals.

Disturbed behaviour can be the result of a seriously deprived upbringing, and in certain circumstances it may be best for the child to be taken into local authority care. He may attend an assessment unit first, so that a decision can be made as to which type of accommodation would be suitable. This may involve psychological testing. The accommodation chosen might be a community home, or if the child were particularly disturbed and disruptive, a youth treatment centre. There are also private children's homes, some specifically for disturbed youngsters, to which local authorities may send children in their care. The fees are paid by the authority. See also DELINQUENCY.

Consent to treatment

In most cases the requirement for a patient to consent to treatment is the same for patients of the mental health services as for any others. If your GP recommends a DRUG you do not want to take, or your psychiatrist advises ECT which you do not want to undergo, you have the right under common law to refuse it.

No formal procedure is involved in obtaining your consent to taking medicine: if you accept the doctor's prescription you are deemed to be consenting to the treatment. For ECT, and the much rarer cases of PSYCHOSURGERY, you would be asked to sign a consent form. If there is anything on the form which you do not understand, or if you still have some questions to ask the psychiatrist, do not sign the form until these matters are cleared up. Your consent would usually be held to be valid only if you were given adequate information, were competent to make the decision and did so without being pressured or deceived in any way. Competence to understand the issues can raise problems in the case of a severely mentally ill person who is in hospital voluntarily. He might not be capable of giving informed consent, and in law he should therefore not be treated. This may leave the patient without the treatment he needs. In this situation it may be necessary to detain the patient using the compulsory admission powers outlined in the next chapter. Alternatively, the treatment may have to be delayed until the patient gives his consent.

Psychosurgery can never be performed without the patient's consent and a second doctor's opinion that the operation is necessary. A nurse and someone else (such as a social worker) who have been involved in the patient's treatment must also be consulted. There is therefore no possibility of a doctor deciding alone to perform brain surgery against the wishes of the patient. These provisions also apply to the rare use of surgically implanted hormones in male sex offenders to reduce their sex drive. (A regulation to this effect is expected in the near future in Northern Ireland.) However, in Scotland these provisions apply only to compulsorily detained patients. Informal patients would have only to consent to psychosurgery – a second opinion would not be legally necessary.

For all other treatments (ie those not involving surgery), patients who are in hospital voluntarily must give their consent before treatment is administered. As already stated, there would not be a formal request for consent before a tablet was handed to a patient – by accepting it, the patient indicates his consent to take it. If he refused, the nurse or doctor could not force him to swallow it.

As the next chapter explains, there are circumstances in which patients can be forcibly admitted to or detained in hospital. They are sometimes called formal patients. The section on compulsory treatment gives details of the conditions under which patients may be treated without their consent.

The only time when informal patients can be treated without their consent is in an emergency when the patient or others are in a serious and immediate danger. Treating a case of attempted SUICIDE by drug overdose would be an example. This applies to any medical patient, not just to those who are mentally ill – and to any type of treatment, not just psychiatric treatment.

12

Compulsory hospital care

About five per cent of mentally ill patients in hospital in England and Wales are detained there under the Mental Health Act 1983 (see later in this chapter for information on Scotland and Northern Ireland). A few living outside hospitals, but affected by the powers of this Act, are under guardianship orders. The information in this chapter refers only to these people and need not concern the vast majority of patients who have entered hospital voluntarily – that is, informal patients. If hospital admission is considered necessary, a patient will always be given the opportunity of agreeing to admission before the powers of the Act are resorted to.

Each of the provisions of the Act is made in a numbered section of the legislation. The relevant section numbers are given in this chapter because they are sometimes used as an abbreviation for the full name of the legal powers. Patients detained under the Act are sometimes said to be 'on a section' or 'sectioned'.

Who can be detained?
The Act refers to 'mentally disordered' people, which includes those who suffer from mental illness, mental impairment (mental handicap with special features), and PSYCHOPATHIC DISORDER (see Chapter 5). The Act does not define mental illness, but a psychopathic disorder is defined as a persistent disorder of the mind which 'results in abnormally aggressive or seriously irresponsible conduct'.

The provisions concerning mental impairment are not considered further in this chapter. Powers relating to mental illness sometimes differ from those for psychopathic disorder. Sexual deviancy, dependence on drugs or alcohol, promiscuity and other types of immoral conduct are not classified as mental disorders but they may be associated with such disorders.

Compulsory admission is possible only if the nature or the degree of the mental disorder warrants the patient's detention in hospital. The detention must also be necessary for at least one of the following reasons:

- in the interests of the patient's own health
- in the interests of his safety
- to protect others.

Compulsory admission powers

Various legal requirements must be met before someone can be compulsorily admitted. These vary according to the urgency of the situation and the length of the proposed detention.

An important figure in the legislation is the approved social worker. (The post of mental welfare officer no longer exists.) He is a qualified social worker who has been specially trained and approved by the local authority as competent to work with mentally disordered people. He must always look for alternatives to compulsory admission.

The Act frequently refers to the 'nearest relative' which is defined in the legislation. As an example, a spouse is a nearer relative than a son or daughter; a parent is nearer than a brother or sister. There are also several criteria referring to the person with whom the patient has lived. In some circumstances a non-relative would therefore be considered the 'nearest relative'.

Medical practitioners (doctors) recommending compulsory admissions must have examined the patient themselves. If two recommendations are needed for an admission, only one should ordinarily be from a doctor working at the hospital where the patient is to go. The other will often be from the patient's GP.

Section 2: Admission for assessment – this lasts for up to 28 days in order that the patient's mental condition can be assessed, and treated if necessary. The application for admission is made by the nearest relative or by an approved social worker, in which case he must try to inform the nearest relative of the application. Two medical practitioners must recommend in writing that the patient be admitted.

Section 3: Admission for treatment – this lasts for up to six months, can then be renewed for a further six months, and thereafter renewed annually. The general conditions for compulsory admission apply; in addition, if the patient has a psychopathic disorder, it must be treatable. This means that the treatment must be likely to relieve his condition, or at least prevent it getting worse. A mentally disordered person who has neither a mental illness, psychopathic disorder nor mental impairment cannot be admitted under this section.

An application is made as under Section 2. If the nearest relative objects, an approved social worker may not make an application. If the social worker considers the objection to be unreasonable, he may apply to a County Court for the nearest relative's function to pass to someone else. This might be to the local authority, the approved social worker himself, or another relative who supports the application.

For a patient to be detained for more than six months, the responsible medical officer (normally the consultant) has to make a psychiatric examination and a medical report, and consult at least one other person involved in his care. As with the original admission order, a renewed period of detention for a patient with a psychopathic disorder is permitted only if the condition is treatable. This also applies if a mentally ill patient is to be detained for more than six months, unless he would be unable to care for himself or obtain the care he needs, or to guard himself against serious exploitation. In these cases a renewed order for detention may be issued.

Section 4: Emergency admission – this lasts for up to 72 hours and is used if it is urgently necessary for the patient to be detained, and there is not time to comply with Section 2. Only one medical recommendation is required – preferably from a doctor who knows the patient, such as his GP. The application may be made by an approved social worker or by the nearest relative; the applicant must have seen the patient within the past 24 hours, as must the doctor.

If a second medical recommendation is produced within 72 hours of the patient entering hospital, he may subsequently be detained as under Section 2.

Section 5: Holding powers – the first part of this section states that patients already in hospital informally can also be detained under Sections 2 and 3, provided the legal requirements are met. The rest of Section 5 gives 'holding powers' to certain doctors and nurses so that they can detain an informal hospital patient for a limited period. This would be necessary if a patient had entered hospital voluntarily, but then tried to leave when his condition merited detention in the hospital under the terms of the Act. Without these powers, the doctors would have to let the patient leave, and then an approved social worker or the nearest relative would have to apply for compulsory admission under Section 2, 3 or 4. In this time the patient, or other people, might have suffered.

If the doctor in charge of an informal in-patient's care considers that an application for admission should be made, the patient may be detained in the hospital for up to 72 hours. This doctor may delegate his holding power to one other doctor if he is not at the hospital. If neither of these doctors is available, a registered mental nurse may detain a patient for up to six hours.

On rare occasions, no one with holding powers under the Act is available when an informal patient with a mental disorder needs to be restrained because his behaviour represents an immediate danger to himself or others. Only in this situation may others (in practice, usually nurses) exercise their common law right to restrain such a person. The force they can use, and the length of detention, are limited.

Guardianship

The aim of these powers is to enable a patient who requires care, but will not accept it informally, to remain in the community, thus avoiding compulsory admission to hospital. An application may be made by an approved social worker or the nearest relative for a person aged 16 or over; two medical recommendations are required. A guardianship order has several points in common with Section 3 – for example, it has the same time limits and the nearest relative may veto an application.

The guardian appointed may be the local social services department or an individual, such as the nearest relative. The guardian may require the patient to live at a specified place, and to attend for medical treatment, education, training or employment. He can also require that a doctor, social worker, or anyone else be able to see the patient. While an order under these sections appears to give the guardian a great deal of authority, there are limitations on his powers. He cannot, for example, force a patient to accept treatment, only to attend for it – see 'Compulsory treatment' below. There are penalties if a guardian mistreats or wilfully neglects a patient.

Removal to a place of safety

Two sections of the Act allow people who appear to be mentally disordered to be removed to a 'place of safety' for up to 72 hours. For example, a police officer might find such a person in a public place and consider him to be in immediate need of care and control, for the patient's welfare or for the protection of others. The person would be taken for instance to a hospital or residential accommodation (preferably not a police station). He would then be examined by a doctor and interviewed by an approved social worker.

A Justice of the Peace can issue a warrant for premises to be searched for an apparently mentally disordered person. There must be reasonable grounds for suspecting that he is being mistreated or neglected, or that he is alone and unable to care for himself.

Requests from the nearest relative

If the nearest relative considers that compulsory admission might be necessary for a mentally disordered person, he can request the social services department to instruct an approved social worker to consider the case. Though the law is somewhat ambiguous, this seems to mean that the social worker must interview the person. Only if he is then satisfied that compulsory admission is unavoidable may the social worker make an application under the Act. The approved social worker has to inform the nearest relative in writing if he does not wish to apply for the patient's admission.

Compulsory treatment

Consent to treatment by informal patients is discussed at the end of Chapter 11. In many cases detained patients may be compulsorily treated, although this does not mean that treatment is automatically forced upon them. The aim is always to obtain the patient's consent to treatment. If this is refused, and the responsible doctor feels that treatment is necessary, certain procedures must be followed before hospital staff can resort to forcible treatment. Patients detained under Sections 4 and 5 or the 'place of safety' powers, or remanded for report (see 'Mentally disordered offenders' below), may not be compulsorily treated. They are considered as informal patients in this respect.

As described in Chapter 11, PSYCHOSURGERY and the surgical implantation of hormones may never be performed without the patient's consent and a second opinion – even if he is compulsorily detained.

ECT may be given only if the patient consents, or if a second doctor confirms that the treatment is necessary to relieve the patient's condition, or at least prevent it getting worse. A nurse and someone else (such as a social worker) who have been involved in the patient's treatment must also be consulted.

DRUGS may be given for three months without either the patient's consent or a second opinion. After that, drug treatment is subject to the same restrictions as ECT.

Any other forms of treatment for mental disorder can be given without the patient's consent or a second opinion. This provision is unlikely to be used very often, except for general nursing care. Most of the psychiatric treatments not already covered fall into the category of PSYCHOTHERAPY. While a patient could be compelled to attend a psychotherapy session, it would be impossible to make him co-operate with the therapist, and the session would achieve little, if anything.

If a patient is being treated compulsorily, his case is monitored by the **Mental Health Act Commission** on behalf of the Secretary of State for Social Services. When a detention order is to be renewed, the doctor in charge of the patient's case must report to the Commission on the patient's condition and the treatment being given. The Commission may also request such a report at any other time. Authority to administer compulsory treatment on the basis of a second opinion may be withdrawn at any time by the Commission.

One exception to the above regulations is any 'immediately necessary' treatment. In certain circumstances, detained patients (except those already mentioned) may be treated without their consent and without a second opinion. The precise circumstances depend on the nature of the proposed treatment. A greater emergency is necessary to warrant irreversible and hazardous treatment, than reversible or non-hazardous treatment. However, examples of such forms of treatment are not given in the Act. Apart from surgery, which is clearly irreversible, it is not clear how other treatments would be classified.

Rights while detained
Correspondence
Detained patients may receive all letters addressed to them, unless they are in a special hospital (see below). If they write to someone else, the hospital must allow the letter to be sent, unless that person has asked not to receive correspondence from the patient.

This also applies if the patient is detained in a special hospital. In addition, such hospitals may withhold letters sent by a patient if it is considered that they would cause distress or danger. (The possibility of hospital staff being distressed by the contents is not grounds for withholding a letter.) Letters addressed to a special hospital patient may be withheld if they threaten his safety or that of others.

In general, letters may not be withheld if they are to or from certain people and organisations, such as MPs, the Court of Protection, Mental Health Review Tribunals, Community Health Councils and hospital managers.

Voting
Compulsorily detained patients may not vote.

Complaints
One of the functions of the **Mental Health Act Commission** is to investigate complaints from detained patients, or from anyone else, in connection with powers under the Act. A patient who wishes to complain about an incident which happened during his detention may do so either during or after his detention. He should normally first complain to the hospital managers, and complain to the Commission only if he is still dissatisfied. There is no bar to direct contact with the Commission – such as while Commissioners are visiting the hospital.

Other people may also contact the Commission directly, but the complaint must refer to the powers of the Mental Health Act. They may, for example, complain about compulsory treatment, but not about an alleged theft of the detained patient's property – only the patient himself could do that.

The Commission may refer certain types of complaint to other procedures set up for dealing with them. (These are further described in Chapter 11 and *A Patient's Guide to the National Health Service* published by Consumers' Association and the Patients Association.)

Legal action

A detained patient can sue for compensation if there has been an improper motive in detaining him, or if the medical recommendations turn out to have been wrong because of negligence by the doctors. In order to sue he will need the permission of the High Court to bring a civil action, or of the Director of Public Prosecutions for a criminal action. This will be granted only if there are reasonable grounds for believing that the patient has a case. This permission is not needed if the patient intends to sue the Secretary of State for Social Services or the health authority. Without it, however, legal action cannot be brought against hospital staff, social services departments or nearest relatives. If a patient's case were successful he would then be discharged from hospital.

Leaving hospital

A detained patient is not necessarily kept in hospital continuously until his discharge. The doctor in charge of his case may grant him 'leave of absence', either for a limited period, or indefinitely. The patient may then go home until the end of the period of leave, or until his doctor recalls him to hospital, or until six months have passed, when the detention order automatically ends.

A patient leaving the hospital without his doctor's authorisation can be compulsorily returned. If he is absent for 28 days (or a shorter period, depending on the type of detention order), he is automatically discharged. It is a criminal offence to help a detained patient to abscond.

If a patient is absent from the hospital when the detention order expires he cannot be brought back to the hospital.

There are three types of discharge for detained patients whose detention orders have not yet expired. (This does not apply to mentally disordered offenders under hospital orders with restrictions – see below.) The nearest relative must be informed of a detained patient's imminent discharge, unless either of them has specifically requested otherwise.

1 A patient detained in a hospital or mental nursing home can ask the doctor in charge of his care to discharge him, or to cancel the detention order so that he becomes an informal patient. If the doctor refuses, the patient may ask the managers of the hospital or nursing home for discharge, and they will arrange a managers' hearing, which will be attended by members of the District Health Authority. Three or more of these members may discharge a patient. A guardianship order can be cancelled by the doctor in charge of the patient's case, or by the responsible social services department.

2 The patient's nearest relative can order his discharge if the patient is detained under Section 2 or 3 (for assessment or treatment) or under a

guardianship order. If the patient is in hospital, the relative should write to the hospital managers saying that in 72 hours he intends to discharge the patient. The responsible medical officer may then issue a barring certificate, preventing the patient being discharged if he thinks the patient would be a danger to himself or others. The relative could not use this procedure again for six months, but could apply within 28 days for a Mental Health Review Tribunal (see below), for a patient detained for treatment but not for assessment. If no barring certificate is issued the relative can collect the patient 72 hours after the managers have received the letter. With a guardianship order the nearest relative need only put his intention to discharge the patient in writing; he need not give 72 hours' notice and a barring certificate cannot be issued.

3 **Mental Health Review Tribunals** (MHRTs) can order a patient's discharge, but there is a limit to how often he, or his nearest relative, may apply for this. Certain patients are also automatically referred for a Tribunal hearing. The hospital managers must inform patients of their rights regarding MHRT hearings and legal aid provisions. Unless the patient objects, his nearest relative is also given this information. Social workers, nurses and doctors may all be involved in providing advice, and questions should be put to them. Expert help is also available through MIND, where the legal department helps patients and relatives applying to a Tribunal. Requests for information and help should be sent in writing, unless it is an urgent case and you have already written.

Legal aid can be used to pay for a solicitor and an independent psychiatric or social enquiry report. MIND and the **Law Society** will arrange representation for patients applying to an MHRT. The patient has a right to be heard at the Tribunal and can have a friend or relative to present his case, although this person could not be paid out of legal aid. If arrangements for the patient's future care outside hospital can be described at the hearing, this should help his case.

The rules governing when a patient's case may be heard by a Tribunal vary according to the type of detention:

- Admission for assessment – the patient may apply within 14 days of entering hospital
- Admission for treatment – the patient may apply within six months of admission, and then once during each period for which the detention order is renewed. The nearest relative can apply only if he has tried to order the patient's discharge and a barring certificate was issued (see above). If no applications are made in the first six months, the hospital managers must refer the patient for a hearing. Thereafter they must ensure that he has a hearing every three years

- Guardianship – the patient only may apply as under Admission for treatment
- If a patient's nearest relative tried to veto a patient's admission for treatment, and the approved social worker succeeded in having a County Court remove his right to do so, the relative could apply to an MHRT. This would have to be within one year of the patient's admission. In many cases, the court will name another relative as nearest relative, and this person will have the usual rights of the next of kin.

Mentally disordered offenders may likewise apply to an MHRT – see below.

The Tribunal may order the patient's discharge at its discretion, but it must do so if certain criteria are met. An MHRT may direct that discharge be delayed until arrangements for the patient's future care are made. It may also recommend that a patient be given leave of absence, or be transferred to another hospital or into guardianship.

Care after discharge

The District Health Authority and social services department of the local authority must provide after-care for patients who have been detained for treatment and for mentally disordered offenders who have been in hospital. They may do this through co-operation with voluntary agencies. This duty continues until the person no longer needs after-care – for example, in terms of accommodation and medical care.

Mentally disordered offenders

Compulsory detention of mentally disordered offenders is covered by different Sections of the Mental Health Act. These are briefly described below.

Section 35: Remand for report – this lasts for periods of up to 28 days, renewable until the patient has been detained for 12 weeks. A doctor must give evidence at the person's trial that there is reason to suspect he is suffering from a mental disorder, and that the only practical way of obtaining a medical report is to detain him in hospital. Such a patient cannot be compulsorily treated.

Section 36: Remand for treatment – the duration is the same as under Section 35, but two doctors must give evidence at the trial. People suffering from mental illness, but not from psychopathic disorder, may be detained under this Section and compulsorily treated if necessary (see above).

Section 37: Hospital order – this may be made at the time of sentencing the offender, and in certain circumstances the court has no option but to do so (see CRIME in Chapter 13). The order has the same duration as a Section 3 Admission for treatment (up to six months). The requirements for the condition to be treatable in some cases are the same as under Section 3. In some circumstances, the court can add restrictions as to the conditions under which the patient may be released. These are sometimes for a specified period, but are usually indefinite ('without limit of time'). The patient is then ineligible for leave of absence, transfer, or discharge by the hospital managers without the Home Secretary's permission. Nor can the nearest relative order the patient's discharge. The patient may, however, be discharged by a Mental Health Review Tribunal. (The Tribunal in these cases will be chaired by a Judge.) He may appeal to a Tribunal during the second six months of his detention, and then yearly. If no applications are submitted, his case will be referred automatically every three years to a Tribunal. As with non-offender patients, the Tribunal must order the patient's discharge if relevant criteria are met. If the discharge is not absolute, it can be conditional on the patient attending a hospital for treatment. If he fails to do so, he may be returned to the hospital for as long as the restriction order is in force. When there is no restriction order, the patient can also be discharged by the hospital managers. In addition to the above rights of application to a Tribunal, the patient's nearest relative may apply equally frequently.

Section 38: Interim hospital order – this initially lasts for a specified period of up to 12 weeks and can be renewed for periods of 28 days, until the patient has been detained for six months. Two medical recommendations are required and the patient may be compulsorily treated. This order is used when there is doubt whether a hospital order is appropriate – the decision is made while the patient is detained.

Guardianship – this is applied for under Section 37, as for a hospital order, and has the same effect as the guardianship described above for people who have not committed an offence. The patient has the same right to apply to a Mental Health Review Tribunal as a non-offender under guardianship. In addition his nearest relative may apply within the first year of the order's duration, and thereafter yearly.

Transfer of prisoners – the Act provides for prisoners to be transferred to hospital if their mental condition makes this necessary. Two medical recommendations are required.

Scotland

The equivalent legislation here is the Mental Health (Scotland) Act 1984. Mental disorder is defined for the purposes of the Act as mental illness or mental handicap, however caused or manifested. If the mental disorder is a persistent one, manifested only by abnormally aggressive or seriously irresponsible conduct (not defined, as in the English Act, as 'psychopathic'), the person may be detained only if treatment is likely to alleviate or prevent deterioration of his condition.

189

To avoid repetition, only aspects of this Act which differ from English legislation are listed below.

In Scotland there are only two, not three, ways in which a patient may be compulsorily admitted:

Application for admission – this is very similar to the English 'admission for treatment'. The mental health officer is the Scottish equivalent of an approved social worker. Applications are submitted to a Sheriff for approval, and the patient (or his representative) and his nearest relative must be given the chance to voice any objections. The **Mental Welfare Commission** and local authority must be informed of a detention.

Emergency admission – the doctor making the recommendation must try to obtain the consent of the nearest relative or of a mental health officer. In any case the nearest relative or someone living with the patient must be informed of the emergency admission as must the Mental Welfare Commission.

Short term detention – this power can be used after an emergency admission for up to 28 days on the recommendation of one doctor. Where possible, the consent must be obtained of the nearest relative or of the mental health officer. If he does not know of the detention, this relative should be informed, and the local authority and Mental Welfare Commission must be told.

Holding powers – a fully qualified nurse may detain an informal patient for up to two hours. The hospital authorities and Mental Welfare Commission must be notified.

Guardianship – this is very similar to guardianship in England and Wales. The applications are made as for an 'application for admission', except that a mental health officer's recommendation is always required.

Removal to a place of safety – as under English law, except that Sheriffs may also issue warrants.

Compulsory treatment – as under English law, except that the regulations requiring consent and a second opinion for surgical treatment are not extended to include informal as well as detained patients (see 'Consent to treatment' at the end of Chapter 11).

Rights while detained – correspondence and voting rights are the same as in England and Wales. The Mental Welfare Commission has a duty to exercise protective functions for mentally disordered people who may be incapable of protecting their own interests. This includes detained and informal patients.

Legal action – the restrictions on a patient wishing to bring legal action if there has been an improper motive or negligence in detaining him, are different in Scotland: it is not necessary for the patient to obtain the permission of either the Court of Session or the Director of Public Prosecutions.

Leaving hospital – leave of absence may be granted as in England and

Wales. If it is for more than 28 days the Mental Welfare Commission must be given the patient's address. Patients have the right of appeal to a Sheriff against short-term detention. When a patient is detained under the 'application for admission' procedure, a medical report must be prepared during the fourth week of a patient's detention. If the grounds for admission are no longer satisfied the patient must be discharged. After any renewal of an order under this section of the Act, a patient may appeal to the Sheriff for discharge. The nearest relative can secure a patient's discharge by giving seven days' notice of his intention. There are no Mental Health Review Tribunals in Scotland, but patients may appeal to the Mental Welfare Commission, which may review cases and order discharges at any time.

Care after discharge – the local authority must co-operate with health boards and voluntary organisations to provide after-care services for people who have been, or still are, suffering from mental disorder.

Mentally disordered offenders – hospital orders and guardianship orders are much the same as in England and Wales. They have very similar effects to Scottish applications for admission and guardianship orders for non-offender patients. Restriction orders can be added, as in England, and these patients are usually referred to as 'state patients'. Offenders detained under any of these orders may appeal for discharge by the Sheriff.

Northern Ireland

New mental health legislation is being introduced as the Mental Health (Northern Ireland) Order 1985. As for the Scottish legislation, only those points which differ from the situation in England and Wales are mentioned below.

The legislation defines mental disorder as mental illness, mental handicap and any other disorder or disability of mind. This is the only UK mental health legislation to define mental illness: 'a state of mind which affects the person's thinking, perceiving, emotion or judgement to the extent that he requires care or medical treatment in his own interests or the interests of other persons'. There is no category of psychopathic disorder, and the legislation excludes personality disorder as a form of mental disorder, in addition to those exclusions made in the English Act. As in England and Wales, compulsory admission is possible only if the nature or degree of the mental disorder warrants the patient's detention in hospital. The new Northern Ireland legislation will then require that failure to detain him would create a substantial likelihood (or risk) of serious physical harm to himself or others.

Admission for assessment – this is the only form of compulsory admission. The application may be made by an approved social worker or the nearest relative. As in England and Wales, the nearest relative may object, and the social worker then has the same option of applying for a court order. However, if he considers that admission is necessary as a matter of urgency, and that applying for a court order would involve an undesirable delay, the social worker may apply to a Justice of the Peace for authority to override the relative's objection. Only one medical recommendation is required for admission, ideally from the patient's own doctor or one who knows him. Any patient detained for treatment is first held for an assessment period of up to 14 days. Within 48 hours of his admission, the patient must be examined by a consultant psychiatrist. Two more examinations are required before the patient can be detained for treatment. A medical report must state that the patient is suffering from mental illness or severe mental impairment. The periods of detention are then as in English law. A provision unique to the Northern Ireland legislation is that a detention for assessment, if the patient is then discharged without treatment, will be disregarded for certain purposes. The person will not be obliged to disclose any information, for example in a job interview, about such periods of detention. In court and other judicial cases he would, however, have to declare this fact if required.

Holding powers – the differences from the English Act are that any doctor on the hospital staff may use this power, but only for up to 48 hours.

Guardianship – this must be necessary in the interests of the welfare of the patient. A recommendation is required from an approved social worker stating that this is the case. If a social worker makes the application the same conditions apply as for an admission for assessment.

Removal to a place of safety – the provisions are very similar to those in the English Act, except that detention is limited to 48 hours.

Compulsory treatment – these provisions are very similar to the English legislation. Consent and a second opinion are required for any patient (detained or not) to receive PSYCHOSURGERY. (The surgical implantation of hormones to reduce male sexual drive will probably also be covered by this part of the legislation.)

Rights while detained – complaints may be made to the **Mental Health Commission for Northern Ireland** which, like the Scottish Mental Welfare Commission, has a duty to review the care and treatment of all mentally disordered people. Unlike the Scottish Commission, however, it has no power to discharge detained patients (this power is lodged with the **Northern Ireland Mental Health Review Tribunal**).

Leaving hospital – patients may be discharged in the same ways as in England and Wales, except that the Health and Social Services Board is the equivalent of the District Health Authority. The nearest relative of any patient (detained or not) must be informed of his imminent discharge, unless either of them has specifically requested otherwise.

Care after discharge – the Health and Social Services Board has a duty to 'promote the treatment, welfare and care of persons suffering from mental disorder'.

Secure facilities

A minority of compulsorily detained patients need to be sent to secure facilities because they represent a serious danger to the public as a result of their violent or criminal tendencies. Some are mentally disordered offenders who have either been sent straight to these facilities (the usual case), or been transferred from prisons. The remainder of those kept in secure facilities were detained in ordinary hospitals until their disruptive behaviour made it impossible for them to remain.

There are four 'special hospitals' in England – Rampton, Broadmoor, and Park Lane and Moss Side on the same site. The equivalent facility in Scotland is the State Hospital, Carstairs. There are no such secure hospitals in Northern Ireland, but the English special hospitals accept patients from there.

Regional secure units are gradually being created for a level of security between that of special and ordinary hospitals. They are for patients who are too difficult or dangerous to remain in a hospital, but who do not require the highest security either. As well as the increasing number of regional secure units, there are interim secure units at several hospitals. This might be just a single ward at the hospital where doors are kept locked. If the patient's behaviour does not improve and he needs long-term high security, he may be transferred to a special hospital. If it does, he can quickly rejoin the normal hospital routine. A patient would, however, probably spend one or two years at the unit. Some hospitals have locked or security wards which are not interim secure units.

In Scotland most mental illness hospitals have some form of secure facility for this type of patient.

Regional secure units are planned in Wales but some mental illness hospitals there and in Northern Ireland have intensive care or secure units.

Mentally ill offenders may be accommodated in ordinary NHS or special hospitals, or in regional secure units. Some prisons also have hospital facilities where mentally ill patients can be cared for. There is a unique psychiatric prison called Grendon Underwood which is run as a therapeutic community – every aspect of life in the prison is part of the therapy, not just the therapy sessions. The prison officers run GROUP THERAPY discussions aimed at helping the prisoners to alter their attitudes and their behaviour. Drama therapy (see OCCUPATIONAL THERAPY) is also used.

The **Matthew Trust** gives practical and professional help to patients and former patients of the four special hospitals in England and to prisoners who have a history of mental illness.

13

Living with mental illness

For many sufferers an episode of mental illness or an emotional problem will be over in a matter of months. You may have used the services described in Chapters 9 and 11, or contacted one of the organisations specialising in the conditions listed in Chapters 5 and 6. You may have benefited from one or more types of treatment, and now be ready to resume your normal way of life. If the illness has not been a long, serious one, this will be relatively easy, particularly if you have understanding relatives and friends to help you.

There are two groups of people for whom recovery is not so straight-forward. The first are those who have had a long illness, perhaps requiring several years of hospital treatment. Some lack the support of a family when they recover sufficiently to return home. Rehabilitation and resettlement services aim to smooth the transition from psychiatric care to independent living.

A second group of mentally ill people do not recover fully after their treatment. The worst period is over, and they no longer need to be in hospital, but they do not return to their former state of mental health. They may suffer another serious episode in the future, or remain below their mental par for many years.

It is often said that not enough is done for those people with mental illness living in the community (ie outside hospital). It is therefore particularly important that those in need of such support are aware of its existence and of how to obtain it. This chapter looks at the non-medical needs of people who have been, or still are, suffering from mental illness, and who are not living in hospital.

Rehabilitation

This is the process of helping former patients to resume a normal daily life after a period of mental illness. Often, it means preparing those who have spent some time in hospital for life in the community. This may mean teaching them new skills, or encouraging them to make the most of the abilities they already possess – sometimes a lack of self-confidence is the major problem. This should begin while the person is still in hospital, so that the way back to an independent life, taking responsibility for himself, has already been paved by the time he is discharged. OCCUPATIONAL and INDUSTRIAL THERAPY described in Chapter 4 are the two main forms this preparation takes (see EMPLOYMENT later in this chapter). Adult education classes are also arranged at some psychiatric units and mental illness hospitals. These are particularly useful for those whose difficulties with reading, writing and arithmetic could handicap their ability to cope with everyday life. Obtaining 'O' levels through these classes could also improve the patient's job prospects. Training may be arranged in the domestic skills necessary for living independently – such as household budgeting, cooking and housekeeping.

Attitudes about what the future holds may affect the success of a person's rehabilitation programme. It is important to find a balance between denying that you face any problems, and believing that you will never achieve anything. The truth lies somewhere in between, and it is the job of those in charge of rehabilitation programmes to help patients realise this. Some programmes include social skills training (see BEHAVIOUR THERAPY) for those whose difficulties with relationships of various kinds are currently a handicap. These difficulties might prevent them making friends outside the hospital, or working under a supervisor.

When patients are discharged their family should be informed (though this is a legal requirement for informal patients only under the new Northern Ireland legislation). There should be a definite plan of what happens next – somewhere to live, something to do during the day, someone to turn to when problems arise. The professions most involved in supporting former patients are social workers and community psychiatric nurses. If nothing seems to have been arranged before you are about to leave the hospital, talk to a doctor, nurse or social worker there. You may be asked to sign a form permitting the release of some information about you to the social worker who is to take over your case. This will be kept confidential.

Local authorities have some obligations to help mentally ill people in the community, though the level of this provision is not specified. There must, for example, be accommodation, day centres and social workers to support mentally ill people – but the numbers of these vary around the country. Leisure facilities are not obligatory provisions. In many areas voluntary organisations supplement these services, either providing a facility for which the local authority pays, or offering an independent service.

People who live in north or east London may use the many facilities of the **Psychiatric Rehabilitation Association**. Members are referred by GPs, social workers or relatives or they contact the Association themselves. Some of the services are described in more detail later in this chapter. Others include home-visits by the Association staff and individual COUNSELLING. Their aim is to help and encourage people who have been mentally ill to play an active part in the community. The Association will also help groups of patients and others to set up projects in other areas.

Those who have been in the Armed Services or Merchant Navy, especially in active or long service, may be helped by the **Ex-Services Mental Welfare Society**. The Society runs a Veterans' Home and a Hostel for men who might otherwise be homeless, and two Treatment Centres which give accommodation for up to 500 men and women per year to give carers a break. Their Welfare Officers visit those who suffer from psychiatric disabilities, either at home or in hospitals throughout the UK, most being referred by social workers or other ex-service organisations. The Welfare Officers also deal extensively with applications and appeals to War Pensions Tribunals. The Society offers general advice and limited financial help.

Other organisations concentrate on providing one type of service – for example, accommodation or employment – and are described later in this chapter. Small local schemes also provide help of this kind. The section at the end of Chapter 9 gives advice on finding out what is available in your area.

Accommodation

This is not a problem for the former patient who is able to return to a family home, but some are not ready for this, or no longer have a home. The hospital should always arrange accommodation before discharging such a patient. Sometimes an accommodation officer has this responsibility; otherwise a social worker will make the arrangements.

There are a few health authority schemes, but accommodation is usually provided by local authorities and voluntary organisations. These take not only former hospital patients – mentally ill people who have been living in their own homes or other accommodation may also be eligible. The schemes offer varying degrees of support and the best solution is often to use one or two on the way to full independence in your own home. These are some of the alternatives:

Group homes are usually in large converted houses, rather than purpose-built. The group may be any size from three or four to about twenty people. When the schemes start, a group of hospital patients who are ready to leave at about the same time may be selected as the first residents. They are helped to settle in by the hospital and social services staff, and may attend classes in domestic skills before leaving the hospital. If problems arise after the residents have moved in, the hospital or social workers may become involved. Homes run as therapeutic communities (like the hospital wards described in Chapter 11) place great emphasis on everyone contributing to the smooth running of the home. No one is employed to 'look after' the residents. Some examples of therapeutic communities run by voluntary organisations are described opposite.

The weekly accommodation charge, and the agreement signed by each resident, may form a tenancy controlled by the Rent Act, or merely a licence to live in the group home with no rights under the Act. The terms of the agreement should be fully explained to prospective residents. For example, it should be made clear whether a resident can live in the home permanently if he so wishes. Some homes set a time limit on the period of residence; others allow the residents to choose for themselves whether to make this their long-term home, or a 'stepping-stone' to a more independent way of life. Group homes which specifically aim to form this bridge between hospital and independence are called 'halfway' homes.

Hostels vary enormously because the term is used for several forms of accommodation. One type of hostel provides little more than somewhere to sleep and eat – there is no active attempt to help the residents achieve a more satisfactory way of life. Other hostels function very much as group homes – sometimes acting as 'halfway' accommodation, but also providing longer-term accommodation. Some provide more intensive support than group homes, with medical staff available at all times, and other staff to help organise day-time activities.

Sheltered flats and **bed-sitters** provide the least degree of professional support and are suitable for those who want to live independently but still need someone to monitor their progress. Sometimes a housing authority will make a number of council flats in a block available specifically for people recovering from mental illness. A housing officer might work with a social worker to help the person settle into the new accommodation. The social worker may then visit once a week to collect the rent and check that the person is coping. In other schemes the accommodation may be purpose-built by a voluntary organisation. Some sheltered accommodation schemes have volunteer helpers who call in on the residents to provide practical help and be 'neighbourly'.

Bed-and-board accommodation is provided by people who let the spare rooms in their homes and may cook meals for the residents. Any professional services the residents require must be obtained just as if they were living in their own homes. Such lodgings do not necessarily provide any care for them, and no arrangements are automatically made for regular visits by a social worker, for example. One disadvantage with this type of accommodation is that the proprietors may not allow residents to be in their rooms during certain times of the day.

If a patient needs accommodation on leaving hospital this is usually provided in the local authority area where he formerly lived. Only this local authority has any obligations towards the patient. If he has no home, and used to live in the area, the authority must find him accommodation. They may be willing to pay for him to live in certain types of accommodation in another area. This is called 'sponsoring'. However, a patient cannot leave hospital, move to an area where he has never lived before, and then demand special accommodation from that local authority.

Organisations providing accommodation
The following are some of the voluntary organisations providing accommodation for former hospital patients and people who still suffer from mental illness and emotional problems.

The **Richmond Fellowship** – provides residential homes of various types for adults and children, all of which are run as therapeutic communities. Every aspect of life at the home is geared towards improvement in the residents' mental state. Some people need to learn how to live with others, and also how to be independent and self-sufficient. So there are no cooks and cleaners, and everyone shares in the shopping, preparing meals, housework and organising social activities. The staff at the homes encourage residents to face up to their problems, and to find ways of dealing with them. There are regular meetings of all those who live in the home – staff and residents – and also opportunities for individual discussions. Each home has a group of local volunteers who provide support for the residents. The group homes are 'halfway' houses providing accommodation for three months to five years. Many of these houses have an average stay of about eight months, though there are some Community Residences where people typically stay longer. There are usually fifteen to twenty residents, male and female, who share a large ordinary house. Some houses are specifically for people who have been suffering from SCHIZOPHRENIA, ALCOHOL or DRUG DEPENDENCE. If a family needs to live in a therapeutic community for a while, children can be accommodated with one or both parents. The problem in these cases is less often that one member has been diagnosed as mentally ill, but that the parents for some reason need help in coping with their children. A number of homes accept adolescents without their parents. In these homes specialist and remedial education or vocational training are provided when necessary.

Whether those wishing to live in a Richmond Fellowship home are currently in hospital or in their own home, a recommendation from their social worker, psychiatrist or probation officer is required. The home then keeps in touch with whoever provides the referral. Generally the cost of the accommodation may at least be partly met by the local authority where the resident normally lives. Adults may then pay the

199

remainder of the weekly charge out of their own social security benefits or earned income. Some people are eligible for a residential care allowance if their local authority does not sponsor their place at a home. The Home Office pays for the stays of some young people on probation. Children and adolescents, who have not usually been in hospital before they join a group home, may attend only during the day. Some people using the Richmond Fellowship facilities, particularly for a child, pay the full cost themselves.

The **Mental After Care Association** – runs registered homes and hostels in south-east England for men and women recovering from mental illness who are aged 16 to 69 when they apply for a place. Most of those living in their residential homes are over retirement age, and many spend their last years there. They are encouraged to join in social activities in the community as well as the home, and everyone contributes in some way to the running of the establishment. The hostels are sometimes used for shorter 'halfway' stays before the residents move to more independent accommodation, and the rehabilitation programme is aimed at this. However, residents may find that they are unable to move on, and no time limit is set for their stay. Some have jobs near the hostel. The resident staff are trained and the Association's social workers make regular visits to the homes and hostels and offer COUNSELLING. Most people are referred to the Association by hospitals, local authorities or the probation service. Mentally ill people who are being looked after in their own homes by relatives may also be accepted for very short holiday stays. Fees can usually be met from DHSS benefit payments if they are not paid by the local authority or the individual.

Guideposts – accommodation is in group homes, hostels, flats and bedsitters. A 'fair rent', fixed by the local rent officer, is charged for flats and bedsitters and the residents become tenants as in any other rented accommodation. A social worker and community nurse are allocated to each group home, and a team of local volunteers helps residents at each of the residential schemes. Whenever hospital patients are to be discharged to a Guideposts project, they are first given a training course at the hospital to prepare them for their new way of life. For some, the Guideposts accommodation is a stepping-stone to returning to their families after a long hospital stay.

The **Psychiatric Rehabilitation Association** – offers a variety of accommodation in north and east London. In the group homes residents share the running of the home and live as a family, without any residential staff. For those preferring more independence there are 'cluster' flats for one or two people. Group Home Visitors make regular visits to both types of accommodation, partly to collect the rent, but also to give advice and to monitor how the residents are coping. Those who have more serious problems, but do not need to be in hospital, may apply for a place in the Intensive Care Accommodation. This is very much like the group homes, but with residential staff. Residents may eventually move into local authority housing.

The **Arbours Association** – described in Chapter 9 for its PSYCHOTHERAPY service, also has three long-stay households in London which are run as therapeutic communities. Two psychotherapists are responsible for each house. There are regular meetings of everyone living at each house, and residents are encouraged to work at their own problems, and to help each other. Individual psychotherapy is available. As in all therapeutic communities, the residents share the shopping, cooking and domestic chores. Some have jobs or study locally. The financial arrangements are similar to those for Richmond Fellowship accommodation.

Community Action Halfway Homes – these offer accommodation in Sheffield for people aged 18 to 40 leaving local mental illness hospitals. One halfway house, and two threequarter-way houses, provide more independence but support from staff and volunteers when needed; there are no resident workers.

Mental health associations – these are involved in accommodation schemes in various ways. Some local associations affiliated to MIND in England and Wales work with the local authority to set up accommodation. For example, MIND in Waltham Forest is working with the health and local authorities to provide ordinary housing. They can be contacted through MIND's **South-East office**. MIND's Housing Team at the head office can provide advice on accommodation. The **Northern Ireland Association for Mental Health** has a group home development programme. Local associations affiliated to the **Scottish Association for Mental Health** are involved in establishing or assisting the development of various types of accommodation.

Financial help

One type of financial help has already been mentioned – local authority contributions towards the cost of accommodation in certain voluntary organisation schemes. Social security benefits are an important means of financing mentally ill people at home or in residential care. There are 'basic support benefits', 'special needs benefits', and 'benefits for supported accommodation needs'. People sometimes fail to claim all the benefits to which they are entitled. Benefits are applied for at the local social security (DHSS) office, or by sending off the forms attached to the leaflets obtainable there or at post offices. The local DHSS office will advise you on benefits. Other sources of advice are social workers, the local Citizens Advice Bureau and specialist welfare rights offices. Local mental health associations should also be able to help, especially if they have a Welfare Rights Officer or Adviser. The local **Disablement Income**

Group may be able to answer queries on financial problems, and also publishes guides to benefits and allowances.

Three books, which may be kept by your local reference library, give detailed information on all the financial benefits available: *National Welfare Benefits Handbook* and *Rights Guide to Non Means Tested Social Security Benefits*, both published by the **Child Poverty Action Group**; and *Disability Rights Handbook* published by the **Disability Alliance Educational and Research Association**. The Alliance also has a telephone advice service (Mon–Fri, 2–4 p.m.) for queries on social security problems for those who have been unable to obtain help locally.

A very brief summary of the financial help available is given below. Most benefit rates change each year. Some more radical changes in benefits are likely from 1987, subject to legislation.

Sickness benefit – paid for up to six months to those physically or mentally incapable of work. For employed people, statutory sick pay paid by the employer already replaces sickness benefit for the first eight weeks, and under new legislation will replace it altogether. See DHSS leaflet NI.16.

Invalidity benefit – paid to those still incapable of work after 28 weeks. See leaflet NI.16A.

Severe disablement allowance – replaces the former non-contributory invalidity pension. New claimants over the age of 20 have to be assessed as being 80 per cent disabled, as well as incapable of work. Anyone already receiving mobility or attendance allowance (see below) is assumed to be 80 per cent disabled. See leaflet NI.252.

Mobility allowance – paid (subject to an upper age limit) to those who are unable, or virtually unable, to walk, if this is likely to persist for a year. See leaflet NI.211.

Attendance allowance – paid to those who need attention or supervision from someone else either by day or by night, and at a higher rate if both day- and night-time help is required. This must have been the case for over six months. The care does not have to be provided by the same person continuously, and the carer(s) need not live permanently with the person being helped. See leaflet NI.205.

Invalid care allowance – paid to some people looking after a person entitled to attendance allowance. See leaflet NI.212, and FINANCE in Chapter 14.

Supplementary benefit – available to anyone who is not in full-time work and has less than a certain amount to live on, according to their dependants and commitments. Savings must be below a set level. The benefit may be increased by 'exceptional circumstances additions' – for example, to cover the cost of laundry because of incontinence, or domestic assistance. 'Exceptional needs payments' or single payments are available in certain circumstances for individual purchases which would not be covered by the person's weekly benefits – for example, furniture. See leaflet SB.1.

Housing benefits – to help with rent and/or rates. Application forms can be obtained from your local council offices and leaflet RR.1, also available from social security offices, gives more details. A special rate relief can be claimed by people whose homes have been altered because of their disability.

Family income supplement – available to families with income below a set level (according to the number of dependants), in which the head of the family has a full-time job. See claim form FIS.1.

Earnings – affect different benefits in different ways. Some, like mobility allowance and attendance allowance, are not affected at all. With supplementary benefit, any earnings over the limit reduce the benefit received. With sickness benefit, invalidity benefit and severe disablement allowance earnings below the limit do not affect benefit if the 'work' is 'therapeutic'. The local office will want details of the work.

Help with prescription charges – if DRUGS are prescribed for your mental illness you may find the prescription charges difficult to afford. Check whether you are entitled to free prescriptions by obtaining leaflet P.11 from a post office or social security office. Those eligible include pensioners, people receiving family income supplement or supplementary benefit, and those requiring continuous drug treatment for EPILEPSY, or suffering from a permanent disability making them housebound. This last category refers to physical disability and could in theory include someone suffering severely from a DEMENTIA such as ALZHEIMER'S DISEASE. A GP or hospital doctor may be willing to endorse an application from such a person.

If you do not qualify for free prescriptions you can still save money by buying a pre-payment certificate lasting four or twelve months. These work like season tickets because you pay in advance and can then have as many prescriptions as you need with no charge while the certificate is valid. The certificates are worth buying if you are likely to need more than five items in four months, or more than 15 items in a year. However, if you actually obtain fewer items than this during the relevant period you cannot claim any refund.

Help with travel costs – if you are receiving family income supplement or supplementary benefit or have an income below a certain level, you may claim a refund of fares for travelling to hospital (or other health facility). See leaflet H.11.

Charitable funds – sometimes available to supplement the social security benefits described above. Various conditions are usually imposed, such as where you live or the care you have received. A doctor's recommendation or other professional endorsement of your application may be necessary. The application may have to be for a specific type of purchase. Among the charities which provide funds for mentally ill people in financial difficulty are:

Queen Adelaide's Fund; Ex-Services Mental Welfare Society (other forces organisations, and trade and professional organisations have benevolent funds); charities to help sufferers from specific disorders (see Chapter 5); **Counsel and Care for the Elderly** (grants for people over pension age only); local branches of Round Table and Rotary Clubs; Mayor's Fund or similar fund run by a borough or metropolitan council.

General advice on the availability of charitable funds can be obtained from the local Citizens Advice Bureau, local mental health associations, Counsel and Care for the Elderly and the **Charities Aid Foundation**'s publication, *Directory of Grant-making Trusts* (available in many reference libraries). The **Family Welfare Association** publishes a useful reference book called *The Charities Digest* which may be available at your reference library.

Employment

An episode of mental illness will almost certainly affect your ability to carry out your job as efficiently as you did before. Poor concentration and a slower rate of working (occasionally a more frantic rate), are common. Colleagues at work may be surprised at the change in your performance – your boss may be disappointed. You may wish to discuss your problem briefly and explain what help you have sought. If you are not well enough to work you should take sick-leave in the normal way. It is worth considering taking a week of your annual holiday if you are not this ill, just to rest and relax. Some employers are very understanding about this type of leave if the situation is explained frankly.

A short rest, with whatever COUNSELLING, PSYCHOTHERAPY or DRUGS you need, may leave you as fit to continue your job as you were before. In this case you will need no advice on employment. However, for some people an episode of more severe mental illness has a less happy outcome. After a long illness some sufferers have no job and a reduced ability to work and to find employment. The rest of this section is for these people.

Rehabilitation aimed at helping patients to return to normal employment begins while they are still in hospital. OCCUPATIONAL and INDUSTRIAL THERAPY are provided in most hospitals with this in mind. Patients may attend Re-employment Training Units where a succession of jobs are practised for several hours a day, each being slightly more demanding than the last. There are also Industrial Units, some of which accept mentally ill people living outside the hospital who need to get used to the work environment again.

On discharge, many patients who are fit to work will be able to return to their former jobs. The psychiatrist who has been in charge of a patient's care will advise him on whether to go back or to register as sick. Some former patients continue working in the hospital industrial unit. For those who are ready to progress to a more realistic work environment, but not to an ordinary job, there are sheltered workshops providing light industrial tasks. The next step is a sheltered industrial scheme run by a local authority or voluntary organisation. The actual job is the same as that done by the other employees but a supervisor takes a special interest in the mentally ill person, helping him with any difficulties. Most such placements are in jobs such as gardening, factory work or street cleaning. An alternative is to attend an Employment Rehabilitation Centre. A few of these run special courses of up to a year for those who have been mentally ill. Guidance is given in areas such as bench engineering, commercial and clerical work, and gardening. At the end of the course the Centre tries to find a suitable job for each person. Some examples of organisations providing bridges between hospital rehabilitation and ordinary employment are given below.

Of those who take advantage of these various forms of rehabilitation, some will not be able to make the final step in competing for a job. Sheltered employment will then be a long-term choice, rather than a 'halfway' step. Those who do go on to apply for jobs may benefit from some help in this, especially with high unemployment creating more competition for jobs. The Disablement Resettlement Officer (DRO) at the local Job Centre may be able to help, and he can put your name on the Disabled Person's (Employment) Register once you qualify for invalidity benefit (see previous section). Any company which employs 20 or more people must have at least three per cent of its staff registered as disabled. One of the advantages of having your name on the register is that you may be able to obtain a job under this scheme. The register has two sections, both with long waiting lists. Those in the first section are usually found ordinary jobs, while those in the second section are more likely to go into sheltered employment.

Most people find job interviews nerve-wracking, but they can be especially difficult if your self-confidence is at a low ebb after a period of mental illness. If you are able to get advice on applying for jobs and attending interviews, either through a rehabilitation programme, or a voluntary organisation, this is well worth having. Practice sessions are particularly helpful, so that you learn how to create a good impression. Employers are looking for people with energy, who are able to express themselves and seem willing to accept responsibility. Think before the interview why they should give the job to you, rather than to the other applicants – because of your previous experience, personal qualities and so on.

If you are applying for a job after a relatively long period of mental illness during which you did not work, it can be difficult to know how to explain this. Some people do not mention their illness when they apply and obtain jobs without their employers knowing their medical history. This is not possible when applying for a job in local or central government because a medical reference is always obtained. Your GP cannot divulge any information on your medical record without your permission – you may be asked to give this on a job application. If this is likely, see your GP first and discuss with him the fact that you are looking for work. It is important for him to tell your prospective employer how well you are now, and this may not be apparent from your medical record. Even if you are not obliged to reveal your medical history there is a danger in evading the issue. In an interview your attempts to dodge a direct question as to why you have not been working in the past may arouse unfounded suspicions in the interviewer's mind. Try to answer questions unemotionally, stressing that you are now recovered and eager to return to work. If you do obtain the job your contract could become invalid if your medical history, such as bouts of mental illness or EPILEPSY, later came to light and you had omitted these facts from your application form. New legislation in Northern Ireland allows certain periods of detention to be disregarded under the law except in some judicial proceedings (see NORTHERN IRELAND in Chapter 12).

Dismissal

Assuming that your job contract has not been invalidated as described above, your employer could not fairly dismiss you simply because you have a history of mental illness. You could be dismissed only if a doctor stated that in future you are unlikely to be able to do your job satisfactorily. Thus if you become mentally ill while you are employed, and a doctor is of the opinion that you will not be able to work again for a year, your employer could dismiss you. An employee can also be dismissed for poor performance at his job, and this might be the case for someone whose mental illness has left him less competent to work. In both these instances an employer must explain his intentions – he cannot dismiss you without warning. If you think you have been unfairly dismissed you have the right to appeal to an industrial tribunal within three months. The Legal Advice Department at MIND head office will be able to advise you if your dismissal was connected with mental illness.

Organisations providing employment

Examples of organisations providing employment for people suffering or recovering from mental illness:

Industrial Therapy Organisation (Thames) Ltd – one of a number of such organisations in England and Northern Ireland which provide training courses as a stepping-stone to an ordinary job and way of life. The men and women who attend the course are referred by hospitals,

GPs, social workers, Disablement Resettlement Officers and so on. They live in their own homes, or other accommodation in the community, and attend the course for an average of six to eight months, but no more than a year. They are paid a weekly training allowance and experience the true pace of a working day.

Remploy Ltd provides sheltered employment at factories in Great Britain. Many of the employees are mentally ill, and they usually stay at the factory, rather than moving on to other employment. Prospective employees are selected by Disablement Resettlement Officers. Remploy factories involve furniture, textiles and leather goods, assembly and packing.

The **Psychiatric Rehabilitation Association** has a number of industrial units in north and east London. A day centre provides a variety of simple jobs for those who require a daily occupation which is no more challenging than this, or as a preparation for more demanding work. Some, for example, move on to an Industrial Education Unit. Workers at the day centre and at the attached unit manufacture, repair and adapt aids for physically disabled people. Another Industrial Education Unit manufactures PVC products. The Association also runs a Shop Assistant Training Scheme.

The **Peter Bedford Trust** operates in Islington and Hackney providing employment programmes, mainly for older people, who have spent a considerable time in hospital. They may at a later stage be offered accommodation. The Trust recruits from local hospitals and social services departments.

The **Richmond Fellowship** runs a workshop primarily for young people who have left a psychiatric hospital, but Disablement Resettlement Officers also make referrals. Training under three craft supervisors continues for up to a year and it is hoped that the young people will then be able to find a job.

Local mental health associations affiliated to MIND and to the **Scottish Association for Mental Health** run a variety of employment schemes.

Day care and social clubs

The day hospitals described in Chapter 11 are health authority facilities offering medical treatment as well as OCCUPATIONAL THERAPY and recreational activities. Day centres and similar facilities are run by local authorities and voluntary organisations. They do not offer treatment, although various types of therapy may be available. A community psychiatric nurse might spend some time at the centre. The main emphasis is on providing activities which will fill the day as constructively as possible for a mentally ill person who is not working.

Day centres are run in numerous ways – some are open Monday to Friday, morning and afternoon, others only on a few days a week. Most organise some activities during the day, and also encourage those attending to get to know each other. Some offer individual COUNSELLING; some are run as therapeutic communities. Mentally ill people may be referred to the centre by health or social services staff as a step between leaving hospital and living a completely independent life. Some will continue to use the centre for many years as a source of day-time activity and companionship. Day centres may cater specifically for the needs of mentally ill people, or elderly mentally ill people, or for a wider range of needs including those who are physically disabled. As well as providing a change and a stimulating environment for the person, the day centre gives the carer some relief.

Some centres are run less formally and those who use them drop in from time to time as they wish. These social centres may have facilities for playing music, making coffee or simply chatting with volunteers who are sympathetic to their mental or emotional problems. Voluntary organisations are more likely than local authorities to set up this type of centre.

There are also clubs which primarily serve meals – lunch or dinner – but which may also organise social events.

The section at the end of Chapter 9 tells you how to find out what is available in your area; these are a few examples:

Leeds MIND runs the 157 Centre which opens two days a week as a social centre. Activities include art therapy, creative writing, a music group, COUNSELLING and advice on welfare rights. It is a free service for members, most of whom approach the Centre directly without a referral. New members are invited to attend sessions in coping with STRESS, RELAXATION, social skills and yoga.

The **Psychiatric Rehabilitation Association** covering north and east London runs a Diners' Club each weekday evening, a day centre where further education classes are available, and evening centres providing leisure activities such as films, listening to guest speakers, discussion groups, musical entertainment, and outings to places of interest.

LINK: **Glasgow Association for Mental Health** runs six clubs.

The **Northern Ireland Association for Mental Health** runs 30 Beacon House Clubs. Each has at least one club leader, plus voluntary helpers. The activities include art classes, relaxation and discussion groups, dressmaking and music. Members must be referred by the health or social services or other caring agencies.

Help at home

After a long stay in hospital it may be difficult to get back into the routine of looking after your home. You may even be doing this for the first time and find it difficult to cope. Depending on the sort of accommodation you have, advice may be available from those providing it. A social worker or community psychiatric nurse will also be able to give you advice.

It may be that you need more practical help, particularly if you also have some physical illness or disability, or if you are elderly. Social services departments (or the equivalent) offer a number of domestic services. Home helps come to your home for a few hours a week to do your housework, but not other chores such as decorating or gardening, though they may do your shopping. Some areas have intensive home help services, sometimes called domestic aides, home care, or home-maker services.

Meals on Wheels are often supplied by the **Women's Royal Voluntary Service**, though they are paid for by the local authority. This is a hot meal delivered to your home at lunchtime.

Laundry services are available in some areas to help with the problems of incontinence, suffered by some people with DEMENTIA, for example. These are discussed in the next chapter.

Being a parent

If you have been suffering from mental illness, and perhaps spent some time in hospital, it can be difficult to resume all the tasks involved in being a parent, especially of young, demanding children. If you are being visited by a social worker, community psychiatric nurse or health visitor (because you have a child under five years), discuss your problems with him or her. These workers can provide advice and may be able to arrange other help for you. A home help (see above) might provide the extra assistance you need during your first few weeks at home. Health and social workers may also know of local schemes and voluntary organisa-tions which help parents.

If parents who are mentally ill are unable to arrange for their children to be adequately cared for, the local authority may have to take over this responsibility and receive the children into care. However, this is by no means an automatic consequence of a parent being admitted to hospital for mental illness, and every effort is first made to look after the children in their own home or to accommodate them elsewhere informally.

Sometimes a parent's mental illness can be disturbing for children and lead to their developing emotional and behaviour problems. This in-creases the strain already felt by the parent. FAMILY THERAPY is often the answer to such situations. As described in the next chapter it is important to seek help if children begin to show such disturbances.

Holidays

A break from the normal routine is important for everyone, but especi-ally those whose lives are more stressful because of mental or emotional problems. If financial difficulties are added to these problems, the possibility of taking a holiday may seem remote, and you may also lack the energy to organise it.

Some social services departments (or the equivalent) organise holiday schemes. It is also possible to use some of the residential facilities described earlier in the chapter under ACCOMMODATION for short holiday stays. The **Psychiatric Rehabilitation Association** and other voluntary organisations arrange group holidays. Some of the organisations listed in Chapter 5 can help with holidays for sufferers of certain conditions. The **Holiday Care Service** provides information for people who have special holiday needs, including those who are mentally ill or have very low incomes.

Legal problems

Generally speaking, people who suffer from mental illness are no different in the eyes of the law from anyone else. The exceptions apply to only a proportion of mentally ill people and concern the matters described in this section, and compulsory detention in hospital which is covered in Chapter 12.

Legal documents and obligations

Certain documents, such as a will, are valid only if they are made by someone who is mentally competent. Everyone is presumed to be so, unless they are proved to be incompetent in a court. A doctor (probably a psychiatrist) would be asked to provide evidence in such a case. The court might then rule that the person is not competent to enter into a civil contract, fulfil his legal obligations, or make a will. There are specific tests to determine whether someone is competent to make a will. For example, he must be able to say what property and relatives he has.

Managing affairs and property – a small proportion of people are unable to manage their own affairs, particularly if they are also elderly and living in hospital. The law provides for the affairs and property of such people to be administered for them. Patients who are compulsorily detained in hospital are not necessarily assumed to be incapable of managing their own affairs.

There is an office of the Supreme Court, called the **Court of Protection**, which considers applications, supported by medical evidence, that a mentally disordered person is incapable of administering his property and affairs. The Court (which does not normally function as a court in the usual sense) can appoint someone else to do this for him. ('Mental disorder' is defined in the Mental Health Act 1983 – see Chapter 12.) If an application is made to the Court of Protection concerning your affairs, you must normally be notified. You then have ten days in which to write to the Court with any objections. If a decision to appoint a 'receiver' to manage your affairs is still made, you have the right of appeal. The arrangement is not necessarily life-long – if the Court is satisfied that you have become capable, at a later date, of managing your affairs, the receiver's powers are revoked. The Lord Chancellor appoints Visitors who see a minority of those concerned each year, partly to report to the Court on the patient's mental capacity. As it is usually a relative who applies to the Court of Protection, more details are given in the next chapter under FINANCE, where the equivalent arrangements in Scotland and Northern Ireland are also described.

People sometimes wish to appoint another person (an 'attorney') to manage their affairs, or some aspect of them. At the time of doing so they must be capable of knowing what they are doing. An 'ordinary' power of attorney is revoked if the person giving the power becomes mentally incapable. The attorney or anyone else could then apply to the Court of Protection for receivership. Legislation has been passed for a new enduring power of attorney which continues if the person becomes mentally incapable. When he believes this is happening the attorney must apply to the Court of Protection for the power of attorney to be registered. If you are suffering from a progressive disorder you may wish to consider this option at an early stage.

More detailed information may be obtained from the **Court of Protection**.

In Scotland the equivalent of a power of attorney is strictly speaking a Factory and Commission, though the English term is often used. Like the ordinary power of attorney in England, this is revoked if the person becomes mentally incapable.

Driving

You must tell the DVLC if you become aware of any physical or mental condition which might affect your ability to drive, whether you are applying for a licence or already hold one. If the condition worsens you must also inform them. Among the examples of relevant conditions given by the DVLC are mental illness, ALCOHOL DEPENDENCE, PARKINSON'S DISEASE and EPILEPSY (a fuller list of examples is given in the Post Office leaflet D. 100). Mental illness is not defined, so you should discuss with your doctor whether your disorder would affect your driving ability. DEMENTIA, including ALZHEIMER'S DISEASE, could well do so. There are specific regulations for people who have had epileptic fits. When you have notified the DVLC of a condition, they will ask your permission to contact your doctor for more information. They may then:

- take no action
- issue a licence for a limited number of years, so that your condition can be reviewed regularly
- refuse or withdraw your licence.

You may appeal to the Magistrate's Court (Sheriff's Court in Scotland) against any decision by the DVLC.

Being a juror
People who are suffering from a mental illness or PSYCHOPATHIC DISORDER, and are therefore in a hospital or nursing home, or regularly seeing a doctor for treatment, are excused from jury service.

Crime
If you are accused of a crime and are mentally ill, your state of mind will be taken into account at some stage. A simple case would be that of a person with DEMENTIA being accused of shoplifting. If the item is returned, and the person's mental condition explained, the matter will probably go no further.

Those who are mentally ill do not commit crimes more often than other people. Mental illness is rarely the sole cause of criminal behaviour, which is usually the result of a combination of factors, including social and personality problems. For this reason the criminal behaviour will not necessarily be stopped by treating the mental illness.

Mentally ill people who do commit crimes, however, are more likely to be charged with violent, sex or drug offences than, for example, burglary. So mental illness may influence the type of crime committed. Some sufferers fear that their behaviour will become wild and violent. If this was not the case before, it is very unlikely to arise simply because they become mentally ill. A theory put forward a few years ago suggested that a genetic abnormality was responsible for violent offences by some men. This has never been proven. Research in the USA has linked crimes by women with PRE-MENSTRUAL TENSION.

Shoplifting by people suffering from DEMENTIA has already been mentioned. It is also a crime sometimes committed by people who are suffering from severe emotional distress, especially women, and sometimes by sufferers from DEPRESSION and EATING DISORDERS. These are not defences for the crime, because their state of mind is not so disturbed that they are unaware of what they are doing. However, a court may sometimes take their mental or emotional problem into account and direct them to receive treatment for it. For example, a probation order with a condition of psychiatric treatment might be issued. This will be done only if the accused person expresses a desire to overcome the problem and receive treatment. A probation officer is then responsible for seeing that the person complies with the order, either by receiving out-patient treatment or entering hospital as an informal patient. If the conditions of the order are not met, the person will be called back to court.

With more serious crimes there are provisions to ensure that those

212

who require medical treatment are sent to hospital, rather than to prison. There are a number of special defences which may be used when the person is brought to trial, sentenced or in prison. Psychiatrists' reports are needed to help the court decide whether a person is, or was at the time of the offence, mentally disordered. They give their opinion as to whether the person was responsible for his actions. The requirements for medical reports if a mentally disordered offender is to be compulsorily admitted to hospital, are described in Chapter 12.

There are two defences which are very rarely used today. One is that the person is 'not guilty by reason of insanity'. This means that the abnormality of his mind substantially impaired his mental responsibility for his actions. He therefore did not know what he was doing, or that it was wrong. A slightly more common defence is that the person is 'unfit to plead' because he could not understand the court proceedings. If the jury accepts either of these defences, the judge must issue a hospital order, with restrictions without limit of time (see Chapter 12).

If a mentally ill person is charged with murder he may plead 'diminished responsibility' for his action. If the jury accepts this, the charge is reduced to manslaughter and the judge may then issue a hospital order, instead of the obligatory life sentence for murder.

The more widely used provisions for mentally disordered offenders are described in Chapter 12.

Anyone accused of a crime obviously requires expert advice and this section has given only a general outline of the legal situation. The Legal Department at MIND head office will advise people of their legal rights – preferably in answer to written enquiries.

The **Portia Trust** helps emotionally disturbed women who have committed a crime. Their counsellors will give advice by telephone or letter to women whose mental state was the major factor in a crime such as shoplifting or baby-snatching. The counsellors sometimes go to court with an accused woman.

14

Living with a mentally ill person

The information in the last chapter, written for people with a mental illness, will also help anyone living with a sufferer to advise him and make any necessary arrangements. This chapter is specifically for those who are living with someone who is mentally ill. Caring for such a person is a very important role because you can help your relative or friend to receive services which he might otherwise not know about, or have the determination to obtain. Use the suggestions at the end of Chapter 9 to find out what services are available in your area for mentally ill people.

There is an increasing number of services for carers, too. Some of these, aimed at carers of specific groups of people, are mentioned in the rest of this chapter, and in Chapters 5 and 6. There is also a general organisation called the **Association of Carers**. For a small annual membership fee they provide carers with practical information and also try to put them in touch with other carers in a similar situation. They are particularly interested in helping carers themselves avoid mental illness. There is a network of local groups of carers who meet regularly.

When you contact the local mental health association to find out about services in your area, ask if the association runs a group for relatives.

Helping someone to recover

Patients recovering from mental illness sometimes suffer one of two types of problem which you can watch for. One is a serious lack of self-confidence in their own ability to cope with STRESS. They may therefore shy away from any remotely difficult task or situation. Others react as if nothing has happened and expect to resume their previous lifestyle immediately.

Your attitude can have a significant effect on how well your relative recovers. For example, you can encourage him to take advantage of REHABILITATION facilities, such as attending an industrial unit after leaving hospital, or returning to work (see Chapter 13). You can

214

persuade him to take any medicine prescribed and to attend follow-up appointments at the hospital. The difficulties of getting someone to seek help initially are described in Chapter 10. Ensuring that they persevere with treatment is not always easy, particularly if they are suffering from MANIA or SCHIZOPHRENIA but do not require hospital care. As discussed at the end of Chapter 11, there is a fundamental right to refuse treatment, unless the person's mental condition warrants compulsory detention in hospital. You can only try to persuade your relative of the benefit to be gained from treatment, and discuss the situation with his doctor if you fail.

Relatives may also experience the two types of reaction described at the beginning of this section. Striking the right balance in what you expect of your relative at home may require the advice of his psychiatrist or others involved in his care. You may feel that the person should not be expected to help with the running of the house, but this will not necessarily be in his best interests. It may well be better for him to assume a gradually increasing amount of responsibility at home, while you continue to make the most demanding decisions for a time. You should not be doing jobs for the person which he can manage himself, because this will make him more, not less dependent, and may undermine his self-esteem.

The opposite problem is expecting far more of your relative than he is capable of achieving. For example, he may not be able to obtain as responsible or well-paid a job as you might have hoped for. This may be a temporary or permanent situation, but expressing your disappointment can only make the person feel disheartened.

It is important for a mentally ill person who has been in hospital or some special form of accommodation, to resume contact with the ordinary community. While day centres and clubs have a very useful role, you can also help your relative to participate in other general activities – for instance, a club connected with a hobby.

Once he is recovering, it is natural for a mentally ill person to fear a relapse. By remaining positive yourself about the future, you can help to reduce this anxiety. Respond to signs of the illness returning, but do not be over-vigilant. Everyone occasionally has a sleepless night, makes a nonsensical remark, feels depressed – it does not necessarily herald an episode of mental illness.

Your feelings

It is not only the sufferer who is affected by mental illness, but also those who live with him. Seeing a change in the moods and behaviour of someone close to you can be upsetting and even frightening. Reacting in this way is neither harsh nor unusual. It is quite understandable that if you care about someone, you will be distressed by his suffering. Reading

215

the relevant section in Chapters 5 or 6 on mental illnesses and emotional problems should help to explain some of the changes you have noticed. The 'What can be done' information also gives specific advice on how to help someone suffering from that illness or problem. Some other general tips are:

- You may feel impatient when your relative makes irrational comments – perhaps because of delusions, or because of severe DEPRESSION. There is, however, nothing to be gained by telling him these thoughts are 'nonsense' or 'stupid'. If he knows his feelings are irrational, he will be hurt by your lack of understanding. If he does not, no amount of reasoning will change his view. The best course is sometimes just to listen and show that you are sympathetic about his unhappiness, rather than discussing the actual content of what he says. If he presses you for a comment, you could say that your view of the situation is different, that you cannot believe things are the way he sees them. This is neither colluding with him, nor contradicting what he says. Of course, if he has an emotional problem, rather than symptoms of a severe mental illness, it is very helpful to discuss the reasons for his worries.

- Bear in mind that severely mentally ill people do not always express themselves well, or fully understand what is said to them. Make allowances for this.

- Your relative may make hurtful comments to you, which are especially difficult to bear when in fact you are doing your best to help him. However hard it seems, the most helpful reaction is not to be upset or angry at what he says.

- The phrase 'snap out of it' may spring readily to mind, but someone diagnosed as mentally ill will not be able to do so.

It is also understandable if you feel resentful about the task of full-time caring, such as an elderly relative may require (see below). This is especially likely if you had other plans – such as a paid job – or if you can no longer give as much time as you would like to your partner and children. These feelings may in turn cause you to feel guilty. This is unnecessary, as is blaming yourself for your relative's mental illness, or fretting about how you could have been kinder to him in the past. As described in Chapter 2, mental illness is the result of many factors – known and probably some as yet unknown. You may also feel worried about your relative's future health, or how you are going to cope. It is certainly not unknown for the strain of caring to cause such problems as insomnia, frequent headaches and DEPRESSION. Professional help in coping with all these feelings is available, in particular from GPs, community psychiatric nurses and social workers.

If an illness lasts for a long time it can be very wearing for the family, as well as for the sufferer. It is important to have interests outside the home, and to keep in contact with friends and other relatives. You may feel disinclined to invite people to your home because of your relative's unpredictable behaviour. There is no simple solution to this, but it may be possible to discuss it with him before someone visits, and so reduce the chances of an embarrassing incident. A different problem is the mentally ill person who refuses to see any visitors and appears 'unsociable'. This withdrawal is part of the illness, however, and needs to be tolerated like other symptoms. With all such problems you may find your visitors far more understanding of your position than you had feared.

Marriage

A brief spell of mental illness is not likely to put an intolerable strain on a marriage, unless there were already problems with the relationship. More persistent illness or emotional problems suffered by one partner may, however, have a more serious effect. The mentally ill person may cease showing any affection, and a loss of interest in sex is a common symptom. While understanding the reason for this, a partner may still find the situation difficult to live with. The advice in Chapter 6 on MARITAL and SEXUAL PROBLEMS is relevant for those living with someone who is mentally ill.

A marriage may also be strained when neither partner is suffering from a mental illness, but because the couple are caring for a mentally ill relative in their house – perhaps a child, or an elderly parent. A partner is an easy foil for frustration and anger felt about this responsibility, which are concealed from the mentally ill relative. Support of this kind may enable the couple to continue in their caring role when the strain might otherwise be intolerable. But it is important to recognise the effect it has on the marriage. Discussing this openly in calmer moments, and acknowledging the value of this support to each other, will help, as will specialist advice for marital problems.

Children

There are a number of ways in which you as a carer may be concerned about your children. It may be a child who is the mentally ill or emotionally disturbed member of the family. On the other hand you may be worried about the effect on children of living with a mentally ill adult – their other parent or a grandparent, for example.

The special services described in Chapter 11 are generally as concerned for the parent of a disturbed child as for the patient. Children are often referred to specialist services for CONDUCT DISORDERS (see Chapter 3). These can be extremely wearing on the parents and distressing for brothers and sisters. A family approach, if not formal FAMILY

THERAPY, is therefore often used. It is easy for parents to lose patience with children who are experiencing mental or emotional disorders, and so it is important to seek help before this harms your relationship with the child.

Most parents probably worry at some stage about an aspect of their child's behaviour and wonder whether it is 'normal'. As discussed in Chapter 1, this is an impossible criterion to define. Children have markedly different patterns of development which need not be indicative of any mental problem. Often difficulties arise because of the parents' anxiety over the possibility of a disturbance, rather than the child or adolescent actually having a disorder. If you are worried, see your GP so that he can either reassure you or put you in touch with the necessary services. Signs that your child may have a problem which he cannot express verbally include wetting the bed or soiling his clothes when you thought toilet-training was complete; becoming increasingly reluctant to go to school (see PHOBIAS); or disrupting family life by continuous screaming or temper tantrums. Do not leave the matter until you are forever scolding the child in frustration at his behaviour or frightening him with your own anxiety – see your GP.

Adolescence can be a difficult time for the teenager and his family. Some rebellious behaviour is to be expected if he is going to become independent. Though your patience may be strained you need not worry unduly about the odd incident. Prolonged difficulties may, however, warrant professional help, as do ALCOHOL and DRUG DEPENDENCE, and 'vandalism' (see DELINQUENCY). Teenage girls are especially vulnerable to EATING DISORDERS, but do not be over-cautious and start nagging your daughter if she simply refuses a pudding. SEXUAL PROBLEMS also concern parents, but may perhaps be reduced by frank discussions on the subject before a child reaches adolescence. Parents of adolescents who are out late every night might wish they were quiet and home-loving, but teenagers who are extremely reluctant to go out and have no friends may need some professional help.

If it is your partner or another adult in the house who is mentally ill, the effect on your child will depend to some extent on how you explain this and react to it yourself. Except for a child too young to understand any explanation, it is not a good idea to avoid the subject completely. A child whose parent begins to act in a way he does not expect will be confused and perhaps frightened. Explain that this is because the person is not feeling well at the moment, that it is not in any way the child's fault. If he is old enough, explain the need to be patient and understanding, and try to be so yourself. Caring for a mentally ill person can be demanding and time-consuming, but children also need your attention, and feeling ignored may be one reason for their being unhappy in this situation.

A sensitive child may try to hide his own feelings so as not to add to your problems. Others become naughty or violent because they cannot cope with these feelings. While it is important for the two of you to discuss the subject, it may be easier for the child to talk to someone outside the home, so that he does not have to worry whether he should be voicing such feelings to a parent. A close relative or friend, particularly if they have children of a similar age, may also be able to take your child on trips which you have had to abandon.

If you are worried about a child's reaction to living with a mentally ill relative, discuss it with your GP. He may refer you to one of the specialist children's services. Staff here can discuss the matter with your child, and advise you on how to help him.

Elderly relatives

By no means all elderly people become mentally ill, but of those who do, less than ten per cent move into hospitals or residential homes. Many of the rest are cared for by younger relatives. Two of the most common mental illnesses in elderly people are DEPRESSION and DEMENTIA, including ALZHEIMER'S DISEASE. It is important to remember, however, that mental problems in elderly people may have less serious causes that are quite easily treated. If CONFUSION, restlessness, insomnia or other symptoms are worrying you, try to persuade the elderly person to see a GP – or contact him yourself. A slightly worsening memory, or occasional feelings of sadness or worry, are not any more serious in an elderly person than in a younger one.

Of all the mental conditions described in this book, dementia is among the most difficult for relatives to cope with. (Not all sufferers are elderly, and many of the comments in this section refer also to the relatives of younger people who have dementia.) The physical problems connected with feeding, personal hygiene and mobility can be very tiring. It is also difficult to accept, for example, that the parent who once cared for you now needs to be cared for. Some people with severe dementia may seem no more capable than a child, but it is important not to speak to them as if they were. Help them to retain their dignity and self-esteem by speaking patiently, explaining matters that confuse them, and encouraging them to do things of which they are still capable. It helps to reduce confusion if a regular routine is followed in the house. When the person is particularly slow at a task, try to be patient so that he does not panic.

There will inevitably be times when you feel exasperated by the person you care for. Poor memory and reduced inhibitions can cause people with dementia to repeat the same question again and again, or to behave in an embarrassing way. They may even be aggressive, and will probably show little or no gratitude for the efforts you make. Over the years they may become unrecognisable as the person you once knew. Some relatives experience a kind of BEREAVEMENT – a feeling that the person they loved has gone, although he is still alive. Grief in this situation is very understandable and it will help to talk to someone about it. The COUNSELLING services described in Chapter 9, or perhaps a BEREAVEMENT support service, may be able to help you.

Some sufferers from dementia eventually become incontinent – do not be too embarrassed to ask for help with this problem. Talk to your GP or the elderly person's hospital doctor about it – there are a number of causes of incontinence, and it can sometimes be treated. Otherwise, ask any professionals with whom you are in contact what services are available locally to help with laundry and so on.

An elderly person's confusion is sometimes increased by poor eyesight and/or hearing. Make sure your relative has glasses or a hearing aid if necessary. Poorly fitting dentures can make speech incoherent and interfere with eating. If it is very difficult to get your relative to a dentist, call the District Dental Officer at the health authority offices and ask if any local dentist will make home visits.

Aids, such as by the bath or lavatory, or even an adaptation to your home, will help some of the physical problems an elderly person may suffer. Ask the social services department (or equivalent) if an occupational therapist could visit your home. If you would also like some advice on arranging activities for your relative, mention this when you call. If your elderly relative cannot bathe himself, but will not let you help, ask your GP if a bath attendant can visit.

As stated elsewhere in this chapter, it is important not to forget your own needs as a carer. Professional and voluntary workers are increasingly providing services and support for those who care for elderly mentally ill people. One type of help is the relatives' support group. This is a regular meeting of people who are caring for someone who is elderly and suffering from dementia, or from any other mental illness in the case of some groups. They have two functions, and a particular group may emphasise one more than the other. One aim is to provide practical information, either by sharing experiences and 'tips', or through talks from professional workers. The other purpose of group meetings is to give moral support and a chance to express the frustrations and anxieties which every carer feels. It can be very helpful to hear that others have similar feelings, especially if you had been ashamed of them and imagined that you were the only person to feel that way. If nothing else, the group provides a regular social occasion away from the full-time pressures of caring, though of course you may need to arrange for someone else to take over while you are out. Groups are sometimes set up by voluntary organisations, such as local mental health associations. Others are run from hospital departments where the elderly mentally ill people are treated – their relatives are then invited to join the group. If there is no group in your area, and you would like to start one, talk to the community psychiatric nurse, social worker or hospital staff who are involved in your relative's care. MIND publishes a leaflet on support groups called 'Who cares about relatives?'.

There is also an increasing number of schemes providing someone to come into your home while you are away. This can be on a regular basis allowing you to keep a part-time job, for example, or to attend meetings. You may just need someone occasionally, perhaps while you go on holiday, or if you are ill. Some services are free, others charge for the time spent at your home – which may be anything from an hour to a fortnight with many schemes. Voluntary organisations, such as mental health associations affiliated to MIND or **Age Concern** groups, run schemes, as do some social services departments (or the equivalent). They are given a variety of titles which usually include the word 'sitter' or 'sitting-in'. Most offer daytime, evening or weekend sitting-in; some will also stay overnight. In some areas the social services night-sitting service is run jointly with the health authority night-nursing service. Most of these services put a lot of thought into matching the sitter to the elderly person. The sitter's function is not just to supervise, but to create a friendly relationship with the elderly person, as a good neighbour would, and this is impossible if there is a clash of personalities.

Another way for you to have a break during the day is for your relative to attend a day centre or club specifically for elderly mentally ill people (see DAY CENTRES in Chapter 13). A few centres are also open to elderly people who are not mentally ill to create a more mixed group of people.

The hundreds of schemes providing these services are invaluable to carers of elderly mentally ill people. To find out what is operating in your area use the advice at the end of Chapter 9. Local groups of the **National Council for Carers and their Elderly Dependants** offer support, as well as information on services.

It is a sad fact that a few schemes have had to stop because of lack of interest from local people who felt that they should be able to cope alone with the task of caring for an elderly mentally ill relative. You are entitled to a break from the demands of this, and it is neither weak nor inconsiderate to your relative to accept help. In fact it is in everyone's interest that you have some time to yourself. If you do not, the strain will eventually make you irritable and exhausted – perhaps to the point where you can no longer cope at all.

Some examples of the many available schemes are:

- **Support for Relatives of the Elderly Mentally Infirm** – a sitting-in service and group of day centres to relieve carers in the Bath area
- Relatives' psychotherapy group at St James Hospital in Portsmouth
- **Domiciliary care attendant scheme** in North Tyneside – a care and

221

sitting-in service providing practical help to carers and/or mentally ill (or handicapped) people.

However much you wish to avoid it, there may come a time when you can no longer care for your elderly relative at home. If hospital care is not required the options are a local authority, voluntary or private residential home which accepts mentally ill residents, or a private or voluntary nursing home. Information on the various types of accommodation, and the fees payable, is available from **Age Concern England** and from **Counsel and Care for the Elderly**. Consumers' Association's book *Where to Live after Retirement* will also help you.

Holidays

A holiday will refresh you, and if it is not possible for the mentally ill person to go with you, there are various ways of overcoming the problem. He could, for example, go on holiday himself to somewhere providing special care for mentally ill people (see HOLIDAYS in the previous chapter). Particularly if the person is elderly, it may be possible to arrange for a holiday admission to a hospital or residential home. If the local authority agrees that you need a rest from caring, they may contribute towards the cost of your relative's holiday. Talk to the social worker about this if you are in contact with one, or telephone the social services department (or equivalent).

In some areas there are 'sitting-in' schemes whereby someone comes into your home while you are away (see the previous section). 'Fostering' schemes work in the opposite way – your relative goes to stay for a few weeks with those who will care for him.

Finance

Long-term mental illness in one member of the family can often cause financial difficulties. The person might have been the major breadwinner, and now be unable to work or at least to earn at his previous salary level. You may have to give up your job to care for him.

Chapter 13 lists the main sources of financial help in these situations – be sure your relative is claiming all his entitlements.

Invalid care allowance – payable to someone of working age who spends 35 or more hours a week looking after a person entitled to an attendance allowance. The carer must not be earning more than a few pounds a week from paid employment. In the case of mental illness, attendance allowance is probably more likely to be payable when the person being cared for is suffering from a DEMENTIA. The rules state that only men and single women may claim invalid care allowance – married women and those living with a partner are ineligible. However, this rule is currently being challenged in the courts and married women may in future be able to claim. Supplementary benefit may be payable on top or in place of invalid care allowance.

Travel costs – if you are receiving supplementary benefit and are visiting a close relative (or in some circumstances a more distant relation), in a hospital, hostel or residential home, you are entitled to an additional amount to cover the travel costs. See leaflet H.11 available at post offices and social security offices.

Court of Protection – if you are looking after someone who can no longer manage his own affairs, you may need to apply for a Court of Protection Order (described under LEGAL PROBLEMS in Chapter 13). This is most likely to be the case if your relative is elderly and mentally ill. Orders have also been issued in respect of offspring and partners who might, for example, spend all their money because of the nature of their mental disorder. Fees must be paid to the Court of Protection, depending on the person's income, although these are sometimes waived on grounds of hardship. Unless the person's estate is relatively small, a receiver is appointed to manage the person's affairs, as the Court approves or directs. Anyone can apply for an Order but the person's relatives must be notified first. When applying, you need to give information about yourself, any other relatives of the patient and about his estate, an explanation of why he cannot manage his own affairs and what authorities you need from the Court. As receiver you have control over your relative's affairs, but the Court will instruct you. Your views will be sought and you may make suggestions, such as ways to enable the person to retain some responsibility. For example, with the Court's permission you could arrange for him to be able to use a bank account independently, but set a limit on the maximum withdrawal. An information leaflet is available from the Court of Protection.

In Scotland there is no Court of Protection, and an application in these circumstances has to be made to the local Sheriff's Court or to the **Court of Session** to appoint a curator bonis. A solicitor is required, and two medical certificates. In an application to the Court of Session, the person normally appointed as curator bonis by the Court would be either a solicitor or an accountant although in certain cases, for example if the person's estate were quite small, a relative could be appointed. It is more common in applications to the Sheriff's Court for a relative to be appointed. The cost of obtaining the appointment of a curator bonis is slightly lower in the Sheriff's Court but the administration fees are the same for both it and the Court of Session. The administration of these estates is supervised by 'the Accountant of Court'.

In Northern Ireland similar provisions to those in England and Wales apply. The **Office of Care and Protection** has the same powers as the English Court of Protection, but it falls within the jurisdiction of the High Court.

Suicide threats

This is one of many specific problems faced by families of mentally and emotionally disturbed people, but it is singled out here because of the particular distress it causes. SUICIDE is described more fully in Chapter 5 and, as stated there, a suicide threat should never be ignored. It may be only a hint in something the person says, or you may notice preparations he is making which could be used in a suicide attempt. Tell the patient's doctor as quickly as possible why you are worried. People do not often commit suicide without some kind of warning, so it is important to take any threats or clues seriously. There is a much greater risk if the person has previously made an attempt – especially within the past three months. If you are still worried having spoken to the person's doctor and would like to talk about your fears, you can call the **Samaritans** (see SUICIDE), who may be able to offer you advice.

There is the danger of becoming over-concerned with the possibility of suicide. If a relative is diagnosed as suffering from DEPRESSION it is not immediately necessary to remove all knives, razor blades and pills from the house. This will serve only to show the person that you imagine him to be seriously mentally disturbed, and thus reduce his self-confidence. If your relative has not even hinted at suicidal feelings, do not raise the subject yourself.

Severe depression, and to a lesser extent SCHIZOPHRENIA, cause a minority of sufferers to take their own lives. The risk is also higher than average among those who are ALCOHOL- or DRUG-DEPENDENT. There are two periods during the course of depression when extra vigilance is warranted. One is if there is any delay between a decision being taken to arrange in-patient treatment and the person's actual admission to hospital. The other danger-time can be, paradoxically, just as his condition begins to improve. As the person's energy returns he may decide to attempt what he previously only thought about.

Emotional blackmail, by threatening suicide to frighten a friend or relative into complying with a demand, is less likely to lead to actual suicide than if the person is suffering from severe depression. Some people may make an attempt, but at first this may involve a relatively low risk of death (parasuicide). More determined efforts may follow, however, and help should certainly be sought for the person.

Getting help

Practical help will relieve some of the strain of caring for a mentally ill person, and services specially geared to the needs of carers for elderly sufferers are described above. Others will help anyone whose life is restricted through caring for someone else. For example, neighbourhood schemes offer help with shopping and transport, as well as volunteers to stay with your relative while you go out. Write to the Information

Service at the **Volunteer Centre** in Hertfordshire for details of your nearest scheme.

To obtain some social services it may be necessary for the person to be registered as disabled with the local authority – a social worker will advise you. If you are trying to obtain any other health or social service, or a benefit, and feel that you are being denied it unfairly, try to find a professional worker to support your appeal – such as a GP, social worker or health visitor. The local Community Health Council or Citizens Advice Bureau can help, as can a relevant voluntary organisation such as **Age Concern** or a mental health association. Persistence pays, as should politeness, and remember to keep a copy of every letter you send.

See also the HELP AT HOME section in Chapter 13.

Organisations which can help

All the organisations mentioned in this book are listed here with their addresses and telephone numbers. Only the head office address is given for national voluntary organisations. To find your local branch look in the telephone directory or contact the headquarters of the association. *A stamped addressed envelope should be sent with enquiries* – overheads are a major problem for the charities in particular. Almost all the associations for sufferers and their families have a small annual subscription and produce regular newsletters for members.

ACCEPT
200 Seagrave Road
London SW6 1RQ
(01) 381 3155

Action Against Allergy
43 The Downs   London SW20 8HG
(01) 947 5082

Age Concern England
Bernard Sunley House
60 Pitcairn Road   Mitcham
Surrey CR4 3LL
(01) 640 5431

Age Concern Northern Ireland
128 Great Victoria Street
Belfast BT2 7BG
(0232) 245729

Age Concern Scotland
33 Castle Street
Edinburgh EH2 3DW
(031) 225 5000

Age Concern Wales
1 Park Grove
Cardiff CF1 3BJ
(0222) 371566

Al-Anon Family Groups
 UK and Eire
61 Great Dover Street
London SE1 4YF
(01) 403 0888

Alateen
see Al-Anon Family Groups

Alcohol Concern
305 Gray's Inn Road
London WC1X 8QF
(01) 833 3471

Alcohol Counselling Service
34 Electric Lane
London SW9 8JT
(01) 737 3579

Alcoholics Anonymous
PO Box 514
11 Redcliffe Gardens
London SW10 9BQ
(01) 352 9779

Alzheimer's Disease Society
3rd Floor Bank Buildings
Fulham Broadway
London SW6 1EP
(01) 381 3177

Andover Crisis and Support
    Centre
17 New Street Andover
Hampshire SP10 5HA
(0264) 66122

Anorexia Anonymous
24 Westmoreland Road
London SW13 9RY
(01) 748 3994

Anorexic Aid
The Priory Centre
11 Priory Road High Wycombe
Bucks HP13 6SL
(0494) 21431

Anorexic Family Aid
National Information Centre
Sackville Place
44 Magdalen Street
Norwich
Norfolk NR3 1JE
(0603) 621414

Aquarius
4 St Georges Street
Northampton NN1 2TN
(0604) 32421

Arbours Association
41a Weston Park
London N8 7BU
(01) 340 7646

Association for Applied
    Hypnosis
33/39 Abbey Park Road
Grimsby
South Humberside DN32 0HS
(0472) 47702

Association for Post-Natal Illness
Institute of Obstetrics and
Gynaecology
Queen Charlotte's Maternity
Hospital
Goldhawk Road
London W6 0X9
(01) 748 4666

Association of Carers
Medway Homes Balfour Road
Rochester Kent ME4 6QU
(0634) 813981

Association of Community
    Health Councils for England
    and Wales
Mark Lemon Suite
254 Seven Sisters Road
London N4 2HZ
(01) 272 5459

Association of Northern Ireland
    District Committees
25–27 Adelaide Street
Belfast BT2 8FH
(0232) 224431

Association of Scottish
    Local Health Councils
21 Torpichen Street
Edinburgh EH3 8HX
(031) 229 2344

Association of Self-Help and
    Community Groups
7 Chesham Terrace
London W13 9HX
(01) 579 5589

Association to Combat
    Huntington's Chorea
(National Administrative Office)
Borough House
34a Station Road Hinckley
Leics LE10 1AP
(0455) 615558
(Family Counselling Service)
108 Battersea High Street
London SW11 3HP
(01) 223 7000

Bethlem Royal Hospital
see Maudsley Hospital

Biosocial Therapy Association
115 Hampstead Way
London NW11 7JN

Board of Social Responsibility of
    the Church of Scotland
121 George Street
Edinburgh EH2 4YN
(031) 225 5722

Brent Consultation Centre
Johnston House
51 Winchester Avenue
London NW6 7TT
(01) 328 0918

British Association for
    Counselling
37a Sheep Street Rugby
Warwickshire CV21 3BX
(0788) 78328

British Association of
    Psychotherapists
121 Hendon Lane London N3 3PR
(01) 346 1747

British Epilepsy Association
Crowthorne House Bigshotte
New Wokingham Road
Wokingham
Berkshire RG11 3AY
(0344) 773122
(North Regional Centre)
313 Chapeltown Road
Leeds LS7 3JT
(0532) 621076

British Homoeopathic
    Association
27a Devonshire Street
London WIN 1RJ
(01) 935 2163

British Hypnotherapy
    Association
67 Upper Berkeley Square
London W1H 7DH
(01) 723 4443

British Society of Experimental
    and Clinical Hypnosis
Psychology Service
St Augustine's Hospital
Chartham, near Canterbury
Kent CT4 7LL

British Society of Medical and
    Dental Hypnosis
42 Links Road
PO Box 6 Ashtead
Surrey KT21 2HT
(037 22) 73522

Brook Advisory Centres
153a East Street
London SE17 2SD
(01) 708 1234

Cancer Help Centre
Grove House Cornwallis Grove
Clifton Bristol BS8 4PG
(0272) 743216

CancerLink
46a Pentonville Road
London N1 9HF
(01) 833 2451

Catholic Marriage Advisory
    Council
15 Lansdowne Road
London W11 3AJ
(01) 727 0141

Centre for Schizophrenia
see Schizophrenia Association of
Great Britain

Charities Aid Foundation
48 Pembury Road
Tonbridge Kent TN9 2JD
(0732) 356323

Chief Electoral Officer (Northern
    Ireland)
Bedford House
16–22 Bedford Street
Belfast BT2 8AA
(0232) 245353

Child Poverty Action Group
1 Macklin Street Drury Lane
London WC2B 5NH

Churches' Council for Health
and Healing
St Marylebone Parish Church
Marylebone Road
London NW1 5LT
(01) 486 9644

Clouds House
see Life-Anew Trust

College of Health
18 Victoria Park Square
London E2 9PF
(01) 980 6263

Colostomy Welfare Group
4th Floor
38/39 Eccleston Square
London SW1V 1PB
(01) 828 5175

Combat
see Association to Combat
Huntington's Chorea

Commissioner for Complaints
(Northern Ireland)
Progressive House
33 Wellington Place
Belfast BT1 6HN
(0232) 233821

Community Action Halfway
Homes
2nd Floor Mudford Buildings
37 Exchange Street
Sheffield S2 5TR
(0742) 754688 (24-hour answering
service)

Compassionate Friends
6 Denmark Street
Bristol BS1 5DQ
(0272) 292778

Contact
2a Ribble Street
Newtownards Road Belfast
(0232) 57848

Counsel and Care for the Elderly
131 Middlesex Street
London E1 7JF
(01) 621 1624

Court of Protection
E & A Section
Staffordshire House
25 Store Street
London WC1E 7BP
(01) 636 6877

Court of Session
The Supreme Court
2 Parliament Square
Edinburgh EH1 1RQ
(031) 225 2595

Cruse
Cruse House 126 Sheen Road
Richmond Surrey TW9 1UR
(01) 940 4818/9047

Depressives Anonymous,
Fellowship of
36 Chestnut Avenue Beverley
North Humberside HU17 9QU
(0482) 860619

Depressives Associated
PO Box 5 Castletown
Portland Dorset DT5 1BQ

Disability Alliance Educational
and Research Association
25 Denmark Street
London WC2H 8NJ
(01) 240 0806

Disablement Income Group
Attlee House
28 Commercial Street
London E1 6LR
(01) 247 2128

Domiciliary Care Attendant
Scheme
Central Office Citadel East
Killingworth Newcastle-upon-Tyne
Tyne & Wear NE12 0YB
(091) 268 2567

Drugline
28 Ballina Street
London SE23 1DR
(01) 291 2341

229

DVLC (Driving Vehicle Licensing Centre)
Drivers Medical Branch
Swansea SA99 1TU
(0792) 42091

Epilepsy Association of Scotland
48 Govan Road   Glasgow G51 1JL
(041) 427 4911

13 Guthrie Street
Edinburgh EH1 1JG
(031) 226 5458

Ex-Services Mental Welfare Society
Broadway House   The Broadway
London SW19 1RL
(01) 543 6333

Families Anonymous
88 Caledonian Road
London N1 9DN
(01) 278 8805

Family Planning Association
27–35 Mortimer Street
London W1N 7RJ
(01) 636 7866

Family Service Units
207 Old Marylebone Road
London NW1 5QP
(01) 402 5175
see also your local phone directory

Family Welfare Association
501 Kingsland Road
London E8 4AU
(01) 254 6251

Foundation for the Study of Infant Deaths
Cot Death Research and Support
5th Floor   4 Grosvenor Place
London SW1X 7HD
(01) 235 1721/245 9421

Gam Anon
see Gamblers Anonymous

Gamblers Anonymous
17/23 Blantyre Street
Cheyne Walk   London SW10 0DT
(01) 352 3060

General Medical Council
44 Hallam Street
London W1N 6AE
(01) 580 7642

Good Practices in Mental Health
380–384 Harrow Road
London W9 2HU
(01) 289 2034

Greater London Alcohol Advisory Service
91–93 Charterhouse Street
London EC1M 6BT
(01) 248 8406

Guideposts
2 Church Green   Witney
Oxon OX8 6AW
(0993) 72886

Health Service Commissioner for England
Church House
Great Smith Street
London SW1P 3BW
(01) 212 7676

Health Service Commissioner for Scotland
2nd Floor   11 Melville Crescent
Edinburgh EH3 7LU
(031) 225 7465

Health Service Commissioner for Wales
4th Floor   Pearl Assurance House
Greyfriars Road
Cardiff CF1 3AG
(0222) 394621

Holiday Care Service
2 Old Bank Chambers
Station Road   Horley
Surrey RH6 9HW
(0293) 774535

Hyperactive Children's Support Group
59 Meadowside   Angmering
Littlehampton
West Sussex BN16 4BW
(0903) 725182 (10 am–3 pm most weekdays)

Hysterectomy Support Group
Riverdell Warren Way
Lower Heswall
Merseyside L10 9HV
and
75 Priory Road
Peterborough
Cambs PE3 6EE

Industrial Therapy Organisation
  (Thames) Ltd
106 Elthorne Park Road
London W7 2JJ
(01) 567 0119

Institute for Complementary
  Medicine
21 Portland Place London W1N 2AF
(01) 636 9543

Institute of Behaviour Therapy
38 Queen Anne Street
London W1M 9LB
(01) 346 9646

Institute of Group Analysis
1 Daleham Gardens
London NW3 5BY
(01) 431 2693

Isis Centre
Little Clarendon Street
Oxford OX1 2HS
(0865) 56648

Jewish Marriage Council
23 Ravenshurst Avenue
London NW4 4EL
(01) 203 6311

(Manchester branch)
Levi House Bury Old Road
Manchester M8 6FX
(061) 740 5764 (answering machine)

Law Society
(For England and Wales)
113 Chancery Lane
London WC2A 1PL
(01) 242 1222

(For Northern Ireland)
Law Society House
90–106 Victoria Street
Belfast BT1 3JZ
(0232) 231614

(For Scotland)
26 Drumsheugh Gardens
Edinburgh EH3 7YR
(031) 226 7411

Leeds MIND
155–157 Woodhouse Lane
Leeds LS2 3EF
(0532) 451662

Life-Anew Trust
Clouds House East Knoyle
Wiltshire SP3 6BE
(074 783) 650

LifeSkills Ltd
3 Brighton Road
London N2 8JU
(01) 346 9646

LINK: Glasgow Association for
  Mental Health
2 Queens Crescent
Glasgow G4 9BW
(041) 332 2541
(and ARC: Advice and Resource
Centre)
(041) 332 2541/3186

London Centre for
  Psychotherapy
19 Fitzjohn's Avenue
London NW3 5JY
(01) 435 0873

London Youth Advisory Centre
26 Prince of Wales Road
London NW5 3LG
(01) 267 4792

Macmillan Cancer Relief Fund
see National Society for Cancer
Relief

Maisner Centre
57a Church Road Hove
East Sussex BN3 2BD
(0273) 729818/29334

Manic Depression Fellowship
51 Sheen Road
Richmond Surrey
(01) 940 6235

Marie Curie Memorial
  Foundation
28 Belgrave Square
London SW1X 8QG
(01) 235 3325

Marriage Guidance Council
see your local phone directory

Mastectomy Association of
  Great Britain
26 Harrison Street
London WC1H 8JG
(01) 837 0908

Matthew Trust
PO Box 604 London SW6 3AG
(01) 736 5976

Maudsley Hospital
Denmark Hill London SE5 8AZ
(01) 703 6333

Meet-A-Mum-Association
  (MAMA)
3 Woodside Avenue
London SE25 5DW
(01) 654 3137

Mental After Care Association
Eagle House 110 Jermyn Street
London SW1Y 6HB
(01) 839 5953

Mental Health Act Commission
write to the address nearest the
hospital:

Room 22 Hepburn House
Marsham Street
London SW1P 4HW
(01) 211 8061/8858

Cressington House
249 St Mary's Road Garston
Liverpool L19 0NF
(051) 427 2061

Spur A Block 5
Government Buildings
Chalfont Drive
Western Boulevard
Nottingham NG8 3RZ
(0602) 292997

Mental Health Commission for
  Northern Ireland
to be established; contact the
Northern Ireland Association for
Mental Health

Mental Health Foundation
8 Hallam Street
London W1N 6DH
(01) 580 0145

Mental Health Review Tribunals
write to the address nearest the
hospital:

Room 1516 Euston Tower
286 Euston Road
London NW1 3DN
(01) 388 1188 (ext 787)

3rd Floor Cressington House
249 St Mary's Road
Garston Liverpool L19 0NF
(051) 494 0095

Spur A Block 5
Government Buildings
Chalfont Drive Western Boulevard
Nottingham NG8 3RZ
(0602) 294222

2nd Floor New Crown Buildings
Cathays Park
Cardiff CF1 3NQ
(0222) 823398/825111

Mental Welfare Commission for
  Scotland
22 Melville Street
Edinburgh EH3 7NS
(031) 225 7034

MIND
22 Harley Street
London W1N 2ED
(01) 637 0741

MIND South-East
24–34 Stephenson Way
London NW1 2HD
(01) 387 2442

MIND publishes and distributes a
wide range of leaflets and books on
mental health. A list and order form
are available from:
MIND Bookshop
155/157 Woodhouse Lane
Leeds LS2 3EF

Mind Your Self Project
see Leeds MIND for address
(0532) 430918

Miscarriage Association
18 Stoneybrook Close
West Bretton Wakefield
West Yorkshire WF4 4TP
(0924) 85515

National Association for
   Premenstrual Syndrome
25 Market Street Guildford
Surrey GU1 4LB
(0483) 572806/572715

National Association for
   Widows
Chell Road Stafford ST16 2QA
(0785) 45465

National Association of Victims
   Support Schemes
17a Electric Lane
London SW9 8LA
(01) 737 2010

National Association of Young
   People's Counselling and
   Advisory Services
17–23 Albion Street
Leicester LE1 6GD
(0533) 554775 (ext 22 and 36)

National Autistic Society
276 Willesden Lane
London NW2 5RB
(01) 451 3844

National Childbirth Trust
9 Queensborough Terrace
London W2 3TB
(01) 221 3833

National Council for Carers and
   their Elderly Dependants
29 Chilworth Mews
London W2 3RG
(01) 262 1451

National Council for the
   Divorced and Separated
13 High Street Little Shelford
Cambridge CB2 5ES
(Telephone contact): (0623) 648297

National Drinkwatchers
   Network
200 Seagrave Road
London SW6 1RQ
(01) 381 3157

National Marriage Guidance
   Council
see your local phone directory under
Marriage

National Schizophrenia
   Fellowship
78 Victoria Road Surbiton
Surrey KT6 4NS
(01) 390 3651

(Relatives' Centre)
17 Cannon Street
Birmingham B2 5EN
(021) 643 7980

National Schizophrenia
   Fellowship (Northern Ireland)
Room 6 Bryson House
Bedford Street
Belfast BT2 7FE
(0232) 248006

National Schizophrenia
   Fellowship (Scotland)
40 Shandwick Place
Edinburgh EH2 4RT
(031) 226 2025

National Society for Cancer
Relief (Macmillan)
Michael Sobell House
30 Dorset Square
London NW1 6QL
(01) 402 8125

National Society for Epilepsy
Chalfont Centre for Epilepsy
(Health Education and Information
Department)
Chalfont St Peter Gerrards Cross
Buckinghamshire SL9 0RJ
(024 07) 3991

National Society for Research
into Allergy
PO Box 45 Hinckley
Leicestershire LE10 1JY
(0455) 635212

Northern Ireland Agoraphobic
Society
Beacon House
84 University Street
Belfast BT7 1HE
(0232) 228474

Northern Ireland Association for
Mental Health
Beacon House
84 University Street
Belfast BT7 1HE
(0232) 228474

Northern Ireland Mental Health
Review Tribunal
Mental Health Branch
Room 3c Dundonald House
Stormont Estate
Belfast BT4 3FF
(0232) 650111

Northern Schizrenia
Fellowship
38 Collingwood Buildings
Collingwood Street
Newcastle-upon-Tyne
Tyne & Wear NE1 1JH
(0632) 614343

Norwich Centre
7 Earlham Road
Norwich NR2 3RA
(0603) 617709

NSPCC
67 Saffron Hill
London EC1N 8RS
(01) 242 1626

Office of Care and Protection
Royal Courts of Justice
Chichester Street
Belfast BT1 3JF
(0232) 235111

Open Door Association
447 Pensby Road Heswall
Merseyside L61 9PQ

Outsiders Club
PO Box 4ZB
London W1A 4ZB
(01) 741 3332/958 3681

Parkinson's Disease Society
36 Portland Place
London W1N 3DG
(01) 323 1174

Patients Association
Room 33 18 Charing Cross Road
London WC2H 0HR
(01) 240 0671

Peter Bedford Trust
Legard Works 17a Legard Road
London N5 1DE
(01) 226 0302/6074

Phobics Society
4 Cheltenham Road
Chorlton-cum-Hardy
Manchester M21 1QN
(061) 881 1937

Portia Trust
15 Senhouse Street Maryport
Cumbria CA15 6AB
(0900) 812114

Pre-Menstrual Tension Advisory
  Service
PO Box 268 Hove
East Sussex BN3 1RW
(0273) 771366

Proudfoot School of Hypnosis
  and Psychotherapy
9 Belvedere Place
Scarborough
North Yorkshire YO11 2QX
(0723) 363638

Psychiatric Rehabilitation
  Association
21a Kingsland High Street
London E8 2JS
(01) 254 9753

Queen Adelaide's Fund
apply through MIND

Relaxation for Living
29 Burwood Park Road
Walton-on-Thames
Surrey KT12 5LH

Remploy Ltd
415 Edgware Road
London NW2 6LR
(01) 452 8020

Richmond Fellowship
8 Addison Road
London W14 8DL
(01) 603 6373

Royal College of Psychiatrists
17 Belgrave Square
London SW1X 8PG
(01) 235 2351

Royal London Homoeopathic
  Hospital
Great Ormond Street
London WC1N 3HR
(01) 837 8833

Samaritans
see your local phone directory

Sanity
Robina The Chase Ashley
near Ringwood
Dorset BH24 2AN

Schizophrenia Association of
  Great Britain
Bryn Hyfryd
The Crescent Bangor
Gwynedd LL57 2AG
(0248) 354048

School of Hypnosis and
  Advanced Psychotherapy
(01) 359 6991 (24-hour answering
machine)

SCODA
1–4 Hatton Place
London EC1N 8ND
(01) 430 2341

Scottish Association for Mental
  Health
40 Shandwick Place
Edinburgh EH2 4RT
(031) 225 4446

Scottish Association of Victims
  Support Schemes
7a Royal Terrace
Edinburgh EH7 5AB
(031) 558 1380

Scottish Marriage Guidance
  Council
26 Frederick Street
Edinburgh EH2 2JR
(031) 225 5006

Self-Help Team
114 Mansfield Road
Nottingham NG1 3HL
(0602) 505838 (24-hour answering
service)

Sexual and Personal
  Relationships of People with a
  Disability, The Association to
  Aid the (SPOD)
286 Camden Road London N7 0BJ
(01) 607 8851

Simpson House, Family
Counselling Centre
52 Queen Street
Edinburgh EH2 3NS
(031) 225 6028/1054

South Wales Association for the
Prevention of Addiction
111 Cowbridge Road East
Cardiff CF1 9AG
(0222) 26113

Stillbirth and Neonatal Death
Society
Argyle House   29–31 Euston Road
London NW1 2SD
(01) 833 2851

Support for Relatives of the
Elderly Mentally Infirm
SREMI Office   St Martin's Hospital
Midford Road   Bath BA2 5RP
(0225) 834152

Tavistock Clinic
120 Belsize Lane   London NW3 5BA
(01) 435 7111 (ext 327)

Tranx
17 Peel Road   Harrow
Middlesex HA3 7QX
(01) 427 2065

Turning Point
Cap House   9/12 Long Lane
London EC1A 9HA
(01) 606 3947

The Volunteer Centre
29 Lower King's Road
Berkhamsted   Herts HP4 2AB
(044 27) 73311

Westminster Pastoral
Foundation
23 Kensington Square
London W8 5HN
(01) 937 6956

Women's Health Concern
Ground Floor   17 Earls Terrace
London W8 6LP
(01) 602 6669

Women's Health Information
Centre
52 Featherstone Street
London EC1Y 8RT
(01) 251 6580

Women's Information Referral
and Enquiry Service
PO Box 20   Oxford
(0865) 240991

Women's Royal Voluntary
Service
17 Old Park Lane
London W1Y 4AJ
(01) 499 6040

and see your local phone directory

Women's Therapy Centre
6 Manor Gardens   London N7 6LA
(01) 263 6200

Woodbourne Clinic
21 Woodbourne Road
Edgbaston   Birmingham B17 8BZ
(021) 429 4511

Woodlands Road Clinic
Middlesbrough
Cleveland TS1 3BL
(0642) 247311

> *Most of the organisations listed
> here ask that a stamped addressed
> envelope or label be sent with
> enquiries – overheads are a major
> problem for the charities in
> particular.*

Index

Main references under each heading appear in **bold** *type*

Other books from Consumers' Association

These books are available from Consumers' Association, Castlemead, Gascoyne Way, Hertford SG14 1LH.

Understanding allergies
by Mary Steel

The running of eyes and sneezing of hayfever and the wheezing and distress caused by asthma are almost universally recognised. Yet there are many other allergic reactions – some mild and merely irritating, others severe and disabling. In this informative and down-to-earth book, ample insights into the complexities of this topical subject are given, covering such conditions as:
- eczema, particularly in infancy   • ear and eye allergies
- urticaria and angioedema   • asthma in childhood and adulthood   • hayfever.

Further chapters are devoted to insect allergies, allergies to drugs, and to the controversial field of clinical ecology and food allergy. Throughout there are helpful suggestions for alleviating the symptoms and coping with the problems that allergy frequently brings.

Understanding cancer

What is cancer – one disease or many? Does it attack every organ of the body? Is the incidence of different cancers related to a person's occupation? These are some of the questions that this book sets out to answer. It deals with the possible causes of cancer – infection, heredity, environment, lifestyle – and with preventive steps which can be taken. The importance of early recognition is stressed, and the roles of the GP, the specialists, health checks and screening are outlined. Brief descriptions are given of the tests that may be done – and, if cancer is diagnosed, the kind of orthodox treatment that may follow: surgery, chemotherapy, hormone therapy, radiotherapy – how they work, side-effects, and success rates. There are also sections on the role of so-called 'alternative' or supplementary treatments and on the importance of mental attitude, how the patient and his or her family can help each other, and on the current state of research into the origins of and ways of curing cancer.

A patient's guide to the
National Health Service

with a foreword by Katharine Whitehorn

Most people have regular contact with the National Health Service even if only for dental check-ups or sight tests. This objective guide to the NHS, developed in conjunction with the Patients Association, explains all aspects of how to get treatment whether as an in- or an out-patient, and what to do if things go wrong.

Topics covered include: • how to choose your GP, dentist or optician   • maternity and child health services
• all aspects of going into hospital   • the care of the elderly
• the roles of different health workers   • questions of medical records and confidentiality, and consent and medical research.

A further chapter examines when and why you might want to consider private treatment as an alternative to that offered by the National Health Service

Living with stress

Stress can cause illness and illness can cause stress: this book looks at the physical and emotional harm that can result unless stress is kept under control and unnecessary stress is eliminated. It outlines the right and wrong ways to counteract stress – from smoking, drinks and drugs (both kinds) to a whole range of beneficial attitudes and activities.

It helps the individual reader to identify the sources of stress in his own life – which may include personality factors, conditions at work or unemployment, marriage or divorce, over-crowding or loneliness – lists the common warning signs and indicates what steps to take in order to adapt successfully, or change what needs to be changed.

The Which? guide to birth control

This illustrated, practical guide looks at all the methods of birth control in Britain today, explains clearly how each of them works, and assesses their safety, effectiveness, availability and acceptability. They include:
- traditional methods such as withdrawal and breastfeeding
- barriers such as condoms, diaphragms, caps, spermicides
- the Pill in all its forms including
the 'morning after' Pill   • injectable contraception
- periodic abstinence   • sterilisation

There is also a chapter on new developments in contraceptive research.

What to do when someone dies

This is a straightforward guide to the practical arrangements that have to be made after a death: getting a doctor's certificate, reporting the death to the coroner, registering the death and getting various death certificates. Differences between burial and cremation procedures are discussed, and the arrangements that have to be made, mainly through the undertaker, for the funeral. The book details the various national insurance benefits that may be claimed.

Also available in a money-off double offer is **Wills and Probate** which explains all aspects of making or not making a will, and how to administer the estate of someone who has died, without the help of a solicitor.